INTERNATIONAL SERIES OF MONOGRAPHS IN

NATURAL PHILOSOPHY

GENERAL EDITOR: D. TER HAAR

VOLUME 31

COLLECTION OF PROBLEMS IN CLASSICAL MECHANICS

COLLECTION OF PROBLEMS IN CLASSICAL MECHANICS

BY

G. L. KOTKIN AND V. G. SERBO

Novosibirsk State University

TRANSLATION EDITOR

D. TER HAAR

PERGAMON PRESS

OXFORD · NEW YORK · TORONTO

SYDNEY · BRAUNSCHWEIG

Pergamon Press Ltd., Headington Hill Hall, Oxford
Pergamon Press Inc., Maxwell House, Fairview Park, Elmsford, New York 10523
Pergamon of Canada Ltd., 207 Queen's Quay West, Toronto 1
Pergamon Press (Aust.) Pty. Ltd., 19a Boundary Street, Rushcutters Bay, N.S.W. 2011, Australia
Vieweg & Sohn GmbH, Burgplatz 1, Braunschweig

First edition 1971

Based on a translation from the Russian book *Sbornik Zadach po Klassicheskoi Mekhanike*, Nauka, 1969

Library of Congress Catalog Card No. 78-124061

PRINTED IN HUNGARY
08 015843 9

Contents

Preface

THIS collection is meant for physics students. Its contents correspond roughly to the mechanics course in the textbooks by Landau and Lifshitz (1960), Goldstein (1950), or ter Haar (1964).

We hope that the reading of this collection will give pleasure not only to students studying mechanics, but also to people who already know it.

We follow the order in which the material is presented by Landau and Lifshitz, except that we start using the Lagrangian equations in § 4. The problems in §§ 1–3 can be solved using the Newtonian equations of motion together with the energy, linear momentum and angular momentum conservation laws.

As a rule, the solution of a problem is not finished with obtaining the required formulae. It is necessary to analyse the results and this is of great interest and by no means a "mechanical" part of the solution. In particular, it is very desirable to study limiting cases. This is useful not only for checking purposes and for an understanding of the solution obtained, but also for a preliminary analysis of the problem which can be used to learn how to find the motion of a system by intuition. It is also very useful to investigate what happens to a solution, if the conditions of the problem are varied. We have, therefore, suggested further problems at the end of several solutions.

Apart from a few exceptions, we have used the notation of the Mechanics volume by Landau and Lifshitz (1960) and this is often not specifically stated. In problems on electrical circuits we use SI units and for problems about the motion of particles in electromagnetic fields, gaussian units.

A large part of the problems were chosen for the practical classes with students from the physics faculty of the Novosibirsk State University for a course in theoretical mechanics given by Yu. I. Kulakov. We want especially to emphasise his role in the choice and critical discussion of a large number of problems. We owe a great debt to I. F. Ginzburg for useful advice and hints which we took into account. We are very grateful to V. D. Krivchenkov whose active interest helped us to persevere until the end.

We wish to express our indebtedness to A. A. Drozdov, G. I. Frolova, K. G. Gan, Yu. N. Kafiev, V. N. Limanskii, V. L. Maksimov, N. M. Matveeva, T. A. Panshina, N. A. Serbo, A. B. Shvachka, A. A. Sysoletin, and A. S. Vaisman, who helped us in formulating the text.

We are grateful to E. A. Kravchenko and A. L. Kotkin whose part in helping us with translating this book into English cannot be overestimated. We are extremely grateful to D. ter Haar for his help in organising an English edition of our book.

We would be grateful for being told of any errors which are still present.

PROBLEMS

Problems

1. Integration of One-dimensional Equations of Motion

1.1. Describe the motion of a particle in the following potentials $U(x)$:

(a) $U(x) = A(e^{-2\alpha x} - 2e^{-\alpha x})$ (Morse potential Fig. 1a);

(b) $U(x) = -\dfrac{U_0}{\cosh^2 \alpha x}$ (Fig. 1b);

(c) $U(x) = U_0 \tan^2 \alpha x$ (Fig. 1c).

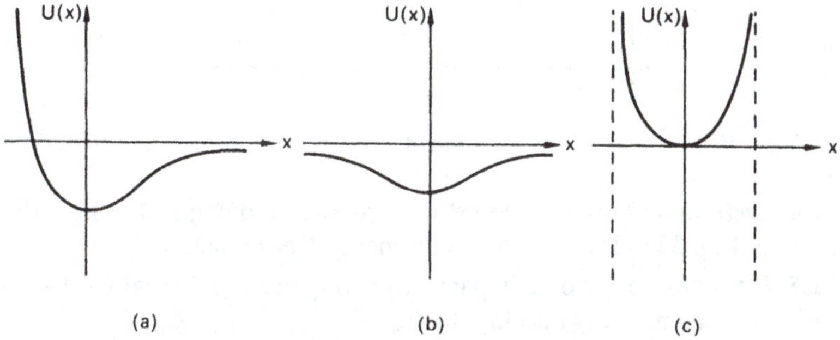

FIG. 1

1.2. Describe the motion of a particle in the potential $U(x) = -Ax^4$, for the case where its energy is equal to zero.

1.3. Give an approximate description of the motion of a particle in a potential $U(x)$ near the turning point $x = a$ (see Fig. 2).

Hint: Use a Taylor expansion of $U(x)$ near the point $x = a$. Consider the cases $U'(a) \neq 0$ and $U'(a) = 0$, $U''(a) \neq 0$.

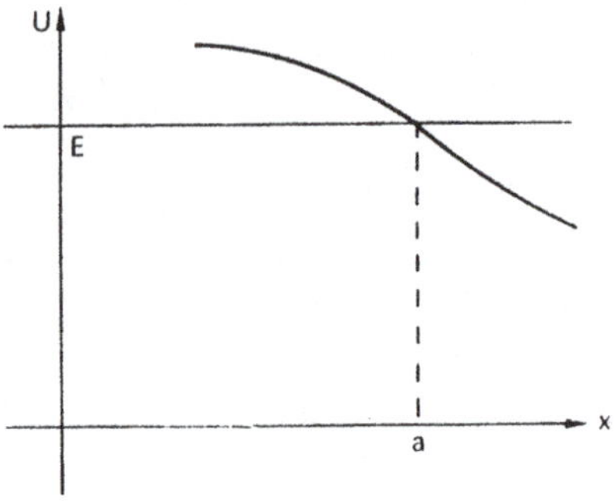

FIG. 2

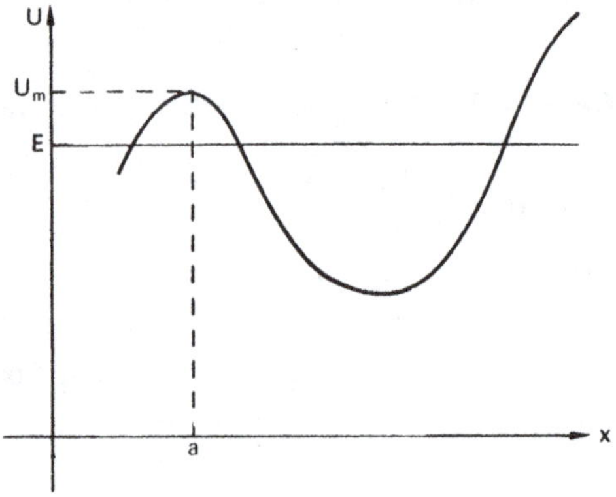

FIG. 3

1.4. Determine how the period of a particle moving in the potential drawn in Fig. 3 tends to infinity as its energy E approaches U_m.

1.5. Estimate the period of a particle moving in the potential $U(x)$ given in Fig. 4, when its energy is close to U_m ($E - U_m \ll U_m - U_{min}$).

Determine how long the particle stays in the range x, $x+dx$.

1.6. A point particle m moves along a circle of radius l in a vertical plane under the influence of the field of gravity (mathematical pendulum). Describe its motion for the case when its kinetic energy E in the lowest point is equal to $2mgl$.

Estimate the period of the pendulum when $E - 2mgl \ll 2mgl$.

1.7. Describe the motion of a mathematical pendulum for an arbitrary value of the energy.

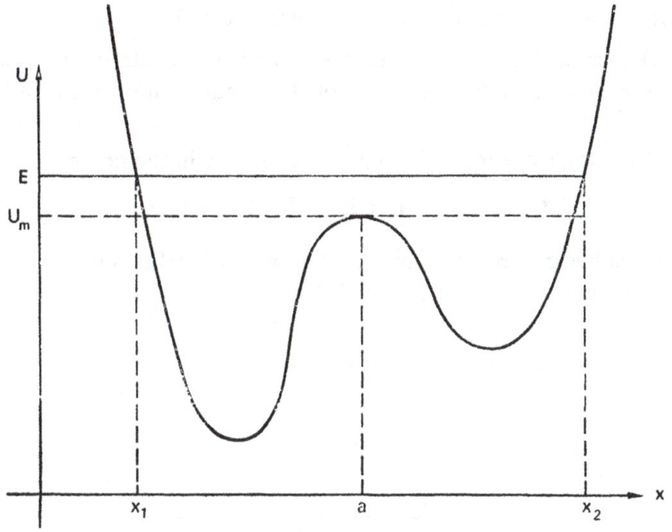

FIG. 4

Hint: The time dependence of the angle the pendulum makes with the vertical can be expressed in terms of elliptic functions (see, for instance, Landau and Lifshitz, 1960, § 37).

1.8. Determine the change in the motion of a particle moving along a section which does not contain turning points when the potential $U(x)$ is changed by a small amount $\delta U(x)$. Consider the applicability of the results obtained for the case of a section near a turning point.

1.9. Find the change in the motion of a particle caused by a small change $\delta U(x)$ in the potential $U(x)$ in the following cases:

(a) $U(x) = \frac{1}{2}m\omega^2x^2$ (harmonic oscillator), $\delta U(x) = \frac{1}{3}m\alpha x^3$;

(b) $U(x) = \alpha x^{-2}$, $x < a$; $U(x) = \infty$, $x > a$, $\delta U(x) = F(x)$.

1.10. Determine the change in the period of a finite orbit of a particle caused by the change in the potential $U(x)$ by a small amount $\delta U(x)$.

1.11. Find the change in the period of a particle moving in a potential $U(x)$ caused by adding to the potential $U(x)$ a small term $\delta U(x)$ in the following cases:

(a) $U(x) = \frac{1}{2}m\omega^2x^2, \quad \delta U(x) = \frac{1}{4}m\beta x^4$;

(b) $U(x) = \frac{1}{2}m\omega^2x^2, \quad \delta U(x) = \frac{1}{3}m\alpha x^3$;

(c) $U(x) = A(e^{-2\alpha x} - 2e^{-\alpha x}), \quad \delta U(x) = -Ve^{\alpha x}\ (V \ll A)$.

2. Motion of a Particle in Three-dimensional Potentials

2.1. Describe qualitatively the motion of a particle in the potential $U = -\alpha/r - \gamma/r^3$ for different values of the angular momentum and of the energy.

2.2. Find the trajectories for a particle moving in the potential

$$U(r) = -V, \quad r < R; \quad U(r) = 0, \quad r > R$$

(Fig. 5: "spherical rectangular potential well") for different values of the angular momentum and of the energy.

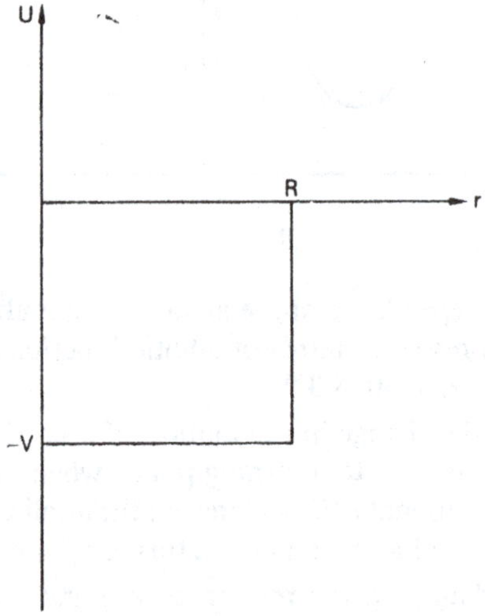

Fig. 5

2.3. Determine the trajectory of a particle in the potential $U = \alpha/r + \beta/r^2$. Give an expression for the change in the direction of the velocity when the particle is scattered as a function of angular momentum and energy.

2.4. Determine the trajectory of a particle in the potential $U = \alpha/r - \beta/r^2$. Find the time it takes the particle to fall to the centre of the potential from a distance r. How many revolutions around the centre will the particle then make?

2.5. Determine the trajectory of a particle in the potential $U = -\alpha/r + \beta/r^2$. Find the angle $\Delta\varphi$ between the directions of the radius vector at two successive passages through the pericentre (that is, when

$r = r_{min}$); find also the period of the radial oscillations, T_r, and the period of revolution, T_φ. Under what conditions will the orbit be a closed one?

2.6. Determine the orbit of a particle in the potential $U = -\alpha/r - \beta/r^2$.

2.7. For what values of the angular momentum M is it possible to have finite orbits in the potential $U(r)$ for the following cases:

(a) $U = -\dfrac{\alpha e^{-\varkappa r}}{r}$,

(b) $U = -Ve^{-\varkappa^2 r^2}$?

2.8. A particle falls from a finite distance towards the centre of the potential $U = -\alpha r^{-n}$. Will it make a finite number of revolutions around the centre? Will it take a finite time to fall towards the centre? Find the equation of the orbit for small r.

2.9. A particle in the potential $U(r)$ flies off to infinity from a distance $r \neq 0$. Is the number of revolutions around the centre, made by the particle, finite for the following cases:

(a) $U = \dfrac{\alpha}{r^n}$,

(b) $U = -\dfrac{\alpha}{r^n}$?

2.10. How long will it take a particle to fall from a distance R to the centre of the potential $U = -\alpha/r$? The initial velocity of the particle is zero. Treat the orbit as a degenerated ellipse.

2.11. Determine the minimum distance between two particles, the one approaching from infinity with an impact parameter ϱ and an initial velocity v and the other one initially at rest. The masses of the particles are m_1 and m_2, and the interaction law is $U = \alpha r^{-n}$.

2.12. Determine in the centre of mass system the finite orbits of two particles of masess m_1 and m_2, and an interaction law $U = -\alpha/r$.

2.13. Determine the position of the focus of a beam of particles close to the beam axis, when the particles are scattered in a potential $U(r)$ under the assumption that a particle flying along the axis is turned back.

2.14. Find the inaccessible region of space for a beam of particles flying along the z-axis with a velocity v and being scattered by a potential $U = \alpha/r$.

2.15. Find the inaccessible region of space for particles flying with a velocity v from a point A in all directions and moving in a potential $U = -\alpha/r$.

2.16. Use the integral of motion $\boldsymbol{A} = [\boldsymbol{v} \wedge \boldsymbol{M}] - \alpha(\boldsymbol{r}/r)$ to find the orbit of a particle moving in the potential $U = -\alpha/r$.

2.17. Determine the change in the angular momentum and energy dependence of the period of radial oscillations of a point particle moving in a potential $U(r)$ when this potential is changed by a small amount $\delta U(r)$.

2.18. Show that the orbit of a particle in the potential $U = -\alpha e^{-r/D}/r$ is a slowly precessing ellipse when $r_{max} \ll D$. Find the velocity of precession.

2.19. Find the precessional velocity of the orbit in the potential $U = -\alpha/r^{1+\varepsilon}$, when $|\varepsilon| \ll 1$.

2.20. Find the change in the period of the radial oscillations, in the period of revolution, and in the angle between the radius vectors at two successive passages through the pericentre

(a) when the energy is changed by a small amount δE, and

(b) when the potential is changed instantaneously by a small amount $\delta U(r)$.

2.21. Find the equation of motion of the orbit of a particle moving in the potential $U(r) = -\alpha/r + \gamma/r^3$, assuming γ/r^3 to be a small correction to the Coulomb field.

2.22. Show that the problem of the motion of two charged particles in a uniform electrical field $\boldsymbol{E}$ can be reduced to the problem of the motion of the centre of mass and that of the motion of a particle in a given potential.

2.23. Under what conditions can the problem of the motion of two charged particles in a uniform magnetic field be separated into the problem of the centre of mass motion and the relative motion problem?

Take the vector potential in the form $\boldsymbol{A} = \frac{1}{2}[\boldsymbol{H} \wedge \boldsymbol{r}]$.

2.24. Express the kinetic energy, the linear momentum, and the angular momentum of a system of N particles in terms of the Jacobi coordinates

$$\xi_j = \frac{m_1\boldsymbol{r}_1 + \ldots + m_j\boldsymbol{r}_j}{m_1 + \ldots + m_j} - \boldsymbol{r}_{j+1}, \quad j = 1, 2, \ldots, N-1;$$

$$\xi_N = \frac{m_1\boldsymbol{r}_1 + \ldots + m_N\boldsymbol{r}_N}{m_1 + \ldots + m_N}.$$

2.25. A particle with a velocity v at infinity collides with another particle of the same mass m which is at rest. Their interaction potential is $U = \alpha/r^n$ and the collision is a central one. Find the point where the first particle comes to rest.

2.26. Prove that

$$(\boldsymbol{M}\cdot\boldsymbol{H})+\frac{e}{2c}([\boldsymbol{r}\wedge\boldsymbol{H}])\cdot[\boldsymbol{r}\wedge\boldsymbol{H}]), \quad \text{where} \quad \boldsymbol{M} = m[\boldsymbol{r}\wedge\boldsymbol{v}],$$

is an integral of motion for a charged particle moving in a uniform magnetic field $\boldsymbol{H}$.

2.27. Give a qualitative description of the motion and the shape of the orbit of a particle moving in the field of a magnetic dipole $\mathcal{M}$ in the plane perpendicular to the dipole. Take the vector potential in the form $\boldsymbol{A} = [\mathcal{M}\wedge\boldsymbol{r}]/r^3$.

2.28. (a) Give a qualitative description of the motion of a charged particle in the potential $U = \frac{1}{2}m\lambda r^2$, where r is the distance from the z-axis (the field of a uniformly charged cylinder), for the case where there is a uniform magnetic field $\boldsymbol{H}$ parallel to the z-axis present.

(b) Find the orbit of a charged particle moving in the potential $U(r)=\alpha/r^2$ in a plane perpendicular to a constant uniform magnetic field $\boldsymbol{H}$.

2.29. A charged particle moves in the Coulomb field $U=-\alpha/r$ in a plane perpendicular to a uniform magnetic field $\boldsymbol{H}$.

Find the orbit of the particle. Study the case where the potential $U(r)$ is a small perturbation and the case when $\boldsymbol{H}$ is small.

2.30. Describe the motion of two identical charged particles in a uniform magnetic field $\boldsymbol{H}$ for the case when their orbits lie in the same plane which is perpendicular to $\boldsymbol{H}$ and where we may consider their interaction energy $U = e^2/r$ to be a small perturbation.

2.31. Show that the quantity

$$(\boldsymbol{F}\cdot[\boldsymbol{v}\wedge\boldsymbol{M}])-\frac{\alpha(\boldsymbol{F}\cdot\boldsymbol{r})}{r}+\frac{1}{2}([\boldsymbol{F}\wedge\boldsymbol{r}]\cdot[\boldsymbol{F}\wedge\boldsymbol{r}])$$

is a constant of motion in the potential $U(\boldsymbol{r})=-\alpha/r-(\boldsymbol{F}\cdot\boldsymbol{r})$. Give the meaning of this integral of motion when $\boldsymbol{F}$ is very small.

2.32. Study the effect of a small extra term $\delta U=-(\boldsymbol{F}\cdot\boldsymbol{r})$ added to the Coulomb potential on the finite orbit of a particle.

(a) Find the average rate of change of the angular momentum, averaged over one period;

(b) Find the time-dependence of the angular momentum, the size, and the orientation of the orbit for the case when the force $\boldsymbol{F}$ lies in the orbital plane;

(c) Do the same as under (b) for the case when the orientation of $\boldsymbol{F}$ is arbitrary.

2.33. Find the systematic displacement of a finite orbit of a charged particle moving in the potential $U(r) = -\alpha/r$ and in the field of a magnetic dipole $\mathcal{M}$, if the effect of the latter may be considered to be a small perturbation. Take the vector potential in the form $\boldsymbol{A} = [\mathcal{M} \wedge \boldsymbol{r}]/r^3$.

Hint: Write down the equations of motion for the vectors $\boldsymbol{M} = m[\boldsymbol{r} \wedge \boldsymbol{v}]$ and $\boldsymbol{B} = [\boldsymbol{v} \wedge \boldsymbol{M}] - \alpha \boldsymbol{r}/r$ averaged over one period, and solve them.

3. Scattering in a Given Field. Collisions between Particles

3.1. Find the differential cross-section for the scattering of particles with initial velocities parallel to the z-axis by smooth elastic surfaces of revolution $\varrho(z)$ for the following cases:

(a) $\varrho = b \sin \dfrac{z}{a}, \qquad 0 \leqq z \leqq \pi a;$

(b) $\varrho = b - \dfrac{a^2}{z}, \qquad \dfrac{a^2}{b} \leqq z < \infty.$

(c) $\varrho = Az^n, \quad n > 0, \quad n \neq 1;$

3.2. Find the surface of revolution which is such that the cross-section for elastic scattering by this surface is the same as the Rutherford scattering cross-section.

3.3. Find the differential cross-section for the scattering of particles by a spherical "potential barrier":

$$U(r) = V, \quad r < a; \qquad U(r) = 0, \quad r > a.$$

3.4. Find the cross-section for the process where a particle falls towards the centre of the potential $U(r)$ when $U(r)$ is given by:

(a) $U(r) = \dfrac{\alpha}{r} - \dfrac{\beta}{r^2};$

(b) $U(r) = \dfrac{\beta}{r^2} - \dfrac{\gamma}{r^4}.$

3.5. Calculate the cross-section for a particle to hit a small sphere of radius R placed at the centre of the potential $U(r)$ for the cases:

(a) $U(r) = -\dfrac{\alpha}{r^n}, \qquad n \geqq 2;$

(b) $U(r) = \dfrac{\beta}{r^2} - \dfrac{\gamma}{r^4}.$

3.6. Find the differential cross-section for the scattering of particles by the potential $U(r) = \alpha/r - \alpha/R$, $r < R$; $U(r) = 0$, $r > R$.

3.7. Find the differential cross-section for the scattering of fast particles ($E \gg V$) by the potential $U(r) = V(1-r^2/R^2)$, $r < R$; $U(r) = 0$, $r > R$.

3.8. Calculate the differential cross-section for small angle scattering in the potential $U(r) = \beta/r^4 - \alpha/r^2$.

3.9. Find the differential cross-section for the scattering of particles by the potential $U(r) = -\alpha/r^2$.

3.10. Find the differential cross-section for the scattering of fast parti cles ($E \gg V$) by the following potentials $U(r)$:

(a) $U(r) = Ve^{-\varkappa^2 r^2};$

(b) $U(r) = \dfrac{V}{1+\varkappa^2 r^2}.$

Study in detail the limiting cases when the deflecting angle is close to its minimum or to its maximum value.

3.11. A beam of particles with their velocities initially parallel to the z-axis is scattered by the fixed ellipsoid

$$\frac{x^2}{a^2}+\frac{y^2}{b^2}+\frac{z^2}{c^2} = 1.$$

Find the differential scattering cross-section for the following cases:

(a) the ellipsoid is smooth and the scattering elastic;
(b) the ellipsoid is smooth and the scattering is inelastic;
(c) the ellipsoid is rough and the scattering elastic.

3.12. Find the differential cross-section for small-angle scattering by the following potentials $U(\boldsymbol{r})$ ($\boldsymbol{a}$ is a constant vector):

(a) $U(\boldsymbol{r}) = \dfrac{(\boldsymbol{a}\cdot\boldsymbol{r})}{r^2};$

(b) $U(\boldsymbol{r}) = \dfrac{(\boldsymbol{a}\cdot\boldsymbol{r})}{r^3}.$

3.13. Find the change in the differential cross-section for the scattering of a particle by the potential $U(r)$ when $U(r)$ is varied by a small amount $\delta U(r)$ for the following cases:

(a) $U(r) = \dfrac{\alpha}{r}, \qquad \delta U(r) = \dfrac{\beta}{r^2};$

(b) $U(r) = \dfrac{\alpha}{r}, \qquad \delta U(r) = \dfrac{\gamma}{r^3};$

(c) $U(r) = \dfrac{\beta}{r^2}, \qquad \delta U(r) = \dfrac{\gamma}{r^3}.$

3.14. Find the differential cross-section as function of the energy acquired by fast particles ($E \gg V_{1,2}$) due to their scattering in the potential $U(r, t) = [V_1(r) + V_2(r) \sin \omega t]e^{-\varkappa^2 r^2}$.

3.15. A particle with velocity V decays into two identical particles. Find the distribution of the secondary particles over the angle of divergence, that is, the angle between the directions at which the two secondary particles fly off. The decay is isotropic in the centre-of-mass system and the velocity of the secondary particles is V_0 in that system.

3.16. Find the energy distribution of secondary particles in the laboratory system, if the angular distribution in the centre-of-mass system is $3 \sin^2 \theta_0 \, d^2\omega/8\pi$ ($d^2\omega = \sin \theta_0 \, d\theta_0 \, d\varphi$), where θ_0 is the angle between the velocity V of the original particle and the direction in which one of the secondary particles flies off in the centre-of-mass system. The velocity of the secondary particles in the centre-of-mass system is V_0.

3.17. An electron moving at infinity with velocity V collides with another electron at rest; the impact parameter is ϱ. Determine the velocities of the two electrons after the collision.

3.18. Find the range of possible values for the angle between the velocity directions after a moving particle of mass m_1 has collided with a particle of mass m_2 at rest.

3.19. Find the differential cross-section for the scattering of inelastic smooth spheres by similar ones at rest.

3.20. Find the change in the intensity of a beam of particles travelling through a volume filled with absorbing centres; their density is n cm^{-3}, and the absorption cross-section is σ.

3.21. Find the number of reactions occurring during a time dt in a volume element d^3r when two beams with velocities V_1 and V_2 and densities n_1 and n_2, respectively, collide. The reaction cross-section is σ.

3.22. A particle of mass M moves in a volume filled with particles of mass m ($\ll M$) which are at rest initially. The cross-section for the scattering of M by m is $d\sigma/d^2\omega = f(\theta)$, and the collisions are assumed to be elastic.

(a) Find the "frictional force" acting on M,

(b) Find the average of the square of the angle over which M is deflected.

4. Lagrangian Equations of Motion. Conservation Laws

4.1. A particle, moving in the potential $U(x) = -Fx$, travels from the point $x = 0$ to the point $x = a$ in a time τ. Find the time-dependence of the position of the particle, assuming it to be of the form $x(t) = At^2+Bt+C$, and determining the constants A, B, and C such that the action is a minimum.

4.2. A particle moves in the xy-plane in the potential $U(x, y) = 0$, $x < 0$; $U(x, y) = V$, $x > 0$, and travels in a time τ from the point $(-a, 0)$ to the point (a, a). Find its position as a function of time, assuming that it satisfies the equations

$$x_{1,2} = A_{1,2}t+B_{1,2},$$
$$y_{1,2} = C_{1,2}t+D_{1,2}.$$

The indices 1 and 2 refer, respectively, to the left-hand ($x < 0$) and right-hand ($x > 0$) half-planes.

4.3. Prove by direct calculation the invariance of the Lagrangian equations of motion under the coordinate transformation

$$q_i = q_i(Q_1, Q_2, \ldots, Q_s, t), \qquad i = 1, 2, \ldots, s.$$

4.4. What is the change in the Lagrangian in order that the Lagrangian equations of motion retain their form under the transformation to new coordinates and "time":

$$q_i = q_i(Q_1, Q_2, \ldots, Q_s, \tau), \qquad i = 1, 2, \ldots, s;$$
$$t = t(Q_1, Q_2, \ldots, Q_s, \tau).$$

4.5. Write down the Lagrangian and the equations of motion for a particle moving in a potential $U(x)$, introducing a "local time" $\tau = t-\lambda x$.

4.6. How does the Lagrangian

$$L = \sqrt{1-\left(\frac{dx}{dt}\right)^2}$$

transform when we change to the coordinate q and "time" τ through the equations:

$$x = q\cosh\lambda+\tau\sinh\lambda,$$
$$t = q\sinh\lambda+\tau\cosh\lambda?$$

4.7. How do the energy and the generalised momenta change under the coordinate transformation

$$q_i = f_i(Q_1, \ldots, Q_s, t), \qquad i = 1, \ldots, s?$$

4.8. How do the energy and the generalised momenta which are conjugate to (a) the spherical polar and (b) the Cartesian coordinates transform under a change to a coordinate system which is rotating around the z-axis?

(a) $\varphi = \varphi'+\Omega t, \qquad r = r';$

(b) $x = x'\cos\Omega t - y'\sin\Omega t,$

$\quad y = x'\sin\Omega t+y'\cos\Omega t.$

4.9. How do the energy and momenta change when we change to a frame of reference which is moving with a velocity $\boldsymbol{V}$? Take the Lagrangian L' in the moving frame of reference in either of two forms:

(a) $L_1' = L(\boldsymbol{r}'+\boldsymbol{V}t, \dot{\boldsymbol{r}}'+\boldsymbol{V}, t)$, where $L(\dot{\boldsymbol{r}}, \boldsymbol{r}, t)$ is the Lagrangian in the original frame of reference;

(b) $L_2' = \sum_a \frac{1}{2}m_a v_a'^2 - U(\boldsymbol{r}'+\boldsymbol{V}t, t)$. Here L_2' differs from L_1' by the total derivative with respect to the time of the function $\left(\boldsymbol{V}\cdot\sum_a m_a\boldsymbol{r}_a'\right)+\frac{1}{2}V^2 t\sum_a m_a$.

4.10. Consider an infinitesimal transformation of the coordinates and the time of the form

$$q_i' = q_i+\varepsilon\Psi_i(q, t), \qquad t' = t+\varepsilon X(q, t), \qquad \varepsilon\to 0.$$

Show that if the action is invariant under this transformation,

$$\int_{t_1}^{t_2} L\left(q, \frac{dq}{dt}, t\right)dt = \int_{t_1'}^{t_2'} L\left(q', \frac{dq'}{dt'}, t'\right)dt',$$

the quantity

$$\sum_i \frac{\partial L}{\partial \dot{q}_i}(\dot{q}_i X - \Psi_i) - LX$$

is an integral of motion.

4.11. Generalise the theorem of the preceding problem to the case when under the transformation of the coordinates and the time the action changes in the following way:

$$\int_{t_1}^{t_2} L\left(q, \frac{dq}{dt}, t\right) dt = \int_{t_1'}^{t_2'} \left\{L\left(q', \frac{dq'}{dt'}, t'\right) + \varepsilon \frac{df(q', t')}{dt'}\right\} dt'.$$

4.12. Find the integrals of motion if the action remains invariant under:

(a) a translation;
(b) a rotation;
(c) a shift in the origin of the time;
(d) a screw shift;
(e) the transformation of problem 4.6.

4.13. Find the integrals of motion for a particle moving in

(a) a uniform field $U(\boldsymbol{r}) = -(\boldsymbol{F} \cdot \boldsymbol{r})$;
(b) a potential $U(\boldsymbol{r})$, where $U(\boldsymbol{r})$ is a homogeneous function,

$$U(\alpha \boldsymbol{r}) = \alpha^n U(\boldsymbol{r});$$

specify for what values of n the similarity transformation leaves the action invariant;
(c) the field of a travelling wave $U(\boldsymbol{r}, t) = U(\boldsymbol{r} - \boldsymbol{V}t)$, where $\boldsymbol{V}$ is a constant vector;
(d) a magnetic field specified by the vector potential $\boldsymbol{A}(\boldsymbol{r})$, where $\boldsymbol{A}(\boldsymbol{r})$ is a homogeneous function;
(e) an electromagnetic field rotating with a constant angular velocity Ω around the z-axis.

4.14. Find the integral of motion corresponding to the Galilean transformations.

Hint: Use the result of problem 4.11.

4.15. Find the integrals of motion of a particle moving in a uniform magnetic field $\boldsymbol{H}$, if the vector potential is given in the form

(a) $\boldsymbol{A} = \frac{1}{2}[\boldsymbol{H} \wedge \boldsymbol{r}]$;
(b) $A_x = A_z = 0, \quad A_y = Hx$.

4.16. Find the integrals of motion of a particle moving in

(a) the field of a magnetic dipole, $A = [\mathcal{M} \wedge \boldsymbol{r}]/r^3$, $\mathcal{M}$ = constant;
(b) the Rubenchik field, $A_\varphi = \mu/r$, $A_r = A_z = 0$.

4.17. Find the equations of motion of a system with the following Lagrangian:

(a) $L(x, \dot{x}) = e^{-x^2}\left(e^{-\dot{x}^2} + 2\dot{x}\int_0^{\dot{x}} e^{-\alpha^2}\,d\alpha\right)$;

(b) $L(x, \dot{x}, t) = \frac{1}{2}e^{\alpha t}(\dot{x}^2 - \omega^2 x^2)$.

4.18. Write down the components of the acceleration vector for a particle

(a) in the system of spherical polars;
(b) for the case of orthogonal coordinates q_i, if the line element is given by the equation

$$ds^2 = h_1^2\,dq_1^2 + h_2^2\,dq_2^2 + h_3^2\,dq_3^2,$$

where $h_i = h_i(q_1, q_2, q_3)$ are the Lamé coefficients.

4.19. Write down the equations of motion of a point particle using arbitrary coordinates q_i which are connected with the Cartesian coordinates x_i by the relations:

(a) $x_i = x_i(q_1, q_2, q_3)$, $\quad i = 1, 2, 3$;

(b) $x_i = x_i(q_1, q_2, q_3, t)$, $\quad i = 1, 2, 3$.

4.20. Verify that one can use the Lagrangians

$$L_1 = \tfrac{1}{2}\mathcal{L}\dot{q}_1^2 - Uq_1, \qquad L_2 = -\frac{q_2^2}{2C} + Uq_2,$$

where $\dot{q}_1 = I$ is the current flowing through the inductance $\mathcal{L}$ in the solenoid from A to B (Fig. 6a), q_2 the charge on the upper plate of the capacitor (Fig. 6b), and U the voltage between A and B ($U = \varphi_B - \varphi_A$), to find the correct "equations of motion" for the q_i and the correct energies.

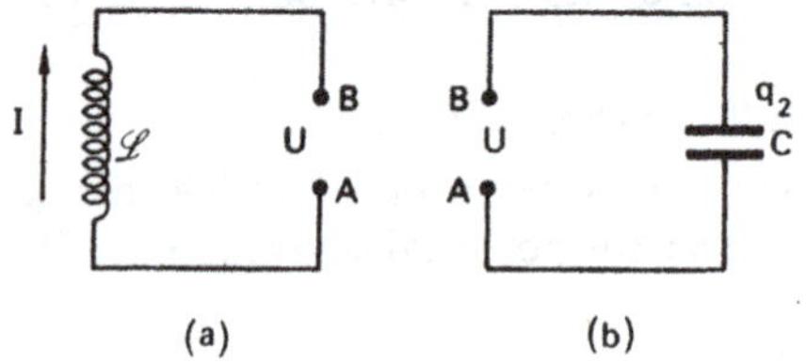

FIG. 6

4.21. Use the additivity property of the Lagrangians and the results of the preceding problem to find the Lagrangians and the Lagrangian equations of motion for the circuits of Figs. 7a, b, c.

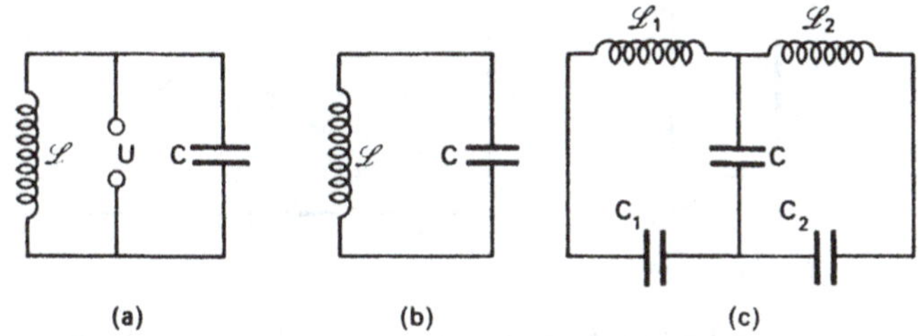

FIG. 7

4.22. Find the Lagrangians for the following systems:

(a) a circuit with a variable capacitor, the movable plate of which is connected to a pendulum of mass m (Fig. 8a), and the capacitance of which is a known function $C(\varphi)$ of the angle φ the pendulum makes with the vertical. The mass of the capacitor plate may be neglected;

(b) a core suspended from a spring with elastic constant $\varkappa$ inside a solenoid with inductance $\mathscr{L}(x)$ which is a given function of the displacement x of the core (Fig. 8b).

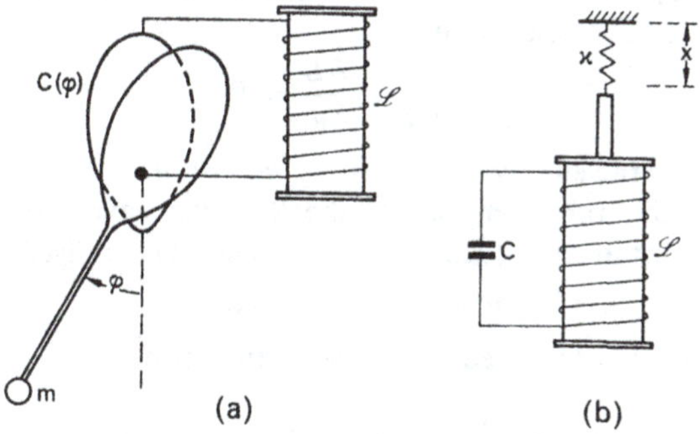

FIG. 8

4.23. A perfectly conducting square frame can rotate around a fixed side AB of length a (Fig. 9). The frame is placed in a constant uniform magnetic field $\boldsymbol{H}$ at right angles to the AB-axis. The inductance of the frame is $\mathscr{L}$, the mass of the side CD is m, and the masses of the other sides may be neglected. Describe qualitatively the motion of the frame.

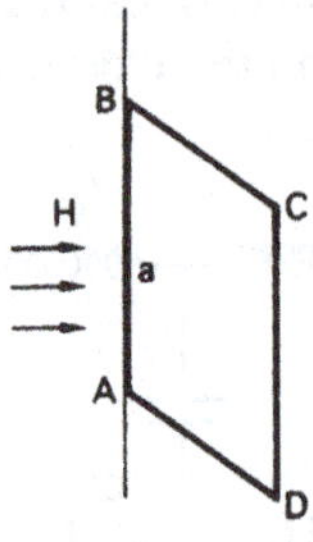

FIG. 9

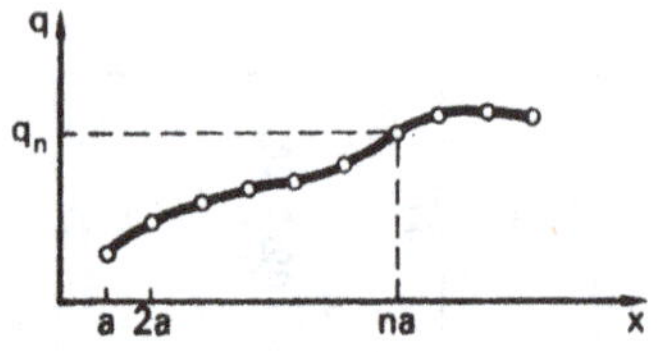

FIG. 10

4.24. Use the method of the Lagrangian or undetermined multipliers to obtain the equations of motion for a particle in the field of gravity when it is constrained to move

(a) along a parabola $z = ax^2$ in a vertical plane;

(b) along a circle of radius l in a vertical plane.

Determine the forces of constraint.

4.25. A particle moves in the field of gravity along a straight line which is rotating uniformly in a vertical plane. Write down the equations of motion and determine the moment of the forces of constraint.

4.26. One can describe the influence of constraints and friction on the motion of a system by introducing generalised constraint and friction forces into the equations of motion:

$$\frac{d}{dt}\frac{\partial L}{\partial \dot{q}_i} - \frac{\partial L}{\partial q_i} = R_i.$$

(a) How does the energy of the system vary with time?

(b) What is the transformation of the R_i which leaves the equations of motion invariant under a transformation to new generalised coordinates:

$$q_i = q_i(Q_1, \ldots, Q_s, t)?$$

4.27. Let the constraint equations be of the form

$$\dot{q}_\beta = \sum_{n=r+1}^{s} b_{\beta n}\dot{q}_n, \quad \beta = 1, \ldots, r,$$

while the Lagrangian $L(q_{r+1}, \ldots, q_s, \dot{q}_1, \ldots, \dot{q}_s, t)$ and the coefficients $b_{\beta n}$ do not depend on the q_β.

Show that the equations of motion can be written in the form

$$\frac{d}{dt}\frac{\partial \mathcal{L}}{\partial \dot{q}_n} - \frac{\partial \mathcal{L}}{\partial q_n} + \sum_{\beta=1}^{r}\frac{\partial L}{\partial \dot{q}_\beta}\sum_{m=r+1}^{s}\left(\frac{\partial b_{\beta m}}{\partial q_n} - \frac{\partial b_{\beta n}}{\partial q_m}\right)\dot{q}_m = 0,$$

where $\tilde{L}(q_{r+1}, \ldots, q_s, \dot{q}_{r+1}, \ldots, \dot{q}_s, t)$ is the function obtained from L by using the constraint equations to eliminate the velocities $\dot{q}_1, \ldots, \dot{q}_r$.

4.28. A continuous string can be thought of as the limiting case of a system of N particles (Fig. 10) which are connected by an elastic thread, in the limit as $N \to \infty$, $a \to 0$, $Na =$ constant. The Lagrangian for a discrete system is

$$L(q_1, \ldots, q_N, \dot{q}_1, \ldots, \dot{q}_N, t) = \sum_{n=1}^{N+1} L_n(q_n, q_n - q_{n-1}, \dot{q}_n, t), \quad (q_0 = q_{N+1} \equiv 0)$$

where q_n is the displacement of the nth particle from its equilibrium position.

(a) Obtain the equations of motion for a continuous system as the limiting case of the Lagrangian equations of motion for a discrete system.

(b) Obtain an expression for the energy of a continuous system as the limiting case of the expression for the energy of a discrete system.

Hint: Introduce the coordinate x of a point on the string together with the expressions obtained as a result of taking the limit as $a \to 0$, $n = x/a \to \infty$:

$$q(x, t) = \lim q_n(t), \qquad \frac{\partial q}{\partial x} = \lim \frac{q_n(t) - q_{n-1}(t)}{a},$$

$$\mathcal{L}\left(x, q, \frac{\partial q}{\partial x}, \frac{\partial q}{\partial t}, t\right) = \lim \frac{L_n(q_n, q_n - q_{n-1}, \dot{q}_n, t)}{a}.$$

4.29. A charged particle moves in a potential $U(\boldsymbol{r})$ and a constant magnetic field $\boldsymbol{H}(\boldsymbol{r})$, where $U(\boldsymbol{r})$ and $\boldsymbol{H}(\boldsymbol{r})$ are homogeneous functions of the coordinates of degrees k and n, respectively, that is, $U(\alpha\boldsymbol{r}) = \alpha^k U(\boldsymbol{r})$, $\boldsymbol{H}(\alpha\boldsymbol{r}) = \alpha^n \boldsymbol{H}(\boldsymbol{r})$. Develop for this system the similarity principle, determining for what value of n it holds.

4.30. Generalise the virial theorem for a system of charged particles in a uniform magnetic field $\boldsymbol{H}$. The potential energy U of the system is a homogeneous function of the coordinates, $U(\alpha\boldsymbol{r}_1, \ldots, \alpha\boldsymbol{r}_s) = \alpha^k U(\boldsymbol{r}_1, \ldots, \boldsymbol{r}_s)$ and the system moves in a bounded region of space with velocities which remain finite.

5. Small Oscillations of Systems with One Degree of Freedom

5.1. Find the frequency of the small oscillations for particles moving in the following potentials:

(a) $U(x) = V \cos \alpha x - Fx$;

(b) $U(x) = V(\alpha^2 x^2 - \sin^2 \alpha x)$.

5.2. Find the frequency of the small oscillations for the system depicted in Fig. 11. The system rotates with an angular velocity Ω in the field of gravity around a vertical axis.

5.3. A point charge q of mass m moves along a circle of radius R in a vertical plane. Another charge q is fixed at the lowest point of the circle (Fig. 12). Find the equilibrium position and the frequency of the small oscillations for the first point charge.

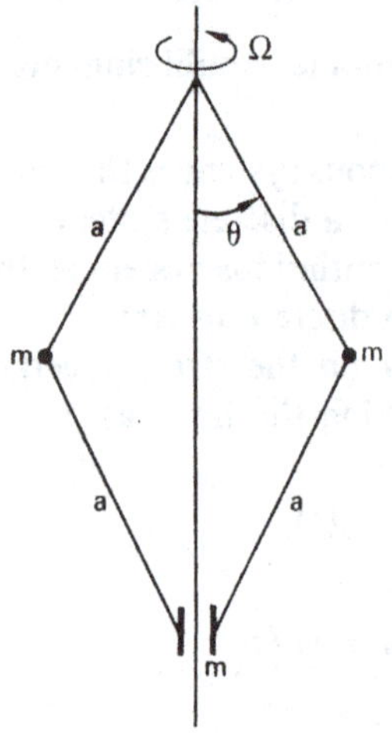

FIG 11

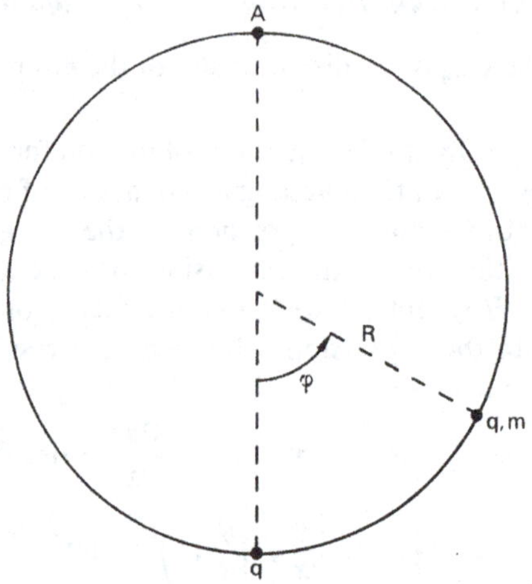

FIG. 12

5.4. Describe the motion along a curve close to a circle for a point particle in the central field $U(r) = -\alpha/r^n$ $(0 < n < 2)$.

5.5. Find the frequencies of the small oscillations of a spherical pendulum (a particle of mass m suspended from a string of length l), if the angle of deflection from the vertical oscillates about the value θ_0.

5.6. Find the correction to the frequency of the small oscillations of a diatomic molecule due to its angular momentum M.

5.7. Determine the eigen-oscillations of the system shown in Fig. 13 for the case when the particle moves (a) horizontally, and (b) vertically.

How does the frequency depend on the tension in the springs in the equilibrium position?

FIG. 13

5.8. Find the eigen-oscillations of the system in Fig. 14 in a uniform field of gravity for the case when the particle can only move vertically.

5.9. Find the stable small oscillations of a pendulum when its point of suspension moves uniformly along a circle of radius R with frequency Ω (Fig. 15). The pendulum length is l ($l \gg R$).

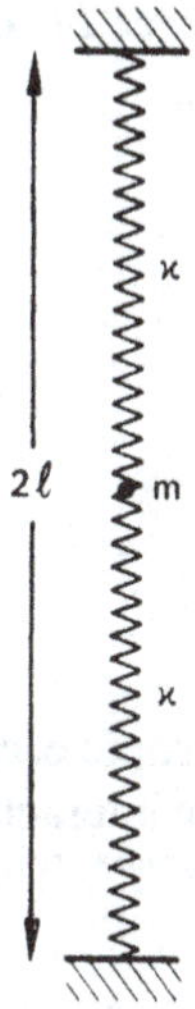

FIG. 14

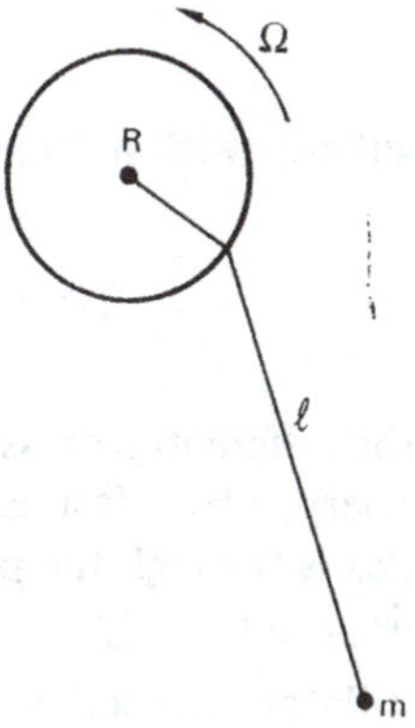

FIG. 15

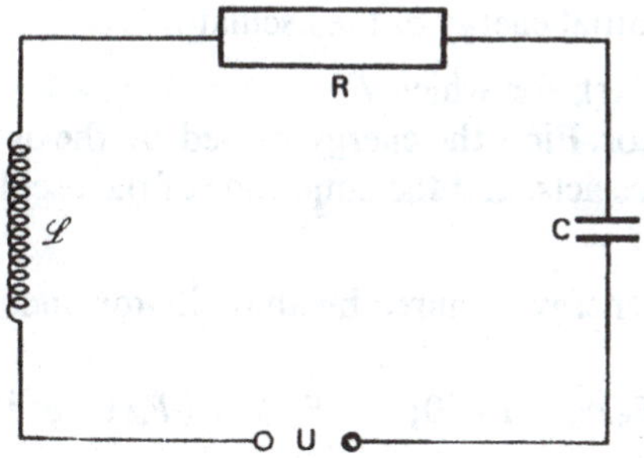

FIG. 16

5.10. Find the stable oscillations in the voltage across a capacitor and the current in a circuit with an e.m.f. $U(t) = U_0 \cos \omega t$ (Fig. 16).

5.11. Describe the motion with friction of an oscillator which initially is at rest and which is acted upon by a force $F(t) = F\cos\gamma t$.

5.12. Determine the energy E acquired by an oscillator under the action of a force $F(t) = Fe^{-(t/\tau)^2}$ during the total time it acts

(a) if the oscillator was at rest at $t = -\infty$;

(b) if the amplitude of the oscillator at $t = -\infty$ was a.

5.13. Describe the motion under the action of a force $F(t)$

(a) of an unstable system described by the equation

$$\ddot{x} - \mu^2 x = \frac{1}{m} F(t);$$

(b) of an oscillator with friction:

$$\ddot{x} + 2\lambda\dot{x} + \omega_0^2 x = \frac{1}{m} F(t).$$

5.14. Find the differential cross-section for an isotropic oscillator to be excited to an energy ε by a fast particle ($E \gg V$) if the interaction between the two particles is through the potential $U(r) = Ve^{-\varkappa^2 r^2}$. The energy of the oscillator is zero initially.

5.15. An oscillator can oscillate only along the z-axis. Find the differential cross-section for the oscillator to be excited to an energy ε by a fast particle ($E \gg V$), if the interaction between the particles is through the potential $U(r) = Ve^{-\varkappa^2 r^2}$. The particle moves along the z-axis with velocity v_∞, and the initial energy of the oscillator is ε_0.

5.16. A force $F(t)$, for which $F(-\infty) = 0$, $F(\infty) = F_0$, acts upon an harmonic oscillator. Find the energy gained by the oscillator during the total time the force acts, and the amplitude of the oscillator as $t \to +\infty$, if it were at rest at $t = -\infty$.

5.17. Find the energy acquired by an oscillator under the action of the force

$$F(t) = \tfrac{1}{2}F_0 e^{\lambda t}, \quad t < 0; \qquad F(t) = \tfrac{1}{2}F_0(1 - e^{-\lambda t}), \quad t > 0.$$

At $t = -\infty$ the energy of the oscillator was E_0.

5.18. Estimate the change in the amplitude of the vibrations of an oscillator when a force $F(t)$ is switched on slowly and smoothly over a period

τ so that $\omega\tau \gg 1$. Assume $F(t)=0$ for $t < 0$, $F(t) = F_0$ for $t > \tau$, while $F^{(k)}(t) \sim F_0/\tau^k$ ($k = 0, 1, \ldots, n+1$) for $0 < t < \tau$ and $F^{(s)}(0) = F^{(s)}(\tau) = 0$ ($s = 1, 2, \ldots, n-1$), while the nth derivative of the force has a discontinuity at $t = 0$ and at $t = \tau$.

5.19. Find the stable oscillations of an oscillator which is acted upon by a periodic force in the following two cases:

(a) $F(t) = (t/\tau - n)F$, when $n\tau \leqq t < (n+1)\tau$ (Fig. 17);

(b) $F(t) = (1 - e^{-\lambda t'})F$, $t' = t - n\tau$, when $n\tau \leqq t < (n+1)\tau$ (Fig. 18).

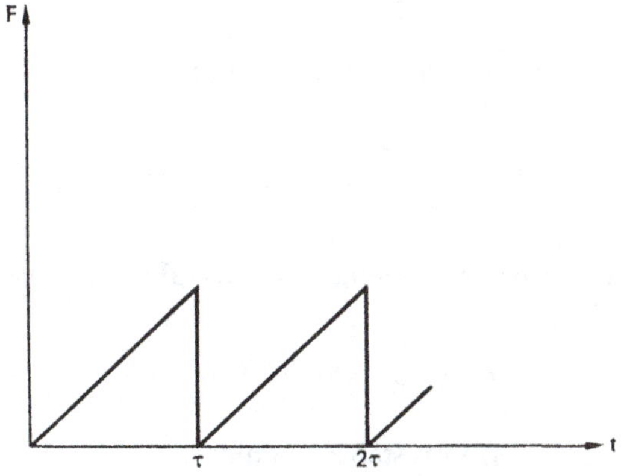

FIG. 17

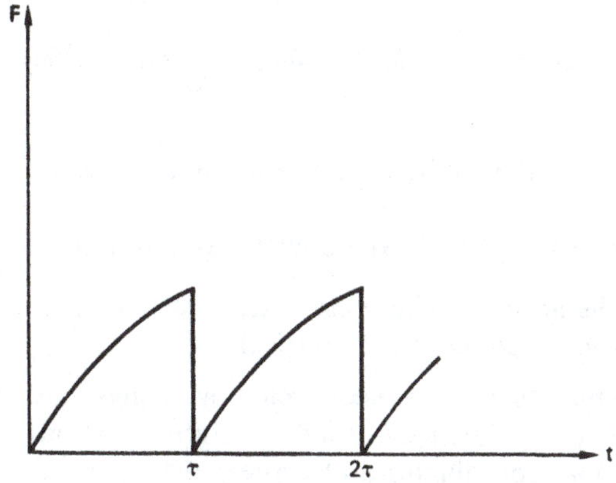

FIG. 18

(c) Find the stable current through the circuit of Fig. 16 in which there is an e.m.f. $U(t) = V(t/\tau - n)$ for $n\tau \leqq t < (n+1)\tau$. The internal resistance of the battery is zero.

5.20. An oscillator with eigen-frequency ω_0 and with a friction force acting upon it given by $f_{fr} = -2m\lambda\dot{x}$ has an additional force $F(t)$ acting upon it.

(a) Find the average work done by $F(t)$ when the oscillator is vibrating in a stable mode for the case when

$$F(t) = f_1 \cos \omega t + f_2 \cos 2\omega t.$$

(b) Repeat the calculations for the case when

$$F(t) = \sum_{n=-\infty}^{+\infty} a_n e^{in\omega t}, \quad a_{-n} = a_n^*.$$

(c) Find the average over a long time interval of the work done by the force

$$F(t) = f_1 \cos \omega_1 t + f_2 \cos \omega_2 t,$$

when the oscillator performs stable vibrations.

(d) Find the total work done by the force

$$F(t) = \int_{-\infty}^{+\infty} \psi(\omega)\, e^{i\omega t}\, d\omega, \quad \psi(-\omega) = \psi^*(\omega)$$

for the case where the oscillator was at rest at $t = -\infty$.

6. Small Oscillations of Systems with Several Degrees of Freedom

6.1. Find the normal oscillations of the system of Fig. 19 for the case when the particles can move only vertically.

6.2. Three masses which are connected by springs move along a circle (Fig. 20). The point A is fixed. Find the eigen-vibrations of the system. Find the normal coordinates and express the Lagrangian in terms of those coordinates.

6.3. Find the eigen-vibrations of a system described by the Lagrangian

$$L = \tfrac{1}{2}(\dot{x}^2+\dot{y}^2)-\tfrac{1}{2}(\omega_1^2x^2+\omega_2^2y^2).$$

What is the trajectory of a point with Cartesian coordinates x, y?

6.4. Find the normal coordinates of the systems with the following Lagrangians:

(a) $L = \frac{1}{2}(\dot{x}^2+\dot{y}^2)-\frac{1}{2}(\omega_1^2x^2+\omega_2^2y^2)+\alpha xy$;

(b) $L = \frac{1}{2}(m_1\dot{x}^2+m_2\dot{y}^2)+\beta\dot{x}\dot{y}-\frac{1}{2}(x^2+y^2)$.

6.5. Find the eigen-oscillations of a system of coupled circuits (Figs. 21a and b).

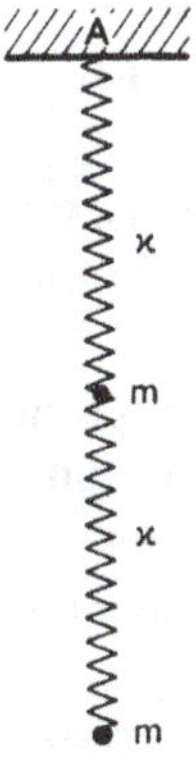

FIG. 19

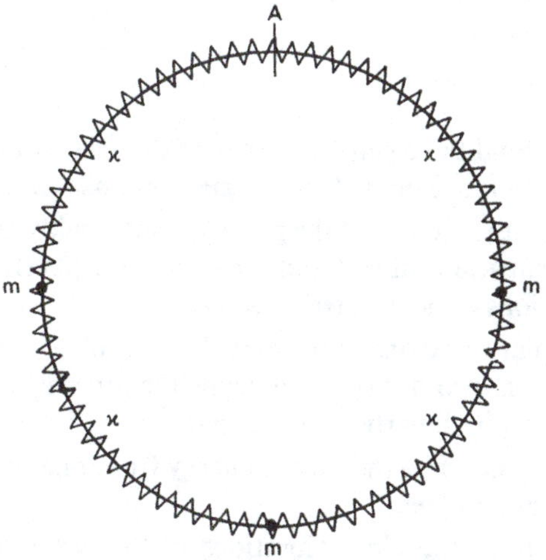

FIG. 20

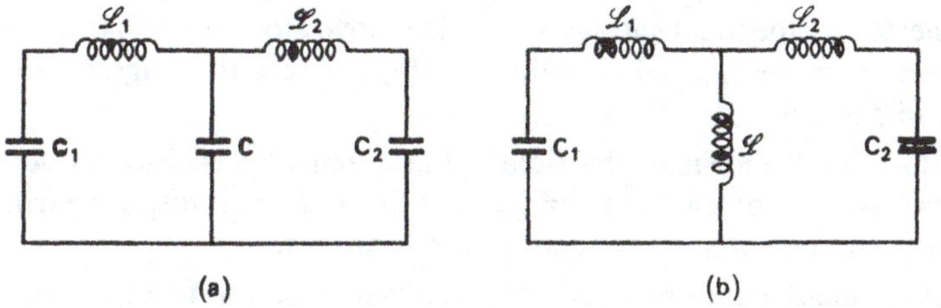

FIG. 21

6.6. Find the normal coordinates of a system of particles which are connected by springs (Fig. 22). The masses can move only along the straight line AB. Find the eigen-vibrations of the system.

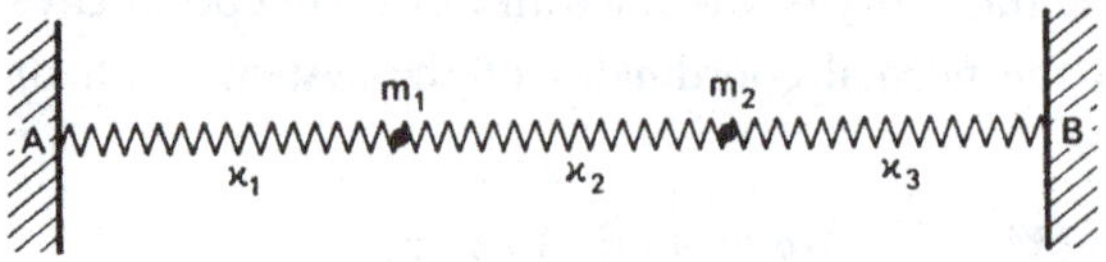

FIG. 22

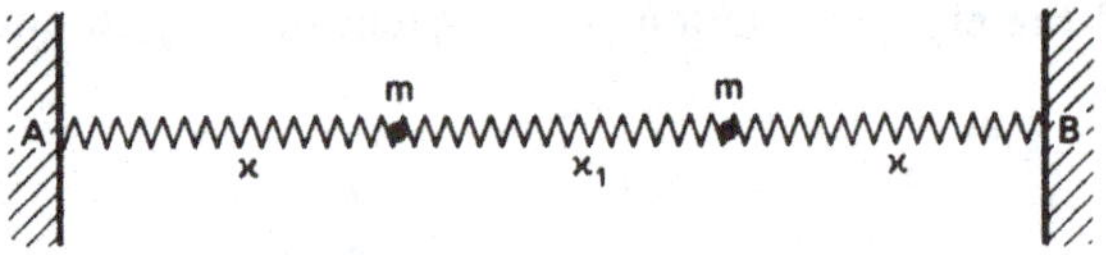

FIG. 23

6.7. Find the eigen-vibrations of the system of Fig. 23 where the particles can move only along the straight line AB

(a) if at $t = 0$ one of the particles moves with velocity v while the second particle is at rest and the displacements from the equilibrium positions of both particles are zero;

(b) if at $t = 0$ one of the particles is displaced from its equilibrium position over a distance a, while the other is at its equilibrium position and both particles are at rest.

6.8. Determine the flux of energy from one particle to the other in the preceding problem.

6.9. Find the eigen-vibrations of the system of Fig. 23 if each of the particles is acted upon by a frictional force which is proportional to its velocity.

6.10. Find the eigen-oscillations of three identical particles which are connected by identical springs and which move along a circle (Fig. 24).

Determine the normal coordinates which reduce the Lagrangian to a sum of squares.

6.11. Find the normal vibrations of the system of particles considered in the preceding problem, if at $t = 0$ one of the particles is displaced from its equilibrium position. The initial velocities are zero.

6.12. Find the normal coordinates of a system of four identical particles moving along a circle (Fig. 25).

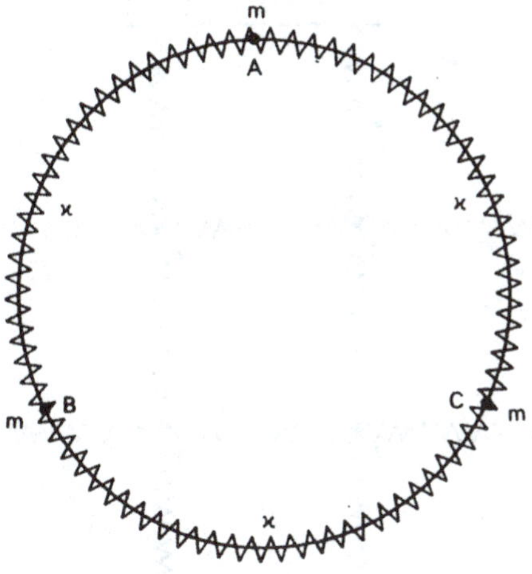

FIG. 24

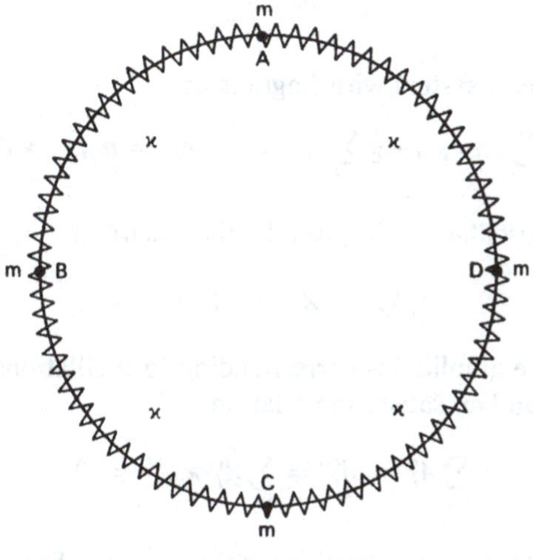

FIG. 25

6.13. Find the eigen-vibrations of the system of particles of Fig. 26 such that the particles do not move out of the plane of the figure. All particles and springs are identical. The tensions in the springs at equilibrium are equal to $f = \varkappa l$, where l is the equilibrium distance between the masses.

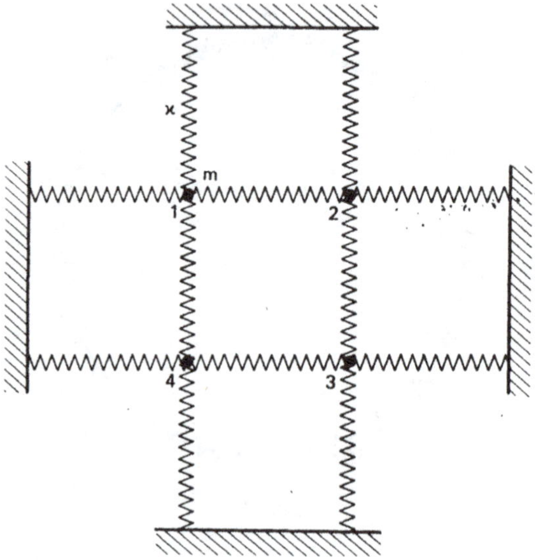

FIG. 26

6.14. Consider a system with Lagrangian

$$L = \tfrac{1}{2}\sum_{i,j} m_{ij}\dot{x}_i\dot{x}_j - \tfrac{1}{2}\sum_{i,j} \varkappa_{ij}x_ix_j, \quad m_{ij} = m_{ji}, \quad \varkappa_{ij} = \varkappa_{ji}.$$

Let their eigen-oscillations be given by the equations

$$x_i^{(l)}(t) = A_i^{(l)} \cos(\omega_l t + \varphi_l).$$

Prove that the amplitudes corresponding to oscillations with different frequencies ω_l and ω_s satisfy the relations

$$\sum_{i,j} A_i^{(s)} m_{ij} A_j^{(l)} = \sum_{i,j} A_i^{(s)} \varkappa_{ij} A_j^{(l)} = 0.$$

6.15. (a) Find the eigen-vibrations of the system of Fig. 27. All particles and springs are identical. The tension in the springs at equilibrium is $f = \varkappa l$, where l is the equilibrium distance between the particles.

(b) Find the eigen-vibrations of the system of four identical particles of Fig. 27 for the case where the mass of particle 5 is put equal to zero. The elasticity coefficients and the tensions at equilibrium are the same as before.

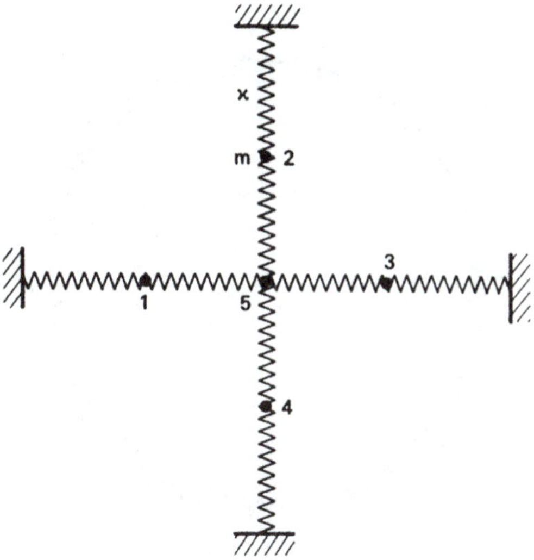

FIG. 27

Hint for both (a) and (b): several of the eigen-vibrations are obvious. The determination of the others can be simplified by using the relations of the preceding problem.

6.16. Find the eigen-vibrations of the system of particles of Fig. 28a; the particles move along a circle.

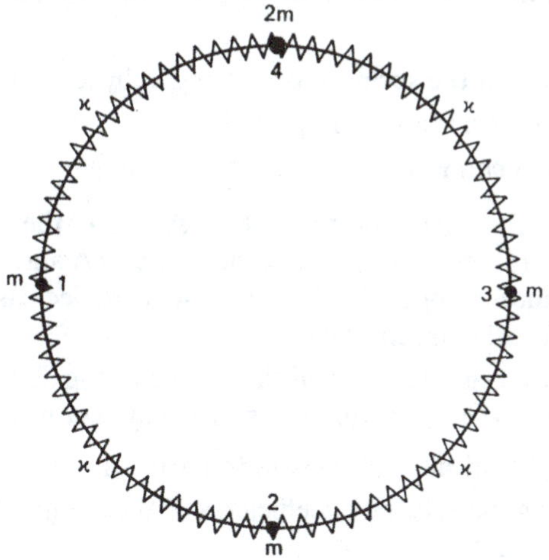

FIG. 28a

FIG. 28b

6.17. Find the eigen-vibrations of a system of four particles moving along a circle (Fig. 28b). All springs are identical and the masses of particles 1 and 3 are m, while those of particles 2 and 4 are M.

6.18. Which of the eigen-vibrations of the system of Fig. 24 remain practically unchanged when the following small changes are made in the system:

(a) the elasticity of the spring AB is changed by a small amount $\delta\varkappa$;

(b) a small mass δm is added to particle C;

(c) a small mass δm_1 is added to particle C and δm_2 to particle B?

6.19. Describe the eigen-vibrations of the system of the preceding problem for the cases (a) and (b) if initially the particles A and C are displaced over equal distances in opposite directions so as to decrease their mutual distance. All velocities are initially zero.

6.20. Find the eigen-vibrations of the system of Fig. 25 which are practically the same as the eigen-vibrations of the system which is obtained

(a) by adding identical small masses to particles A and B;

(b) by changing the elasticity coefficients of the springs AB and CD by equal amounts;

(c) by adding an extra mass to particle A.

6.21. The masses A and C of the system described in problem 6.20(b) are at time $t = 0$ displaced by the same amount from their equilibrium positions in opposite directions so as to decrease their distance apart. Initially all velocities are equal to zero. Describe the eigen-vibrations of the system.

6.22. Determine the eigen-vibrations of the system of Fig. 27 if at $t = 0$ the masses 1 and 4 are displaced over equal distances in the horizontal direction in such a way that their distance apart decreases. At $t = 0$ the velocities of all particles are equal to zero. The tension in the springs is $f = \varkappa l_1$, $l - l_1 \ll l$, where l is the equilibrium distance between the particles (compare problem 6.21).

6.23. Determine the eigen-vibrations of an anisotropic charged harmonic oscillator moving in the potential $U(\boldsymbol{r}) = \frac{1}{2}m(\omega_1^2x^2 + \omega_2^2y^2 + \omega_3^2z^2)$ and in a uniform magnetic field $\boldsymbol{H}$ which is parallel to the z-axis. Consider in particular the following limiting cases:

(a) $|\omega_H| \ll |\omega_1 - \omega_2|$;

(b) $|\omega_H| \gg \omega_{1,2}$;

(c) $\omega_1 = \omega_2 \gg |\omega_H|$,

where $\omega_H = eH/mc$.

6.24. Determine the eigen-vibrations of an anisotropic charged harmonic oscillator moving in a potential $U(\boldsymbol{r}) = \frac{1}{2}m(\omega_1^2x^2 + \omega_2^2y^2 + \omega_3^2z^2)$ and in a weak magnetic field $\boldsymbol{H} = (H_x, 0, H_z)$, considering the effect of the magnetic field to be a small perturbation.

6.25. A mathematical pendulum is part of an electric circuit (Fig. 29). A constant, uniform magnetic field $\boldsymbol{H}$ is applied at right angles to the plane of the figure. Find the eigen-vibrations of this system.

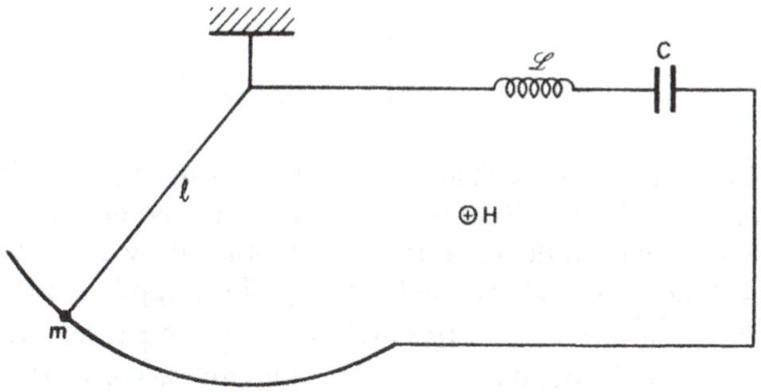

FIG. 29

6.26. Find the stable oscillations of the system of particles of Fig. 19, if the point of suspension A moves vertically according to the equation

(a) $a \cos \omega t$;

(b) $a(t) = a\left(\frac{t}{\tau} - n\right)$ for $n\tau \leqq t < (n+1)\tau$.

Plot a diagram of the frequency-dependence of the amplitude of the vibrations for the case (a). What is the change in the diagram when there is friction present?

6.27. Determine the stable oscillations of the system of Fig. 23 if the point A moves according to the relation $a \cos \omega t$.

6.28. Determine the stable oscillations of the mass m in Fig. 30 moving in a variable uniform field described by the potential $U(\boldsymbol{r}) = -(\boldsymbol{F}(t)\cdot\boldsymbol{r})$ for the following cases:

(a) $\boldsymbol{F}(t) = \boldsymbol{F}_0 \cos \omega t$;

(b) the vector $\boldsymbol{F}$ rotates with constant absolute magnitude with a frequency ω in the plane of the figure.

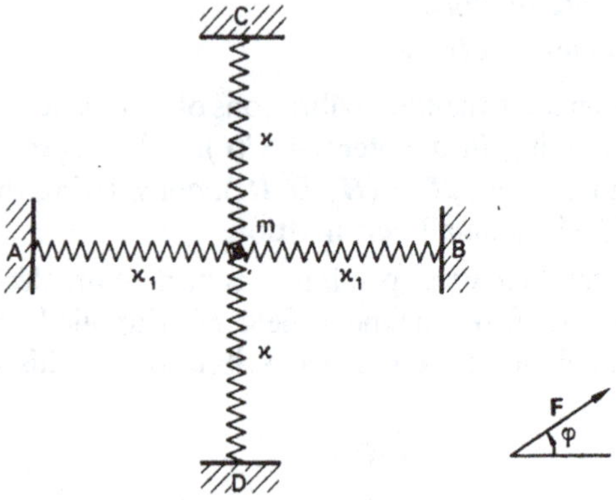

FIG. 30

6.29. Find the stable oscillations of a system of two particles which move along a circle (Fig. 31) for the case when the point A moves along the circle according to the relation $a \cos \omega t$. Study the way the amplitude of the oscillations depends on the frequency of the applied force.

6.30. Find the stable oscillations of the system of particles of Fig. 20 for the case when the point A moves along the circle according to the relation $a \cos \omega t$.

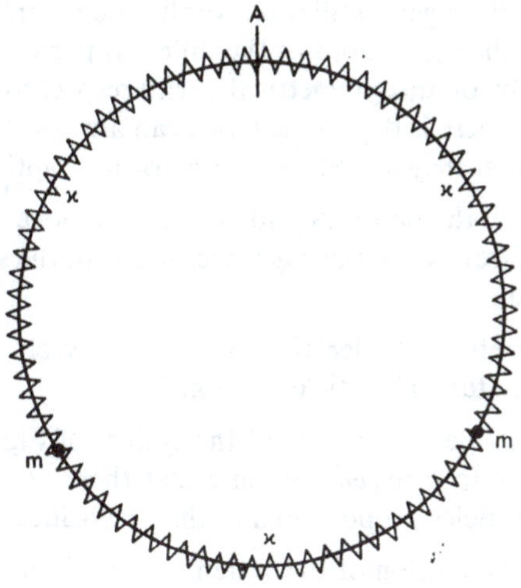

FIG. 31

6.31. We can write the stable oscillations of a system described by the Lagrangian

$$L = \frac{1}{2}\sum_{i,j} m_{ij}\dot{x}_i\dot{x}_j - \frac{1}{2}\sum_{i,j} \varkappa_{ij}x_ix_j + \sum_i x_if_i \cos \omega t$$

in the form

$$x_i(t) = \sum_l \lambda^{(l)}A_i^{(l)} \cos \omega t$$

(see problem 6.14). Why?

Express the coefficients $\lambda^{(l)}$ in terms of the f_i and the $A_i^{(l)}$.

Study the ω-dependence of the $\lambda^{(l)}$.

Show that $\lambda^{(s)} = 0$, if $\sum_i f_iA_i^{(s)} = 0$ for the sth oscillation.

6.32. The system of particles of Fig. 32 is symmetric with respect to the line CD.

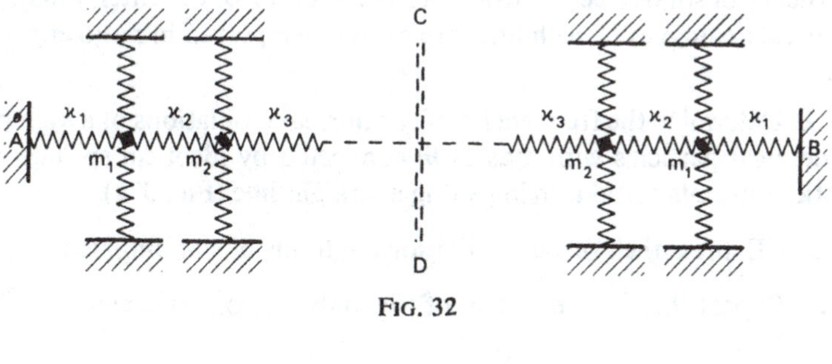

FIG. 32

(a) Show that if the eigen-oscillations of the system are non-degenerate, the amplitudes of the oscillations of the different particles are distributed either symmetrically or antisymmetrically with respect to the centre.

(b) Show that if there is degeneracy, one can always choose the normal oscillations such that they are either symmetrical or antisymmetrical.

6.33. Show that if the points A and B (Fig. 33) move symmetrically or antisymmetrically, several of the eigen-vibrations of the system of Fig. 33 will not be excited.

6.34. Use symmetry considerations to find the vectors of the normal vibrations of the system of particles of Fig. 26.

6.35. Find the stable oscillations of the system of Fig. 23, if the point A moves according to $a \cos \omega t$. Assume that there are frictional forces acting upon the particles proportional to their velocities.

6.36. Describe the motion of the system of Fig. 22 if at $t = 0$ the particles are at rest at their equilibrium positions while the point A moves according to $a \cos \omega t$. Take the masses to be equal ($m_1 = m_2 = m$).

6.37. Determine the eigen-vibrations in a plane of a molecule which has the shape of an equilateral triangle. Assume that the potential energy depends only on the distances between the atoms and that all atoms are the same. The angular momentum is equal to zero up to terms of first order in the amplitude of the oscillations.

6.38. Use symmetry arguments to determine the degree of degeneracy of various frequencies for the case of a "molecule" consisting of four identical atoms which has the form of a regular tetrahedron at equilibrium.

7. Oscillations of Linear Chains

Chains of particles connected by springs are the simplest model used in the theory of solids (see, for example, Wannier, 1959, or Kittel, 1968). The electrical analogues of such lines are r.f. lines employed in radio engineering.

7.1. Determine the frequencies of the normal oscillations of a system of N identical particles with masses m connected by identical springs with elastic constants $\varkappa$ and moving along a straight line (Fig. 33a).

Hint: Express the normal oscillations in terms of standing waves.

7.2. Repeat this for the system of Fig. 33b with one free end.

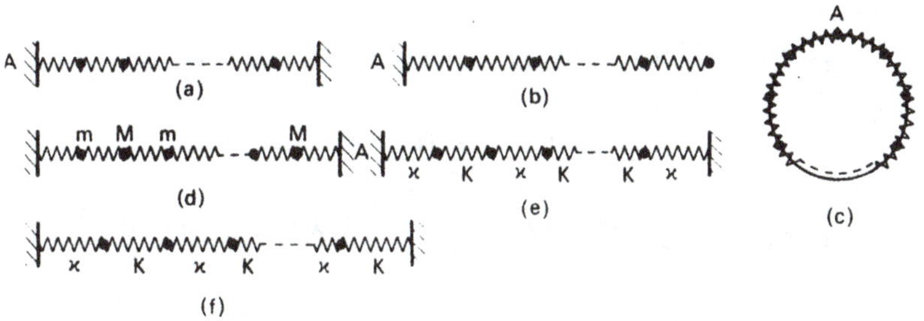

FIG. 33

7.3. Find the eigen-vibrations of N particles which are connected by springs and which can move along a circle (Fig. 33c). All particles and the elastic constants of all springs are the same. Check that if the motion is that of a wave travelling along the circle, the energy flux equals the product of the linear energy density and the group velocity.

7.4. Determine the frequencies of the eigen-vibrations of a system of particles moving along a straight line for the following cases (take the hint of problem 7.1 into account):

(a) $2N$ particles, alternating with masses m and M connected by springs of elastic constant $\varkappa$ (Fig. 33d);

(b) $2N$ particles of mass m connected by springs with alternating elastic constants $\varkappa$ and K (Fig. 33e);

(c) $2N+1$ particles of mass m connected by springs with alternating elastic constants $\varkappa$ and K (Fig. 33f).

7.5. (a) Determine the eigen-vibrations of the system of Fig. 33a if the point A moves according to $a \cos \omega t$.

(b) Do the same for the system of Fig. 33b.

7.6. Do the same for the system of Fig. 33d.

7.7. Determine the eigen-vibrations of a system of N particles which move along a straight line for the following cases:

(a) $m_i = m \neq m_N$, $i = 1, 2, \ldots, N-1$; the elastic constants of all the springs are the same (Fig. 34). Discuss the cases when $m_N \gg m$ and $m_N \ll m$;

(b) $\varkappa_i = \varkappa \neq \varkappa_{N+1}$, $i = 1, 2, \ldots, N$; all the masses are the same (Fig. 35).

Study the cases when $\varkappa_{N+1} \gg \varkappa$ and when $\varkappa_{N+1} \ll \varkappa$.

FIG. 34

FIG. 35

7.8. Consider an elastic rod to be the limiting case of the system of N particles of Fig. 33a in the limit as $N \to \infty$, $a \to 0$, $m \to 0$, where m and a are, respectively, the mass of the particles and the distance between neighbouring particles at equilibrium, while Na and Nm are kept constant. Write down the equations of motion for the oscillations of the rod as the limiting case of the equations of motion of the discrete system.

Hint: Introduce the coordinate of a point of the rod at equilibrium $\xi = na$ and consider the following quantities

$$x(\xi, t) = \lim_{a \to 0} x_n(t), \quad \frac{\partial x}{\partial \xi} = \lim_{a \to 0} \frac{x_n(t) - x_{n-1}(t)}{a}.$$

7.9. Write down the equations of motion for the oscillations of the rod of the preceding problem, taking into account the first non-vanishing correction due to a finite distance a between neighbouring particles.

8. Non-linear Oscillations

8.1. Determine the distortion in the oscillations of a harmonic oscillator which is caused by the presence of anharmonic terms in the potential energy for the following cases:

(a) $\delta U = \frac{1}{4} m\beta x^4$;
(b) $\delta U = \frac{1}{3} m\alpha x^3$.

8.2. Determine the distortion in the oscillations of a harmonic oscillator which is caused by the presence of an anharmonic term, $\delta T = \frac{1}{2} m\gamma x \dot{x}^2$, in the kinetic energy.

8.3. Determine the anharmonic corrections to the oscillations of a pendulum whose point of suspension moves along a circle (Fig. 15; $R \ll l$).

8.4. Determine the oscillations of a harmonic oscillator when there is a force $f_1 \cos \omega_1 t + f_2 \cos \omega_2 t$ acting upon it, taking anharmonic corrections into account for the case when $\delta U = \frac{1}{3} m\alpha x^3$.

8.5. Find the amplitude of the stable oscillations of an anharmonic oscillator which satisfy the equations of motion

$$\ddot{x}+2\lambda\dot{x}+\omega_0^2x+\beta x^3 = f\cos\omega t$$

(a) in the resonance region, $|\omega-\omega_0| \ll \omega_0$;
(b) in the region where there is resonance with the tripled frequency of the force, $|3\omega-\omega_0| \ll \omega_0$ (frequency tripling).

8.6. (a) Determine the amplitude and phase of the stable vibration of a harmonic oscillator under conditions of parametric resonance:

$$\ddot{x}+2\lambda\dot{x}+\omega_0^2(1+h\cos 2\omega t)x+\beta x^3 = 0$$

$$(h \ll 1, \quad |\omega-\omega_0| \ll \omega_0, \quad \beta^{1/2}x \ll \omega_0).$$

(b) Determine the amplitude of the third harmonic in the stable vibration.

8.7. Determine the vibrations of the harmonic oscillator

$$\ddot{x}+\omega_0^2(1+h\cos 2\omega t)x = 0, \quad h \ll 1, \quad |\omega-\omega_0| \ll \omega_0$$

(a) in the region where instability for parametric resonance occurs;
(b) close to the region of instability.

8.8. Let the frequency of a harmonic oscillator $\omega(t)$ change as is indicated in Fig. 36. Find the region where instability against parametric resonance occurs.

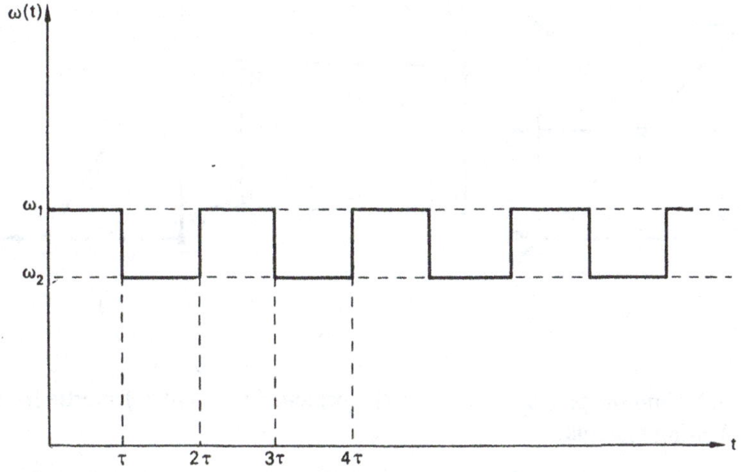

FIG. 36

8.9. Find the frequency of the small vibrations of a pendulum whose point of suspension performs vertical oscillations with a high frequency Ω ($\Omega \gg \sqrt{g/l}$).

8.10. Find the effective potential energy for the following cases:

(a) a particle of mass m moving in the potential

$$U(\boldsymbol{r}) = \frac{\alpha}{|\boldsymbol{r}-\boldsymbol{a}\cos\omega t|} - \frac{\alpha}{|\boldsymbol{r}+\boldsymbol{a}\cos\omega t|}, \qquad r \gg a;$$

(b) a harmonic oscillator moving in the potential

$$U(\boldsymbol{r}) = \frac{(\boldsymbol{a}\cdot\boldsymbol{r})\cos\omega t}{r^3}.$$

8.11. Determine the motion of a fast particle entering the potential field $U(\boldsymbol{r}) = A(x^2-y^2)\sin kz$ at a small angle to the z-axis ($k^2E \gg A$).

9. Rigid-Body Motion. Non-Inertial Coordinate Systems

9.1. At the vertices of a square with side lengths $2a$ masses m and M are located (Fig. 37a). Find the components of the moments of inertia tensor

(a) relative to the x-, y-, and z-axes;
(b) relative to the x'- and y'-axes which are the diagonals of the square.

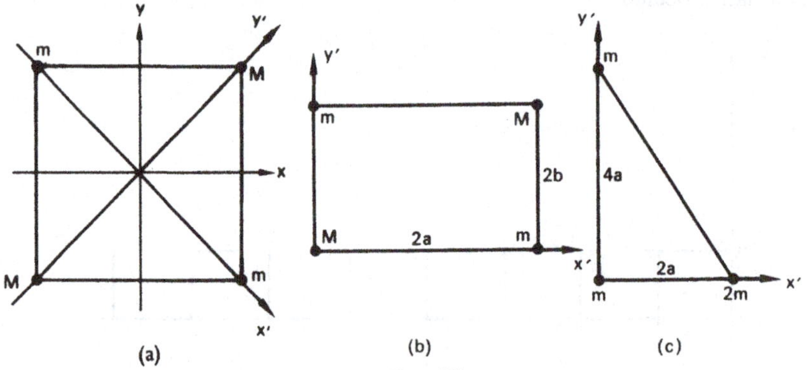

Fig. 37

9.2. Find the principal axes and the principal moments of inertia for the following systems:

(a) masses m and M at the vertices of a rectangle with side lengths $2a$ and $2b$ (Fig. 37b);

(b) masses m and $2m$ at the vertices of a right-angled triangle with side lengths $2a$ and $4a$ (Fig. 37c).

9.3. Give an expression for the moment of inertia I_n with respect to an axis parallel to a unit vector $\boldsymbol{n}$ and passing through the centre of mass in terms of the components of the moment of inertia tensor.

9.4. Determine the principal moments of inertia of a sphere of radius R inside of which there is a spherical cavity of radius r (Fig. 38).

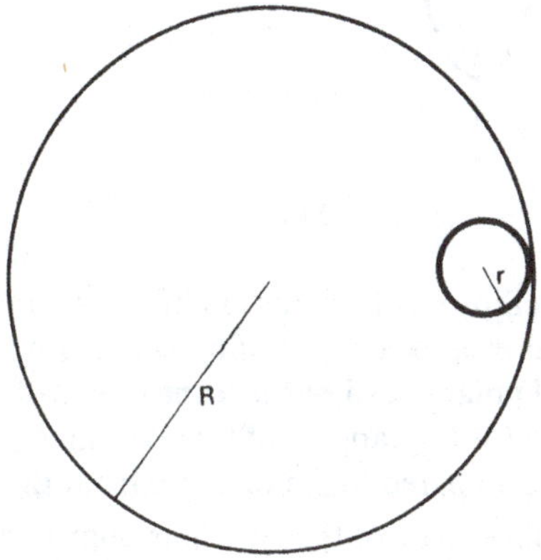

FIG. 38

9.5. Express the components of the mass quadrupole moment tensor,

$$D_{ik} = \int \varrho(3x_i x_k - r^2\delta_{ik})\, d^3r$$

(ϱ is the density), in terms of the components I_{ik} of the moment of inertia tensor.

9.6. Determine the frequency of the small vibrations of a uniform hemisphere which lies on a smooth horizontal surface in the field of gravity.

9.7. A particle moving parallel to the y-axis with a velocity v and with impact parameters ϱ_1 and ϱ_2 is incident upon a uniform ellipsoid with semi-axes a, b $(= a)$, and c (Fig. 39), and sticks to it. Describe the motion of the ellipsoid assuming its mass to be much larger than that of the particle.

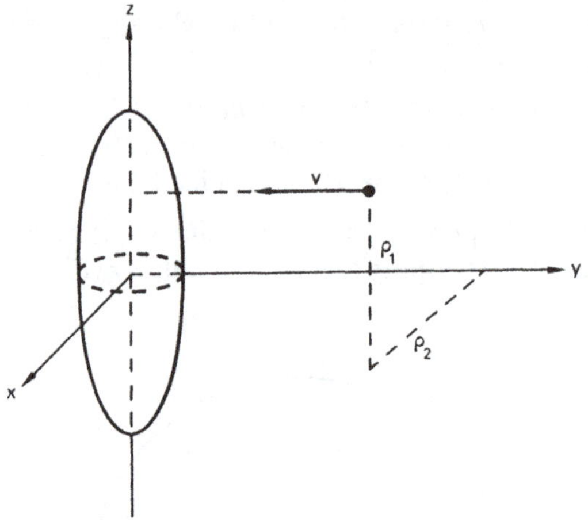

FIG. 39

9.8. An isotropic ellipsoid of revolution of mass m moves in the gravitational field produced by a fixed point of mass M. Use as generalised coordinates the spherical polar coordinates of the centre of mass and the Euler angles and determine the Lagrangian of this system. Assume the size of the ellipsoid to be small compared to the distance from the centre of the field.

Hint: The potential energy of the system is approximately equal to

$$U(\boldsymbol{R}) = m\varphi(R)+\frac{1}{6}\sum_{\alpha,\beta=1}^{3} D_{\alpha\beta}\frac{\partial^2\varphi(R)}{\partial X_\alpha \partial X_\beta},$$

where $\boldsymbol{R} = (X_1, X_2, X_3)$ is the radius vector of the centre of the ellipsoid, $D_{\alpha\beta}$ the mass quadrupole moment tensor (see problem 9.5), and $\varphi(R) = -\gamma M/R$ is the potential of the gravitational field (compare Landau and Lifshitz, 1962, § 41).

9.9. Write down the equations of motion for the components of the angular momentum along moving coordinate axes which are chosen to lie along the principal axes of the moment of inertia tensor.

Integrate these equations for the case of the free motion of a symmetric top.

9.10. Use the Euler equations to study the stability of rotations around the principal axes of the moment of inertia tensor of an asymmetric top.

9.11. (a) A plane disk, symmetric around its axis, rolls over a smooth horizontal plane without friction. Find its motion in the form of quadratures.

Answer in detail the following questions:

Under what conditions does the angle of inclination of the disk to the plane remain constant?

If the disk rolls in such a way that its axis has a fixed (horizontal) direction in space, at what angular velocity will the rotation around this axis be stable?

If the disk rotates around its vertical diameter, at what angular velocity will the motion be stable?

(b) A disk rolls without slipping over a horizontal surface. Find the equations of motion, and answer for this case the same questions as under (a).

(c) Repeat this for a disk which rolls without slip over a horizontal plane, without rotation around a vertical axis.†

(d) A disk rotates, without slipping, around its diameter which is at right angles to an inclined plane, which makes a small angle α with the horizontal, on which the disk is placed. Find the displacement of the disk over a long time interval.

9.12. (a) Find in terms of quadratures the law of motion of an inhomogeneous sphere which is slipping without friction on a horizontal plane. The mass distribution is symmetric with respect to the axis passing through the geometric centre and the centre of mass of the sphere.

Study the effect of small dry friction forces for the case when the motion of the sphere, if the dry friction forces are neglected, would be such that the angle between the vertical and the axis of symmetry remained constant.

(b) Find the equations of motion for the sphere of (a) if it rolls without slipping over a horizontal plane.

(c) Find the equations of motion of this sphere for rolling without slipping down an inclined surface.

9.13. A particle is dropped from a height h with zero initial velocity. Find its displacement from the vertical in the directions of the West and the South.

9.14. A particle moves in a central field potential $U(r)$. Find the equation for its trajectory and describe its motion in a coordinate system which is rotating uniformly with an angular velocity $\boldsymbol{\Omega}$ parallel to its angular momentum $\boldsymbol{M}$.

† This means that the cohesion of the disk to the plane at the point of contact is so firm that the area of contact neither slips not rotates. The energy loss due to rolling friction can be neglected.

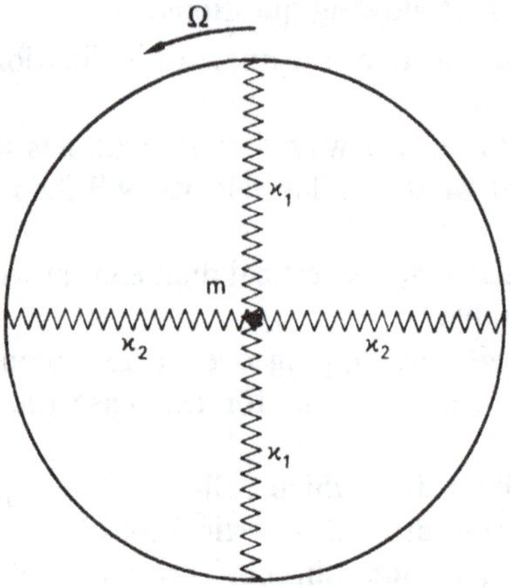

FIG. 40

9.15. Find the small oscillations of a mass m which is fastened to a frame by springs with elastic constants $\varkappa_1$ and $\varkappa_2$. The frame rotates in its own plane with an angular velocity Ω (Fig. 40). The mass moves in the plane of the frame.

9.16. Determine the eigen-oscillations of the three-atomic molecule described in problem 6.37 for the case where its angular momentum $\boldsymbol{M}$ is non-vanishing. Consider the case where the angular momentum is at right angles to the plane of the molecule and where the angular velocity Ω is small: $\Omega \ll \sqrt{\varkappa/m}$, where $\varkappa$ is the elastic constant of the binding.

10. THE HAMILTONIAN EQUATIONS OF MOTION

10.1. Let the Hamiltonian H of a system of particles be invariant under an infinitesimal translation (rotation). Prove the linear (angular) momentum conservation law.

10.2. Use the Euler angles to find the Hamiltonian of a symmetric top for the case when there is no external field acting on the top.

10.3. Determine the Hamiltonian of an anharmonic oscillator, if the Lagrangian is given by the equation

$$L = \tfrac{1}{2}\dot{x}^2 - \tfrac{1}{2}\omega^2 x^2 - \alpha x^3 + \beta x \dot{x}^2.$$

10.4. Describe the motion of a particle with a Hamiltonian

$$H(p, x) = \tfrac{1}{2}p^2 + \tfrac{1}{2}\omega_0^2 x^2 + \lambda(\tfrac{1}{2}p^2 + \tfrac{1}{2}\omega_0^2 x^2)^2.$$

10.5. Find the equations of motion for the case when the Hamiltonian is of the form (a beam of light)

$$H(\boldsymbol{p}, \boldsymbol{r}) = \frac{c\,|\boldsymbol{p}|}{n(\boldsymbol{p}, \boldsymbol{r})}.$$

Determine the trajectory for the case when $n(\boldsymbol{r}) = ax$.

10.6. Find the Lagrangian for the case when the Hamiltonian is

(a) $H(\boldsymbol{p}, \boldsymbol{r}) = \dfrac{p^2}{2m} - (\boldsymbol{a} \cdot \boldsymbol{p}), \quad \boldsymbol{a} = \text{constant};$

(b) $H(\boldsymbol{p}, \boldsymbol{r}) = \dfrac{cp}{n(\boldsymbol{p}, \boldsymbol{r})}.$

10.7. Describe the motion of a charged particle in a uniform magnetic field $\boldsymbol{H}$ by solving the Hamiltonian equations of motion; take the vector potential in the form $A_y = xH$, $A_x = A_z = 0$.

In problems 10.8 to 10.12 we are dealing with the motion of electrons in a metal or semiconductor. Electrons in a solid form a system of particles which interact both with themselves and with the ions which form the crystalline lattice. Their motion is described by quantum mechanics. In solid state theory one is often able to reduce the problem of many interacting particles which form the solid to the problem of the motion of separate free particles (the so-called quasi-particles: electrons or holes, depending on the sign of their charge) for which, however, the momentum dependence $\varepsilon(\boldsymbol{p})$ ("dispersion law") of the energy is complicated.† In many cases it turns out that it is possible to consider the motion of the quasi-particles using classical mechanics. The function $\varepsilon(\boldsymbol{p})$ is periodic with a period which is equal to the period of the so-called reciprocal lattice.‡ Otherwise one can assume that $\varepsilon(\boldsymbol{p})$ has an arbitrary form.

† For instance, for "holes" in germanium and silicon crystals

$$\varepsilon(\boldsymbol{p}) = \{Ap^2 \pm [B^2p^4 + C^2(p_x^2p_y^2 + p_y^2p_z^2 + p_z^2p_x^2)]^{\frac{1}{2}}\}/2m,$$

where the coordinate axes are chosen to coincide with the crystal symmetry axes, m is the electron mass, and the constants A, B, and C have the values

	A	B	C
Ge	−13.1	8.3	12.5
Si	−4.0	1.1	4.1

‡ For instance, for a crystal the lattice of which has a smallest period a in the x-direction, we have $\varepsilon(p_x, p_y, p_z) = \varepsilon(p_x + 2\pi\hbar/a, p_y, p_z)$, where $2\pi\hbar$ is Planck's constant ($\hbar$ is Dirac's constant).

10.8. Obtain the equations of motion using the Hamiltonian $H(\boldsymbol{P}, \boldsymbol{r}) = \varepsilon(\boldsymbol{P}-(e/c)\boldsymbol{A})+e\varphi$ (the electron charge e is taken to be negative).

Hint: Introduce the electron quasi-momentum $\boldsymbol{p} = \boldsymbol{P}-(e/c)\boldsymbol{A}$.

10.9. It is well known that $\varepsilon(\boldsymbol{p})$ is a periodic function of $\boldsymbol{p}$ with a period which is equal to that of the reciprocal lattice, multiplied by $2\pi\hbar$; for instance, for a simple cubic lattice with lattice constant a, the period of $\varepsilon(\boldsymbol{p})$ is equal to $2\pi\hbar/a$.

Describe the motion of an electron in a uniform electric field $\boldsymbol{E}$.

10.10. Determine the integrals of motion of an electron moving in a solid in a uniform magnetic field. What does the "orbit" in momentum space look like?

10.11. Prove that the projection of an electron orbit in a uniform magnetic field onto a plane at right angles to $\boldsymbol{H}$ in coordinate space can be obtained by rotation and change of scale of the orbit in momentum space.

10.12. Express the period of revolution of an electron in a uniform magnetic field in terms of the area $S(E, p_H)$ of the section cut off by the plane $p_H = (\boldsymbol{p}\cdot\boldsymbol{H})/H =$ constant of the surface $\varepsilon(\boldsymbol{p}) = E$ in momentum space.

11. Poisson Brackets. Canonical Transformations

11.1. Evaluate the Poisson brackets

(a) $\{M_i, x_j\}, \quad \{M_i, p_j\}, \quad \{M_i, M_j\};$

(b) $\{(\boldsymbol{a}\cdot\boldsymbol{p}), (\boldsymbol{b}\cdot\boldsymbol{r})\}, \quad \{(\boldsymbol{a}\cdot\boldsymbol{M}), (\boldsymbol{b}\cdot\boldsymbol{r})\}, \quad \{(\boldsymbol{a}\cdot\boldsymbol{M}), (\boldsymbol{b}\cdot\boldsymbol{M})\};$

(c) $\{\boldsymbol{M}, (\boldsymbol{r}\cdot\boldsymbol{p})\}, \quad \{\boldsymbol{p}, r^n\}, \quad \{\boldsymbol{p}, (\boldsymbol{a}\cdot\boldsymbol{r})^2\};$

where x_i, p_i, and M_i are the Cartesian components of the vectors $\boldsymbol{r}$, $\boldsymbol{p}$, and $\boldsymbol{M}$, while $\boldsymbol{a}$ and $\boldsymbol{b}$ are constant vectors.

11.2. Evaluate $\{A_i, A_j\}$ where

$$A_1 = \tfrac{1}{4}(x^2+p_x^2-y^2-p_y^2), \qquad A_2 = \tfrac{1}{2}(xy+p_xp_y),$$
$$A_3 = \tfrac{1}{2}(xp_y-yp_x), \qquad A_4 = x^2+y^2+p_x^2+p_y^2.$$

11.3. Evaluate $\{M_i, \Lambda_{jk}\}$ and $\{\Lambda_{jk}, \Lambda_{il}\}$ where $\Lambda_{ik} = x_ix_k+p_ip_k$.

11.4. Show that $\{M_z, \varphi\} = 0$ where φ is an arbitrary function of the coordinates and momenta of a particle.

Show also that $\{M_z, \boldsymbol{f}\} = [\boldsymbol{k}\wedge\boldsymbol{f}]$, where $\boldsymbol{f}$ is a vector function of the coordinates and momenta of a particle and $\boldsymbol{k}$ the unit vector along the z-axis.

11.5. Evaluate the Poisson brackets $\{\boldsymbol{f}, (\boldsymbol{a}\cdot\boldsymbol{M})\}$ and $\{(\boldsymbol{f}\cdot\boldsymbol{M}), (\boldsymbol{l}\cdot\boldsymbol{M})\}$, where $\boldsymbol{f}$ and $\boldsymbol{l}$ are vector functions of $\boldsymbol{r}$ and $\boldsymbol{p}$ while $\boldsymbol{a}$ is a constant vector.

11.6. Evaluate $\{M_\zeta, M_\xi\}$, where M_ζ and M_ξ are the components of the angular momentum along the Cartesian ζ- and ξ-axes which are fixed in a rotating rigid body.

11.7. Write down the equations of motion for the components of the angular momentum along the axes fixed in a freely rotating rigid body. The Hamiltonian is of the form

$$H = \tfrac{1}{2}\sum_{\alpha,\beta} (I^{-1})_{\alpha\beta} M_\alpha M_\beta .$$

11.8. Write down the equations of motion for the vector $\boldsymbol{M}$ ($\boldsymbol{M} = [\boldsymbol{r}\wedge\boldsymbol{P}]$, where $\boldsymbol{P}$ is the generalised momentum), for the case when the Hamiltonian is $H = -\gamma(\boldsymbol{M}\cdot\boldsymbol{H}) + P^2/2m$, where γ and $\boldsymbol{H}$ are constant. This Hamiltonian is equal to the energy of a magnetic moment $\gamma\boldsymbol{M}$ in a magnetic field $\boldsymbol{H}$.

11.9. Evaluate $\{v_i, v_j\}$ for a particle in a magnetic field.

11.10. Prove that the value of any function $f(p(t), q(t))$ of the coordinates and momenta of a system at time t can be expressed in terms of the values of the p and q at $t = 0$ as follows:

$$f(p(t), q(t)) = f_0 + \frac{t}{1!}\{H, f_0\} + \frac{t^2}{2!}\{H, \{H, f_0\}\} + \dots ,$$

where $f_0 = f(p(0), q(0))$ while $H = H(p(0), q(0))$ is the Hamiltonian. Assume that the series converges.

Apply this formula to evaluate $p(t)$, $q(t)$, $p^2(t)$, and $q^2(t)$ for the following cases:

(a) a particle moving in a uniform field of force;
(b) a harmonic oscillator.

11.11. Evaluate $\boldsymbol{v}(t)$ for the case of a particle moving in a uniform magnetic field using the results of problems 11.9 and 11.10 and writing the Hamiltonian in the form $H = \tfrac{1}{2}mv^2$.

11.12. Prove by direct calculation that the Poisson brackets are invariant under canonical transformations.

11.13. Determine the canonical transformations defined by the following generating functions:

(a) $F(q, Q, t) = \tfrac{1}{2}m\omega(t)\, q^2 \cot Q$.

Write down the equations of motion of a harmonic oscillator with frequency $\omega(t)$ in terms of the variables Q and P;

(b) $$F(q, Q, t) = \frac{1}{2} m\omega \left[q - \frac{F(t)}{m\omega^2} \right]^2 \cot Q.$$

Write down the equations of motion for a harmonic oscillator which is acted upon by a force $F(t)$ in terms of the variables Q and P.

11.14. Determine the generating function $\Psi(p, Q)$ which produces the same canonical transformation as the generating function $F(q, P) = q^2 e^P$.

11.15. What is the condition that a function $\Phi(q, P)$ can be used as a generating function for a canonical transformation?

Consider in particular the example $\Phi(q, P) = q^2 + P^2$.

11.16. Prove that a rotation in q, p-phase space is a canonical transformation for a system with one degree of freedom.

11.17. Consider the small oscillations of an anharmonic oscillator with Hamiltonian

$$H = \tfrac{1}{2}p^2 + \tfrac{1}{2}\omega^2 x^2 + \alpha x^3 + \beta x p^2$$

under the assumption that $\alpha x \ll \omega^2$, $\beta x \ll 1$.

Find the parameters a and b for the canonical transformation produced by the generating function $\Phi = xP + ax^2 P + bP^3$ such that the new Hamiltonian does not contain any anharmonic terms up to first-order terms in $\alpha Q/\omega^2$ and βQ. Determine $x(t)$.

11.18. Determine the parameters a and b for the canonical transformation produced by the generating function $\Phi = xP + ax^3 P + bxP^3$ in such a way that the small oscillations of an anharmonic oscillator described by the Hamiltonian

$$H = \tfrac{1}{2}p^2 + \tfrac{1}{2}\omega_0^2 x^2 + \beta x^4$$

can be reduced to harmonic oscillations in terms of the new variables Q and P. Neglect terms of second order in $\beta Q^2/\omega^2$ in the new Hamiltonian.

11.19. Prove that the following transformation is canonical:

$$x = X \cos \lambda + \frac{P_y}{m\omega} \sin \lambda, \qquad y = Y \cos \lambda + \frac{P_x}{m\omega} \sin \lambda,$$

$$p_x = -m\omega Y \sin \lambda + P_x \cos \lambda, \quad p_y = -m\omega X \sin \lambda + P_y \cos \lambda.$$

Determine the new Hamiltonian $H'(P, Q)$, if the old Hamiltonian is

$$H(p, q) = \frac{p_x^2 + p_y^2}{2m} + \frac{1}{2} m\omega^2 (x^2 + y^2).$$

(Compare problem 11.29.) Describe the motion of a two-dimensional harmonic oscillator for which $Y = P_y = 0$.

11.20. Use the transformation of the preceding problem to reduce the Hamiltonian of an isotropic harmonic oscillator in a magnetic field described by the vector potential $A = (0, Hx, 0)$ to a sum of squares and determine its motion.

11.21. Use a canonical transformation to diagonalise the Hamiltonian of an anisotropic charged harmonic oscillator with potential energy

$$U(\mathbf{r}) = \tfrac{1}{2}m(\omega_1^2x^2+\omega_2^2y^2+\omega_3^2z^2)$$

which is situated in a constant uniform field determined by the vector potential $A = (0, Hx, 0)$.

11.22. Apply the canonical transformation of problem 11.19 to pairs of normal coordinates corresponding to standing waves in the system of particles on a circle considered in problem 7.3 to obtain the coordinates corresponding to travelling waves.

11.23. Prove that the following transformation is a canonical one:

$$x = \frac{1}{\sqrt{m\omega}}(\sqrt{2P_1}\sin Q_1+P_2), \quad y = \frac{1}{\sqrt{m\omega}}(\sqrt{2P_1}\cos Q_1+Q_2),$$

$$p_x = \tfrac{1}{2}\sqrt{m\omega}(\sqrt{2P_1}\cos Q_1-Q_2), \quad p_y = \tfrac{1}{2}\sqrt{m\omega}(-\sqrt{2P_1}\sin Q_1+P_2).$$

Find the Hamiltonian equations of motion for a particle in a magnetic field described by the vector potential $A = (-\tfrac{1}{2}yH, \tfrac{1}{2}xH, 0)$ in terms of the new variables introduced through the above transformation with $\omega = eH/mc$.

11.24. What is the meaning of the canonical transformations produced by the generating function $\Phi(q, P) = \alpha qP$?

11.25. Prove that a gauge transformation of the potentials of the electromagnetic field is a canonical transformation for the coordinates and momenta of charged particles, and find the corresponding generating function.

11.26. It is well known that replacing the Laplacian $L(q, \dot{q}, t)$ by

$$L'(q, \dot{q}, t) = L(q, \dot{q}, t)+\frac{df(q, t)}{dt},$$

where $f(q, t)$ is an arbitrary function, leaves the Lagrangian equations of motion invariant. Prove that this transformation is a canonical one and find its generating function.

11.27. Find the generating function for the canonical transformation which consists in changing $q(t)$ and $p(t)$ to $Q(t) = q(t+\tau)$ and $P(t) = p(t+\tau)$, where τ is constant for the following cases:

(a) a free particle;
(b) motion in a uniform field of force, $U = -Fq$;
(c) a harmonic oscillator.

11.28. Discuss the physical meaning of the canonical transformations produced by the following generating functions:

(a) $\Phi(\boldsymbol{r}, \boldsymbol{P}) = (\boldsymbol{r}\cdot\boldsymbol{P})+(\delta\boldsymbol{a}\cdot\boldsymbol{P})$;

(b) $\Phi(\boldsymbol{r}, \boldsymbol{P}) = (\boldsymbol{r}\cdot\boldsymbol{P})+(\delta\boldsymbol{\varphi}\cdot[\boldsymbol{r}\wedge\boldsymbol{P}])$;

(c) $\Phi(q, P, t) = qP+\delta\tau H(q, P, t)$;

(d) $\Phi(\boldsymbol{r}, \boldsymbol{P}) = (\boldsymbol{r}\cdot\boldsymbol{P})+(r^2+P^2)\delta\alpha$,

where $\boldsymbol{r}$ is the Cartesian radius vector while $\delta\boldsymbol{a}$, $\delta\boldsymbol{\varphi}$, $\delta\tau$, and $\delta\alpha$ are infinitesimal parameters.

11.29. Prove that the canonical transformation produced by the generating function $\Phi(x, y, P_x, P_y) = xP_x+yP_y+\varepsilon(xy+P_xP_y)$ with $\varepsilon\to 0$ is a rotation in phase space.

11.30. Write down the generating functions for the infinitesimal canonical transformations corresponding to

(a) a screw motion;
(b) a Galilean transformation;
(c) a change to a rotating system of reference.

11.31. A canonical transformation is produced by the generating function $\Phi(q, P) = qP+\lambda W(q, P)$, where $\lambda\to 0$. Determine up to first-order terms the change in value of an arbitrary function $f(q, p)$ when we change arguments: $\delta f(q, p) = f(Q, P)-f(q, p)$.

11.32. For the case when the Hamiltonian is

$$H(\boldsymbol{r}, \boldsymbol{p}) = \frac{p^2}{2m}+\frac{(\boldsymbol{a}\cdot\boldsymbol{r})}{r^3}$$

determine $\{H, (\boldsymbol{r}\cdot\boldsymbol{p})\}$ and use the result to obtain an integral of the equations of motion. Use the results of problem 11.24. The vector $\boldsymbol{a}$ is constant.

11.33. Determine how the $\boldsymbol{r}$- and $\boldsymbol{p}$-dependence of M, p^2, $(\boldsymbol{p}\cdot\boldsymbol{r})$, and $H(\boldsymbol{r}, \boldsymbol{p}, t)$ change under the canonical transformations of problem 11.28.

11.34. Show that if

$$\{W_1(q, p), W_2(q, p)\} = 0,$$

the result of applying two successive infinitesimal transformations which are produced by the generating functions

$$\Phi_i(q, P) = qP + \lambda_i W_i(q, P), \quad i = 1, 2, \quad \lambda_i \to 0,$$

will be independent of the order in which they are taken, up to and including second-order terms.

11.35. Determine the canonical transformation which is the result of N successive infinitesimal canonical transformations produced by the generating function $\Phi(q, P) = qP + (\lambda/N)\, W(q, P)$ for the case where $\lambda =$ constant and $N \to \infty$, while $W(q, P)$ is given by the equations

(a) $W(\boldsymbol{r}, \boldsymbol{P}) = ([\boldsymbol{r} \wedge \boldsymbol{P}] \cdot \boldsymbol{a})$, $\quad \boldsymbol{a} =$ constant;

(b) $W(\boldsymbol{r}, \boldsymbol{P}) = ([\boldsymbol{r} \wedge \boldsymbol{P}] \cdot [\boldsymbol{r} \wedge \boldsymbol{P}])$;

(c) $W(q, P) = qP$.

Hint: Construct—and solve for the different concrete forms of W—differential equations which $Q(\lambda)$ and $P(\lambda)$ must satisfy.

11.36. (a) What is the change with time in the volume, the volume in momentum space, and the volume in phase-space which are occupied by a group of particles which move freely along the x-axis? At $t = 0$ the particle coordinates are lying in the interval $x_0 < x < x_0 + \Delta x_0$, and their momenta in the range $p_0 < p < p_0 + \Delta p_0$.

(b) Do the same for particles which move along the x-axis between two walls. Collisions with the walls are absolutely elastic. The particles do not interact with one another.

(c) Do the same for a group of harmonic oscillators.

(d) Do the same for a group of harmonic oscillators with friction.

(e) Do the same for a group of anharmonic oscillators.

(f) We shall describe the particle distribution in phase space at time t by the distribution function $w(x, p, t)$ which is such that $w(x, p, t)\, dx\, dp$ is the number of particles with coordinates in the interval from x to $x + dx$ and momenta in the range from p to $p + dp$. Determine the distribution function of a group of free particles and of a group of harmonic oscillators, if at $t = 0$

$$w(x, p, 0) = \frac{1}{2\pi \Delta x_0 \Delta p_0} \exp\left\{-\frac{(x - X_0)^2}{2\Delta x_0^2} - \frac{(p - P_0)^2}{2\Delta p_0^2}\right\}.$$

12. The Hamilton–Jacobi Equation

12.1. Describe the motion of a particle moving in a potential $U(\boldsymbol{r})$ by using the Hamilton–Jacobi equation for the following cases:

(a) $U(\boldsymbol{r}) = -Fx$;

(b) $U(\boldsymbol{r}) = \frac{1}{2} m(\omega_1^2 x^2 + \omega_2^2 y^2)$.

12.2. Describe the motion of a particle which is scattered in the field of the potential $U(\boldsymbol{r}) = (\boldsymbol{a}\cdot\boldsymbol{r})/r^3$. Express the equation of the trajectory in terms of quadratures; express it analytically for the case when $E\varrho^2 \gg a$, where ϱ is the impact parameter. Before the scattering the velocity of the particle is parallel to $-\boldsymbol{a}$.

12.3. Find the cross-section for the small-angle scattering of particles with velocities before the scattering antiparallel to the z-axis for the cases where the scattering is caused by the following potentials:

(a) $U(\boldsymbol{r}) = \dfrac{a \cos\theta}{r^2}$;

(b) $U(\boldsymbol{r}) = \dfrac{b \cos^2\theta}{r^2}$;

(c) $U(\boldsymbol{r}) = \dfrac{b(\theta)}{r^2}$.

12.4. Find the cross-section for a particle to fall into the centre of one of the following force fields with potential $U(\boldsymbol{r})$:

(a) $U(\boldsymbol{r}) = \dfrac{(\boldsymbol{a}\cdot\boldsymbol{r})}{r^3}$;

(b) $U(\boldsymbol{r}) = \dfrac{(\boldsymbol{a}\cdot\boldsymbol{r})}{r^3} + \dfrac{\lambda}{r}$;

(c) $U(\boldsymbol{r}) = \dfrac{(\boldsymbol{a}\cdot\boldsymbol{r})}{r^3} - \dfrac{\gamma}{r^4}$;

(d) $U(\boldsymbol{r}) = \dfrac{b(\theta)}{r^2}$.

Assuming that all directions of $\boldsymbol{a}$ are equally probable, evaluate the averages of the cross-sections obt ained.

12.5. Find the cross-section for particles to hit a sphere of radius R placed at the centre of the potential $U(\boldsymbol{r}) = (\boldsymbol{a}\cdot\boldsymbol{r})/r^3$.

12.6. Describe the motion of particles which are scattered by and fall towards the centre of the potential field in the following cases:

(a) $U(\boldsymbol{r}) = \dfrac{a\cos\theta}{r^2}$;

(b) $U(\boldsymbol{r}) = -\dfrac{a(1+\sin\theta)}{r^2}$.

Give an expression for the trajectories in terms of quadratures, and also analytically for the case when $E\varrho^2 \gg a$. For the case (a) find also an analytical expression for the case when $E\varrho^2 \ll a$. The quantity ϱ is the impact parameter. Take the initial velocity parallel to the z-axis.

12.7. Describe the motion of a particle falling towards the centre of the potential $U(\boldsymbol{r}) = (\boldsymbol{a}\cdot\boldsymbol{r})/r^3$ for the case when at infinity the particle moved along the straight line $x = -z\tan\alpha$, $y = \varrho$, where ϱ is the impact parameter. The vector $\boldsymbol{a}$ is along the z-axis and the initial spherical coordinates of the particle are $r = \infty$, $\theta = \pi-\alpha$, $\varphi = 0$. Express the trajectory in terms of quadratures, and for the case when $\alpha^2 < 2E\varrho^2/a \ll 1$ also analytically.

12.8. (a) Determine in terms of quadratures the finite orbit of a particle moving in the potential $U(\boldsymbol{r}) = (\boldsymbol{a}\cdot\boldsymbol{r})/r^3 - \alpha/r$ for the case when $M_z = 0$, where the z-axis is taken along the direction of $\boldsymbol{a}$.

(b) Do the same for the potential $U(\boldsymbol{r}) = (\boldsymbol{a}\cdot\boldsymbol{r})/r^3 + \gamma/r^4$.

12.9. Under what condition is the orbit in the preceding problem a closed one?

12.10. Describe qualitatively the motion of a particle in the potential:

$$U(\boldsymbol{r}) = \frac{(\boldsymbol{a}\cdot\boldsymbol{r})}{r^3} - \frac{\alpha}{r}.$$

12.11. Find the values of M for which the orbits in the following potentials are finite:

(a) $U(\boldsymbol{r}) = \dfrac{\gamma}{r^4} - \dfrac{b\cos^2\theta}{r^2}$;

(b) $U(\boldsymbol{r}) = \dfrac{b\cos^2\theta}{r^2} - \dfrac{\alpha}{r}$.

Describe the orbits in both cases.

12.12. Describe the motion in terms of parabolic coordinates for a particle moving in the potential $U(\boldsymbol{r})$ for the following cases:

(a) $U(\boldsymbol{r}) = -\dfrac{\alpha}{r}$;

(b) $U(\boldsymbol{r}) = -\dfrac{\alpha}{r} - (\boldsymbol{F} \cdot \boldsymbol{r})$.

In the case (b) consider only finite orbits and express the orbit in terms of quadratures.

12.13. A particle starts from the origin at an angle α to the z-axis inside a smooth elastic ellipsoid of revolution

$$\frac{x^2}{a^2} + \frac{y^2}{a^2} + \frac{z^2}{b^2} = 1.$$

Find the region inside the ellipsoid which cannot be reached by the particle.

12.14. Describe in terms of quadratures the trajectory of a particle moving in the field of two Coulomb centres,

$$U(\boldsymbol{r}) = \frac{\alpha}{r_1} - \frac{\alpha}{r_2},$$

(see Fig. 41). At infinity the velocity of the particle was parallel to the axis O_2O_1z. Describe the motion of a particle falling onto a "dipole" formed by these centres.

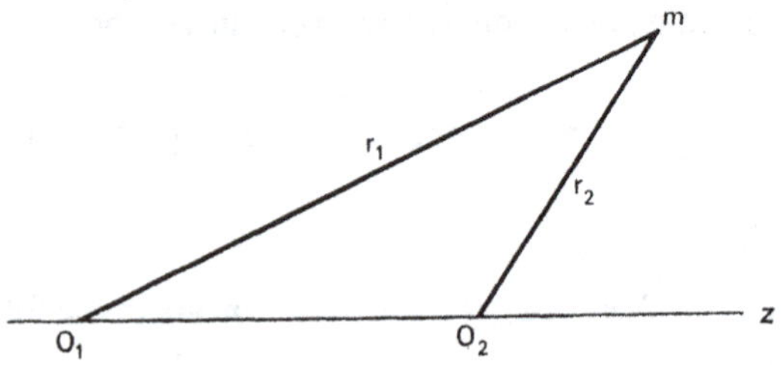

FIG. 41

12.15. A short magnetic lens is produced by a field governed by the vector potential

$$A_\varphi = \frac{r}{2} H(z), \quad A_r = A_z = 0,$$

where $H(z)$ is non-vanishing in the interval $|z| < a$. A beam of electrons close to the z-axis is incident onto the lens from the point $0, 0, z_0$. Find the point $0, 0, z_1$ onto which the beam is focused. Assume that $|z_0|$, $z_1 \gg a$.

Hint: Find the solution of the Hamilton–Jacobi equation in the form of an expansion of $S(r, \varphi, z, t)$ in powers of r:

$$S(r, \varphi, z, t) = -Et + \varphi p_\varphi + f(z) + r\psi(z) + \tfrac{1}{2}r^2\sigma(z) + \dots .$$

12.16. A magnetic lens is produced by a field governed by the vector potential

$$A_\varphi = \tfrac{1}{2}rH(z), \quad A_r = A_z = 0,$$

where

$$H(z) = \frac{H}{1+\varkappa^2 z^2}.$$

A beam of electrons close to the z-axis is incident onto the lens from the point $0, 0, z_0$. Find the points where it will be focused.

Hint: Find a solution of the Hamilton–Jacobi equation as an expansion in r.

12.17. How can one find the action as a function of the coordinates and the time, if the solution of the Hamilton–Jacobi equation is known?

12.18. Formulate and prove the theorem about integrating the equations of motion using the complete solution of the equation

$$\frac{\partial S}{\partial t} + H\left(-\frac{\partial S}{\partial p}, p, t\right) = 0,$$

where $H(q, p, t)$ is the Hamiltonian (Hamilton–Jacobi equation in the momentum representation).

12.19. Use the Hamilton–Jacobi equation in the momentum representation to find the trajectory of a particle moving in a uniform field.

13. Adiabatic Invariants

13.1. A mass m is suspended from a string which passes through a small ring (Fig. 42). Determine the average force exerted upon the ring A by the string when the pendulum performs small oscillations. Find the change in the energy of the pendulum when the ring is slowly displaced vertically.

13.2. A particle moves in a rectangular potential well of width l. Consider the collisions of the particle with the "wall" of the well to find how the energy of the particle will change when l is changed slowly.

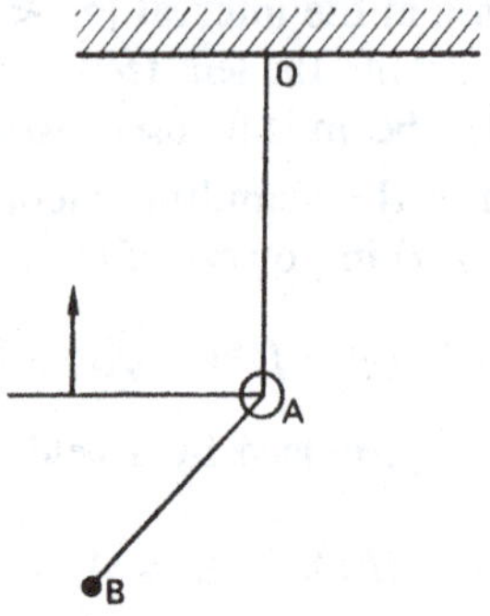

FIG. 42

13.3. A small ball is jumping up and down on an elastic plate in a lift. What is the change in the maximum height the ball reaches if the acceleration of the lift is slowly changed? How does the height vary, if the plate is raised slowly?

13.4. How does the energy of a particle moving in a potential $U(x)$ change when the parameters of the potential change slowly for the following cases:

(a) $U(x) = -\dfrac{U_0}{\cosh^2 \alpha x}$;

(b) $U(x) = U_0 \tan^2 \alpha x$;

(c) $U(x) = A\,|\,x\,|^n$?

Hint: Use the formula (see, e.g., ter Haar, 1964, § 6.2) $T = 2\pi(\partial I/\partial E)$.

13.5. A particle moves down an inclined plane AB (Fig. 43) and is reflected elastically by a wall at the point A. How does the maximum height the particle reaches change when the angle α changes slowly?

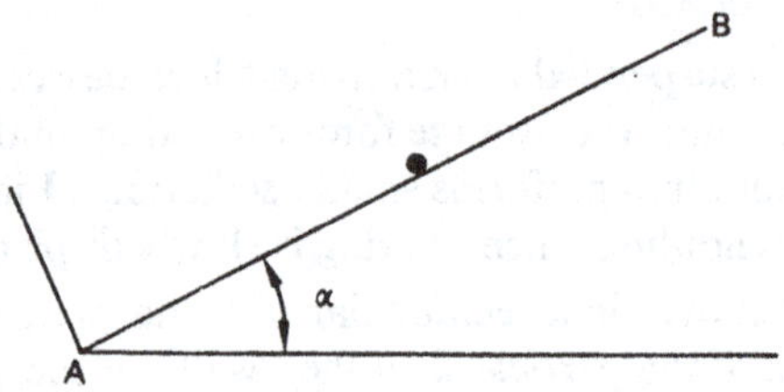

FIG. 43

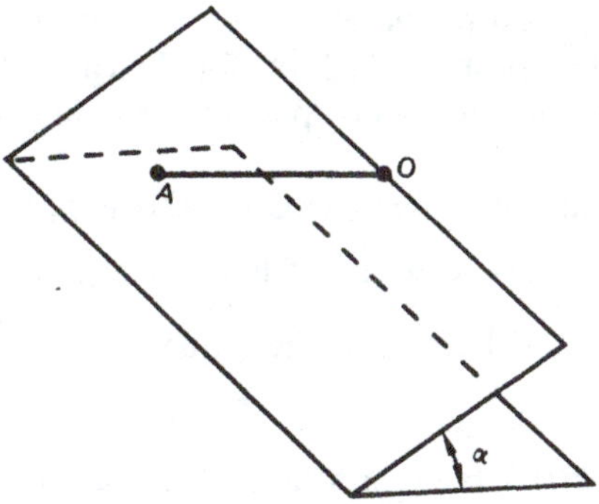

FIG. 44

13.6. A pendulum is placed upon an inclined plane (Fig. 44). How does its amplitude change, when the angle α is changed slowly?

13.7. Determine the adiabatic invariants for a mathematical pendulum for the case when the amplitude of the oscillations is not small.

13.8. (a) Two elastic spherical particles of small radius and with masses m and M, respectively, ($m \ll M$) move along the straight line OA (Fig. 45). At O the particle m is reflected elastically by a wall. Assume that the velocity of the lighter particle at $t = 0$ is much larger than that of the heavier particle and determine the motion of the heavier particle averaged over the period of motion of the lighter particle.

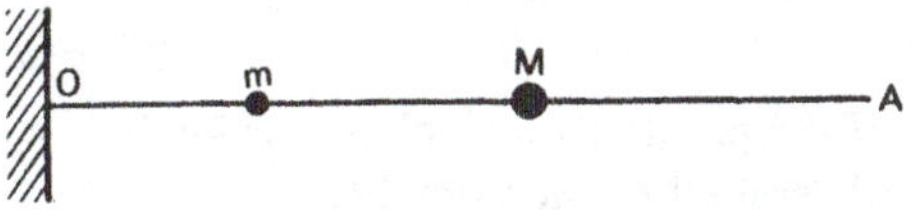

FIG. 45

(b) Two particles of mass M each and one of mass m ($m \ll M$) move along a straight line. The light particle interacts with each of the heavy ones according to a potential

$$U_{1,2}(|x_{1,2} - x|) = -V, \quad |x_{1,2} - x| < a;$$
$$U_{1,2}(|x_{1,2} - x|) = 0, \quad |x_{1,2} - x| > a,$$

where x_1 and x_2 are the coordinates of the heavy particles and x is the coordinate of the light particle. Describe the motion of the system, if at $t = 0$

$$|\dot{x}_1| \sim |\dot{x}_2| \ll |\dot{x}|.$$

13.9. Use the method of successive approximations to solve the equations for P and Q of problem 11.13(a) for the case when the frequency changes slowly ($\dot{\omega} \ll \omega^2$, $\ddot{\omega} \ll \omega\dot{\omega}$) up to and including terms of first order in $\dot{\omega}/\omega^2$.

What is the advantage of the variables P, Q over p, q in this case?

13.10 Check that up to terms of first order in $\dot{\omega}/\omega^2$ the expression $q = \omega^{-\frac{1}{2}} \exp\left(i \int^t \omega\, dt\right)$ satisfies the equation $\ddot{q}+\omega^2(t)q = 0$, where $\dot{\omega}/\omega^2 \sim \omega/\omega\dot{\omega} \ll 1$.

13.11. A force $F(t)$ acts upon a harmonic oscillator. Find the time-dependence of the adiabatic invariant $I(t) = (1/2\pi) \oint p\, dq$.

Find $I(t)$ in particular for the following cases:

(a) $F(t) = at$.

(b) $F(t) = F_0 \sin \Omega t, \quad 0 < t < \frac{\pi}{\Omega}; \quad F(t) = 0, \quad t < 0$ and $\frac{\pi}{\Omega} < t$.

(c) $F(t) = F_0 \sin^2 \Omega t, \quad 0 < t < \frac{\pi}{\Omega}; \quad F(t) = 0, \quad t < 0$ and $\frac{\pi}{\Omega} < t$.

13.12. Find the connection between the volume and the pressure of a "gas" consisting of particles which move parallel to the edges and inside an elastic cube, when the size of the cube changes slowly.

13.13. A particle moves inside an elastic parallelepiped. How does its energy change

(a) if the size of the parallelepiped changes slowly;
(b) if the parallelepiped rotates slowly?

13.14. A particle moves inside an elastic sphere, the radius of which changes slowly. How does its energy change and how does the angle at which it hits the sphere change?

13.15. Determine the change in the energy and in the trajectory of a particle in the following cases:

(a) a finite orbit in the potential

$$U(r) = -\frac{\gamma}{r^n} \qquad (0 < n < 2)$$

when γ changes slowly;

(b) a finite orbit in the potential

$$U(r) = \frac{(\boldsymbol{a}\cdot\boldsymbol{r})}{r^3} + \frac{\gamma}{r^4},$$

when γ changes slowly.

13.16. The string of a spherical pendulum is slowly shortened. How does this affect the motion of the pendulum?

13.17. Determine the change in the energy of a particle moving in a central field potential $U(r)$ when a small extra potential $\delta U(r)$ is slowly "switched on".

13.18. Determine the time-dependence of the energy of a system of two coupled harmonic oscillators with a Lagrangian

$$L = \tfrac{1}{2}m(\dot{x}^2 + \dot{y}^2 - \omega_1^2 x^2 - \omega_2^2 y^2 + 2\alpha xy),$$

when ω_1 changes slowly.

What is the change in the orbit of the point x, y?

13.19. Let the coupling between the oscillators in the preceding problem be small ($\alpha \ll \omega_{1,2}^2$). Prove that if we are far from degeneracy, where $\omega_1 = \omega_2$, the adiabatic invariants calculated neglecting the coupling are conserved, but that they change rapidly when we pass slowly through the region of degeneracy.

13.20. In which range of frequencies $\omega_1(t)$ will the adiabatic invariants of the harmonic oscillators in problem 13.19 change sharply, if the coupling is $\delta U = \beta x^2 y$?

13.21. Determine the shortest distance a particle approaches the edge of a dihedral angle α after being reflected elastically from its faces. The angle at which the particle is incident on one of the faces at a distance l from the edge is φ_0.

Solve this problem by two methods: either by using a reflection method and solving it directly, or by using adiabatic invariants assuming that α and φ_0 are small.

13.22. Determine the boundaries of the region in which a particle moves between two elastic surfaces $y = 0$ and $y = a \cosh \alpha x / \cosh 2\alpha x$. The particle starts at the origin in the xy-plane at an angle φ to the y-axis in the xy-plane and α and φ are small compared to unity. Also determine the period of the oscillations along the x-axis.

13.23. What is the change in the radius and the centre of the orbit of a charged particle moving in a uniform magnetic field which is slowly changing its strength. Take the vector potential in one of the following two forms:

(a) $A_x = 0, \quad A_y = xH(t), \quad A_z = 0;$

(b) $A_r = A_z = 0, \quad A_\varphi = \frac{1}{2}rH(t).$

Explain why the result depends on the form of A.

13.24. Calculate the adiabatic invariants for a charged isotropic harmonic oscillator moving in a uniform magnetic field.

13.25. Consider the following cases of the motion of a charged anisotropic harmonic oscillator in a uniform magnetic field. The potential energy of the harmonic oscillator is of the form

$$U(\mathbf{r}) = \tfrac{1}{2}m(\omega_1^2x^2+\omega_2^2y^2+\omega_3^2z^2),$$

and the magnetic field is along the z-axis. Take the vector potential in the form $A = (0, xH, 0)$ and consider the following cases:

(a) Determine the adiabatic invariants for the harmonic oscillator.

(b) Let initially $H = 0$ and let the trajectory of the orbit fill the rectangle $|x| \leqq a$, $|y| \leqq b$. Find the motion of the oscillator after the magnetic field has slowly increased its strength up to a value which is so high that $\omega_H = eH/mc \gg \omega_{1,2}$.

(c) Let the magnetic field be weak ($\omega_H \ll \omega_1 - \omega_2$) and let the oscillator originally oscillate nearly along the x-axis. What happens to its motion when the value of ω_1 decreases slowly to reach a value $\omega_1' < \omega_2$ such that $\omega_H \ll \omega_2 - \omega_1'$?

13.26. A particle performs a finite motion in a plane at right angles to a magnetic dipole $\mathcal{M}$. What is the change in the energy of the particle when the magnitude of $\mathcal{M}$ changes slowly?

13.27. Determine the period of the oscillations along the z-axis of an electron moving in a magnetic trap. The magnetic field of the trap is symmetric with respect to the z-axis and we have $H_\varphi = 0$, $H_z = H(z)$, $H_r = -\frac{1}{2}rH'(z)$. Consider the following two cases:

(a) $H(z) = H_0\left(1+\lambda \tanh^2 \dfrac{z}{a}\right);$

(b) $H(z) = H_0\left(1+\dfrac{z^2}{a^2}\right).$

13.28. How does the energy and the period of oscillations of an electron moving in the magnetic trap of problem 13.27 change when the field parameters H_0, λ, and a change slowly?

13.29. Determine the change in energy of a particle moving in a central field potential $U(r)$ when a weak uniform magnetic field $\boldsymbol{H}$ is slowly "switched on".

13.30. It is well known that the number of single-valued integrals of motion is increased when the motion becomes degenerate. Find the integrals of motion for the case where a particle moves in the following potentials:

(a) $U(r) = \frac{1}{2}\varkappa r^2$;

(b) $U(r) = \frac{1}{2}m\omega^2(x^2+4y^2)$.

13.31. Find the action and angle variables for the following systems:

(a) a harmonic oscillator;

(b) a particle moving in the potential $U(x) = \infty$, $x < 0$; $U(x) = Fx$, $x > 0$.

13.32. Use the generating function

$$S(x, P) = \int_0^x \sqrt{2m[E-U(x)]}\, dx$$

to perform a canonical transformation for the case of a particle moving in the periodic potential

$$U(x) = 0, \quad na < x < (n+\tfrac{1}{2})a;$$
$$U(x) = V, \quad (n+\tfrac{1}{2})a < x < (n+1)a, \quad n = 0, \pm 1, \pm 2, \ldots,$$

for the case when $E > V$, and where E in the expression for $S(x, P)$ can be derived as function of P from the equation

$$P = \int_0^a \sqrt{2m[E-U(x)]}\, dx.$$

ANSWERS AND SOLUTIONS

Answers and Solutions

1. Integration of One-dimensional Equations of Motion

1.1. (a) The energy of the particle E is determined by the initial values $x(0)$ and $\dot{x}(0)$. The motion follows from the energy conservation law

$$\tfrac{1}{2}m\dot{x}^2 + U(x) = E. \tag{1}$$

When $E \geqq 0$ the particle can move in the region $x \geqq x_1$: the motion is infinite ($E = E'$ in Fig. 46). When $E < 0$ ($E = E''$) the particle moves in the interval $x_2 \leqq x \leqq x_3$: the motion is finite. The turning points are determined from (1) through $U(x_i) = E$:

$$\left.\begin{aligned} x_1 &= \frac{1}{\alpha}\ln\frac{\sqrt{A(A+E)}-A}{E}, \quad \text{when} \quad E > 0,\\ x_1 &= -\frac{\ln 2}{\alpha}, \quad \text{when} \quad E = 0,\\ x_{2,3} &= \frac{1}{\alpha}\ln\frac{A \mp \sqrt{A(A-|E|)}}{|E|}, \quad \text{when} \quad E < 0. \end{aligned}\right\} \tag{2}$$

From (1) we obtain

$$t = \sqrt{\frac{m}{2}}\int_{x(0)}^{x}\frac{dx}{\sqrt{E-U(x)}}, \tag{3}$$

whence

$$x(t) = \frac{1}{\alpha}\ln\frac{A-\sqrt{A(A-|E|)}\cos\left(\alpha t\sqrt{2|E|/m}+C\right)}{|E|}, \quad \text{when} \quad E < 0, \tag{4}$$

$$x(t) = \frac{1}{\alpha}\ln\left[\frac{1}{2}+\frac{A\alpha^2}{m}(t+C)^2\right], \quad \text{when} \quad E = 0, \tag{5}$$

$$x(t) = \frac{1}{\alpha}\ln\frac{\sqrt{A(A+E)}\cosh\left(\alpha t\sqrt{2E/m}+C\right)-A}{E}, \quad \text{when} \quad E > 0. \tag{6}$$

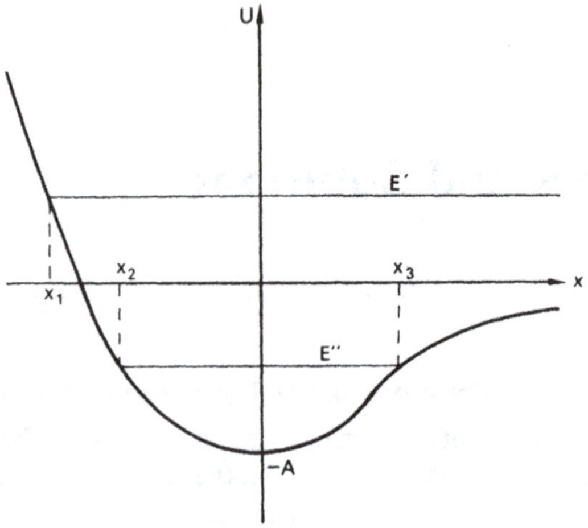

FIG. 46

The constants C are determined by the initial values $x(0)$. For example in (4), when $\dot{x}(0) > 0$

$$C = \arccos \frac{A-|E|\, e^{\alpha x(0)}}{\sqrt{A(A-|E|)}}.$$

The turning points (2) are easily found from (4) to (6).

When $E < 0$ the motion is periodic according to (4) with a period

$$T = \frac{\pi}{\alpha}\sqrt{\frac{2m}{|E|}}.$$

When E is close to the minimum value of $U(x)$, $U_{\min} = -A$, that is, when $A-|E| \ll A$, the period

$$T \approx \frac{\pi}{\alpha}\sqrt{\frac{2m}{A}}\left(1-\frac{A-|E|}{2A}\right)$$

is nearly independent of E. In that case we can write (4) in the form

$$x(t) \approx \frac{1}{\alpha}\ln\frac{A}{|E|}+\frac{1}{\alpha}\ln\left[1-\sqrt{\frac{A-|E|}{A}}\cos\left(\frac{2\pi t}{T}+C\right)\right]$$

$$\approx \frac{1}{\alpha}\ln\frac{A}{|E|}-\frac{1}{\alpha}\sqrt{\frac{A-|E|}{A}}\cos\left(\frac{2\pi t}{T}+C\right). \tag{7}$$

The particle now performs harmonic oscillations near the point $\alpha^{-1}\times \ln(A/|E|)$ with an amplitude determined by the difference $E-U_{\min}$ and with a frequency which is independent of the energy. This kind of motion for an energy close to $U_{\min}$ occurs in nearly every potential (compare the discussion in § 1.5).

When $E \geqq 0$ the particle coming from the right reaches the turning point x_1 (see (2)), turns back, and goes to infinity. Its velocity approaches the value $\sqrt{2E/m}$ from above.

(b)

$$x(t) = \frac{1}{\alpha} \operatorname{arsinh}\left[\sqrt{\frac{|E|+U_0}{|E|}} \sin\left(\alpha t \sqrt{\frac{2|E|}{m}}+C\right)\right], \qquad \text{when} \quad E < 0,$$

$$x(t) = \pm\frac{1}{\alpha} \operatorname{arsinh}\left[\sqrt{\frac{E+U_0}{E}} \sinh\left(\alpha t \sqrt{\frac{2E}{m}}+C\right)\right], \qquad \text{when} \quad E > 0,$$

$$x(t) = \pm\frac{1}{\alpha} \operatorname{arsinh}\left(\alpha t \sqrt{\frac{2U_0}{m}}+C\right), \qquad \text{when} \quad E = 0,$$

where $\operatorname{arsinh} x = \ln\left(x+\sqrt{x^2+1}\right)$ is the inverse of the hyperbolic sine.

(c)

$$x(t) = \frac{1}{\alpha} \arcsin\left[\sqrt{\frac{E}{E+U_0}} \sin\left(\alpha t \sqrt{\frac{2(U_0+E)}{m}}+C\right)\right], \qquad E > 0.$$

Explain why in some of the formulae two signs occur.

1.2.

$$x(t) = \frac{x_0}{1 \pm t x_0 \sqrt{2A/m}}, \qquad x_0 = x(0).$$

The sign in the denominator is the opposite of that of $\dot{x}(0)$. To fix our ideas, let $x(0) > 0$. When $\dot{x}(0) > 0$, the particle reaches infinity after a time $\sqrt{m/2Ax_0^2}$. Of course, for real systems the particle only reaches finite, though long, distances, corresponding to the distance over which the potential has the given form. When $\dot{x}(0) < 0$, the particle asymptotically approaches the point $x = 0$.

1.3. Near the turning point $U(x) \approx E-(x-a)F$, where $F = -U'(a)$, that is, the motion of the particle can be considered to occur under the action of a uniform constant force. Assuming that $x(0) = a$, we get

$$x(t) = a + \frac{Ft^2}{2m}.$$

The further away from the point of $x = a$ we go, the less accurate this formula becomes.

It takes a time $\tau \propto s$ to traverse a short path length s if it is far from a turning point. However, if this path length is at the turning point, $\tau \approx \sqrt{2ms/|F|}$, that is, $\tau \propto \sqrt{s}$.

If $U'(a) = 0$ (see Fig. 47) one must extend the expansion of $U(x)$ to the next term

$$U(x) = E + \tfrac{1}{2}U''(a)(x-a)^2.$$

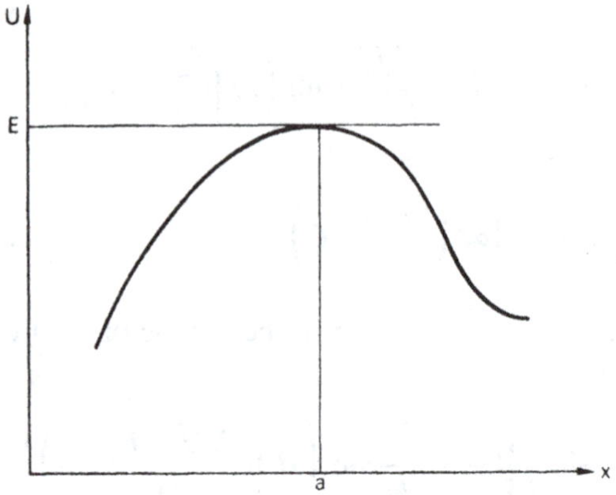

FIG. 47

In that case $x(t) = a + se^{\pm\lambda t}$ with $s = x(0) - a$, $\lambda^2 = -U''(a)/m$, where m is the particle mass, and where the sign in the index is determined by the direction of the velocity at $t = 0$. It takes an infinite time to reach the turning point.

1.4. If $U''(a) \neq 0$, $T \propto \ln \varepsilon$, where $\varepsilon = U_m - E$. If $U''(a) = \ldots = U^{(n-1)}(a) = 0$, $U^{(n)}(a) \neq 0$, we have $T \propto \exp. \{[(1/n) - \frac{1}{2}] \ln \varepsilon\}$.

1.5. The particle moves most slowly near the point $x = a$. Let us first consider the interval $a - \delta < x < a + \delta$ ($\delta \ll L \equiv x_2 - x_1$). To estimate the time T_1 the particle spends in that interval we write $U(x)$ in the form $U(x) = U(a) - \frac{1}{2}\varkappa(x-a)^2$, where $\varkappa = -U''(a)$. We find

$$T_1 = \sqrt{2m}\int_{a-\delta}^{a+\delta} \frac{dx}{\sqrt{E-U(x)}} = 4\sqrt{\frac{m}{\varkappa}} \ln\left(\frac{\delta}{l} + \sqrt{1+\frac{\delta^2}{l^2}}\right),$$

where $l = \sqrt{2\varepsilon/\varkappa}$ and $\varepsilon = E - U_m$. Assuming that ε is so small that

$$l \ll \delta \ll L$$

can be satisfied, we find

$$T_1 \approx 4\sqrt{\frac{m}{\varkappa}}\left(\ln\frac{L}{l} + \ln\frac{2\delta}{L}\right) \approx 4\sqrt{\frac{m}{\varkappa}}\ln\frac{L}{l}. \tag{1}$$

The time T_2 spent by the particle along the intervals $x_1 < x < a-\delta$ and $a+\delta < x < x_2$ satisfies the relation $T_2 \lesssim L/v$, where $\frac{1}{2}mv^2 \sim \frac{1}{2}\varkappa\delta^2$, that is

$$T_2 \lesssim \sqrt{\frac{m}{\varkappa}}\frac{L}{\delta}.$$

When ε decreases, T_1 increases so that, for sufficiently small ε, $T_2 \ll T_1$ and we can then use equation (1) to estimate the period of the motion.

This formula is asymptotically exact. As $\varepsilon \to 0$, its relative error tends to zero as $(\ln \varepsilon)^{-1}$.

If $U''(a) = 0$, but $U^{(iv)}(a) = K \neq 0$, we have

$$T = \left(\frac{6m^2}{\varepsilon K}\right)^{\frac{1}{4}} \int_0^\infty \frac{dx}{\sqrt{1+x^4}} \approx 10.7\left(\frac{m^2}{\varepsilon K}\right)^{\frac{1}{4}}.$$

If we observe the motion of the particle over a long period $t \gg T$, the probability to find the particle between x and $x+dx$ is

$$w(x)\,dx = 2\frac{dt}{T} = \frac{\sqrt{2m}\,dx}{T\sqrt{E-U(x)}}.$$

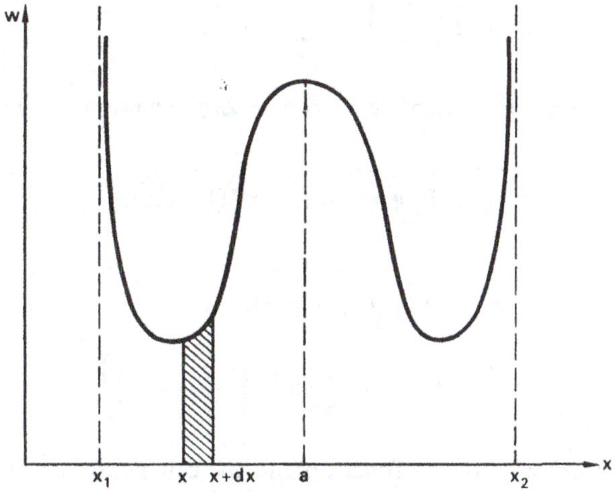

FIG. 48

The x-dependence of the probability w to find the particle at a point x is drawn in Fig. 48. The probability $w(x)\,dx$ is represented by the hatched area (the total area under the curve is unity). For small ε the area under the central maximum gives the main contribution T_1/T to the total area under the curve. In spite of the fact that $w(x) \to \infty$ as $x < x_{1,2}$ the contribution from the regions near the turning points is relatively small.

1.6. We put the value of the potential energy at the lowest point equal to zero. If $E = 2mgl$, we have

$$\varphi(t) = \pi + 4 \arctan \left[\exp\left(\pm 2t\sqrt{g/l}\right) \tan \tfrac{1}{4}(\varphi(0) - \pi)\right],$$

where φ is the angle between the pendulum and the vertical. The sign in the index is the same as that of $\dot{\varphi}(0)$. The pendulum asymptotically approaches its upper position.

In the case $0 < E - 2mgl \ll 2mgl$ the pendulum rotates, slowly crossing its upper position. One can estimate the period of rotation applying the result of the preceding problem:

$$T = \sqrt{\frac{l}{g}} \ln \frac{\varepsilon_0}{E - 2mgl}, \qquad \varepsilon_0 = \tfrac{1}{2}\pi^2 mgl.$$

1.7. We again put the value of the potential energy at the lowest point equal to zero. We then have

$$t = l\sqrt{\frac{m}{2}} \int_0^{\varphi} \frac{d\varphi}{\sqrt{E - mgl(1 - \cos\varphi)}}.$$

The substitution $x = \varkappa \sin \frac{1}{2}\varphi$, $\varkappa = \sqrt{E/2mgl}$ changes the integral to

$$t = \sqrt{\frac{l}{g}} \int_0^{x} \frac{dx}{\sqrt{(1 - x^2)(1 - \varkappa^2 x^2)}},$$

whence

$$x = \operatorname{sn}\left(t\sqrt{\frac{g}{l}} + \psi, \varkappa\right),$$

$$\varphi = 2 \arcsin \left[\frac{1}{\varkappa} \operatorname{sn}\left(t\sqrt{\frac{g}{l}} + \psi, \varkappa\right)\right].$$

(For a definition of the sn function and the other elliptic functions see, for instance, Abramovitz and Stegun, 1965.) The oscillation period is

$T = 4\sqrt{l/g}\,K(\varkappa)$, where $K(\varkappa)$ is the complete elliptic integral of the first kind,

$$K(\varkappa) = \int_0^{\pi/2} \frac{d\xi}{\sqrt{1-\varkappa^2 \sin^2 \xi}}.$$

If $\varkappa > 1$, we get from the substitution $\varkappa x = y$

$$t = \sqrt{\frac{l}{g}}\frac{1}{\varkappa}\int_0^y \frac{dy}{\sqrt{(1-y^2)(1-y^2/\varkappa^2)}},$$

and
$$\varphi = 2 \arcsin\left[\frac{1}{\varkappa^2} \operatorname{sn}\left(\varkappa t\sqrt{\frac{g}{l}}+\psi, \frac{1}{\varkappa}\right)\right].$$

The rotation period of the pendulum is $T = (2/\varkappa)\sqrt{l/g}\,K(1/\varkappa)$.

The following formulae allow us to obtain the period in certain limiting cases:

$$K(\varkappa) = \frac{\pi}{2}\left(1+\frac{1}{4}\varkappa^2\right), \quad \text{when} \quad \varkappa \ll 1;$$

$$K(\varkappa) = \frac{1}{2}\ln\frac{16}{1-\varkappa^2}, \quad \text{when} \quad 1-\varkappa \ll 1.$$

In particular, when $E-2mgl \ll 2mgl$, we have

$$T = \sqrt{\frac{l}{g}}\ln\frac{\varepsilon_0}{E-2mgl},$$

where $\varepsilon_0 = 32mgl$. This result differs from the rather crude evaluation made in the preceding problem in the value of ε_0, that is, in a quantity which does not depend on $E-2mgl$. This difference is small when

$$\frac{E-2mgl}{2mgl} \ll \frac{\pi^2}{64} \approx 0.2.$$

1.8. The motion in the potential $U(x)+\delta U(x)$ is governed by the equation

$$t = \sqrt{\frac{m}{2}}\int_a^x \frac{dx}{\sqrt{E-U(x)-\delta U(x)}}, \tag{1}$$

where we have assumed that at $t = 0$, $x = a$. Expanding the integrand in (1) in powers of $\delta U(x)$, we obtain

$$t = t_0(x)+\delta t(x), \tag{2}$$

where

$$t_0(x) = \sqrt{\frac{m}{2}} \int_a^x \frac{dx}{\sqrt{E-U(x)}}, \tag{3}$$

$$\delta t(x) = \frac{1}{2}\sqrt{\frac{m}{2}} \int_a^x \frac{\delta U(x)\,dx}{[E-U(x)]^{3/2}}. \tag{4}$$

Let the orbit for the case when $\delta U(x) = 0$, which is determined by $t = t_0(x)$, be $x = x_0(t)$. We then have from (2)

$$x = x_0(t-\delta t(x)), \tag{5}$$

where in $\delta t(x)$ we substitute for x the function $x_0(t)$. Expanding (5) in terms of δt, we finally obtain

$$x = x_0(t) - x_0'(t)\,\delta t(x_0(t)). \tag{6}$$

Near a turning point one has to be careful, as the small parameter in the problem so far has been $\delta U/(E-U(x))$ which becomes large near the turning point. Near the turning point $x = x_1$ we may assume

$$\delta U(x) = \delta U(x_1), \quad U(x) = E-(x-x_1)F,$$

where $F = -U'(x_1)$. We assume that $|\delta U'(x_1)| \ll |F|$. The expansion is applicable as long as $|x-x_1| \lesssim \delta x_1$, where $\delta x_1 = -\delta U(x_1)/F$. We then have

$$\delta t = \frac{\sqrt{m}\,\delta U(x_1)}{\sqrt{2F^3(x-x_1)}} + \delta t_0, \tag{7}$$

where the constant δt_0 determines the delay of the particle suffered along its path far from the turning point. When $|x-x_1| \gtrsim \delta x_1$, the first term on the right-hand side of (7) is small; however, when $|x-x_1| < \delta x_1$ it becomes large according to (7) so that it ceases to be a small correction, and (2) is no longer applicable.

We note, however, that equation (6) remains valid right up to the turning point. Indeed, the change in the motion in the vicinity of the turning point consists in a shift of the latter. This result is obtained when we substitute (7) into (6):

$$x(t) = x_0(t) + \delta x_1 - x_0'(t)\,\delta t_0 = x_0(t-\delta t_0) + \delta x_1, \tag{8}$$

where δx_1 satisfies the equation for a turning point,

$$U(x_1+\delta x_1) + \delta U(x_1+\delta x_1) = E,$$

with the required accuracy. This is connected with the fact that near an extremum x is nearly independent of t, even though δt increases when we approach the turning point.

1.9. (a) For the unperturbed motion we have

$$x_0(t) = a \sin \omega t, \quad E = \tfrac{1}{2}ma^2\omega^2. \tag{1}$$

For the correction we have

$$\delta t(x) = \frac{\alpha}{3\omega^3}\left(\sqrt{a^2-x^2}+\frac{a^2}{\sqrt{a^2-x^2}}-2a\right). \tag{2}$$

Substituting (1) and (2) into (6) of the preceding problem, we get

$$x(t) = a \sin \omega t - \frac{\alpha a^3}{3\omega^2} \cos \omega t \left(\cos \omega t + \frac{1}{\cos \omega t} - 2\right).$$

Up to terms of first order in $\alpha a^2/\omega^2$ we have

$$x(t) = a \sin(\omega t+\varphi) - \frac{\alpha a^3}{2\omega^2} - \frac{\alpha a^3}{6\omega^2} \cos 2(\omega t+\varphi),$$

where $\varphi = -2\alpha a^2/3\omega^2$ (compare problem 8.1b).

1.10. The change in period is

$$\delta T = \sqrt{\frac{m}{2}}\left[\int_{x_1+\delta x_1}^{x_2+\delta x_2} \frac{dx}{\sqrt{E-U(x)-\delta U(x)}} - \int_{x_1}^{x_2} \frac{dx}{\sqrt{E-U(x)}}\right]. \tag{1}$$

One cannot expand the integrand in (1) in terms of $\delta U(x)$ since the requirements of the theorem about differentiating improper integrals with respect to a parameter are violated, as the resulting integral diverges. However, we can expand the integrand in terms of $\delta U(x)$ up to terms of first order in $\delta U(x)$ if we write δT in the form

$$\delta T = \sqrt{2m}\frac{\partial}{\partial E}\left[\int_{x_1+\delta x_1}^{x_2+\delta x_2} \sqrt{E-U(x)-\delta U(x)}\, dx - \int_{x_1}^{x_2} \sqrt{E-U(x)}\, dx\right], \tag{2}$$

whence

$$\delta T = -\sqrt{\frac{m}{2}}\frac{\partial}{\partial E}\int_{x_1}^{x_2} \frac{\delta U(x)dx}{\sqrt{E-U(x)}} = -\frac{\partial}{\partial E}(T\langle\delta U\rangle), \tag{3}$$

where

$$\langle\delta U\rangle = \frac{1}{T}\int_0^T \delta U(x(t))\, dt \tag{4}$$

is the time-average of δU.

The time spent near the turning point contributes little to the period, provided, of course, that $U'(x_{1,2}) \neq 0$ (compare problem 1.3). Equation (3) can therefore give a good approximation.

We note that sometimes even small extra terms $\delta U(x)$ may strongly affect the motion (see, for example, problems 1.11(b) and (c)).

Higher-order terms in the expansion of δT in terms of δU can be obtained by similar means:

$$T = \sqrt{\frac{m}{2}} \sum_{n=0}^{\infty} \frac{(-1)^n}{n!} \frac{\partial^n}{\partial E^n} \int_{x_1}^{x_2} \frac{[\delta U(x)]^n \, dx}{\sqrt{E-U(x)}}. \tag{5}$$

The formal expansion (5) may be an asymptotic or even a convergent series.

1.11. (a) According to equation (5) of the preceding problem the correction to the period $2\pi/\omega$ is $-3\pi\beta E/2m\omega^5$ which is small, provided E is sufficiently small,

(b) In Fig. 49 we have given the potential energies $U(x)$ and $U(x)+\delta U(x)$. When $E=E' > U_m = m\omega^6/6\alpha^2$ the extra term clearly means that the particle can move to infinity. When E is close to U_m, the period of oscillation increases without bound (as $|\ln(U_m-E)|$; see problem 1.4) so that one cannot determine the change in period just by a few terms in the series (5) of the preceding problem.

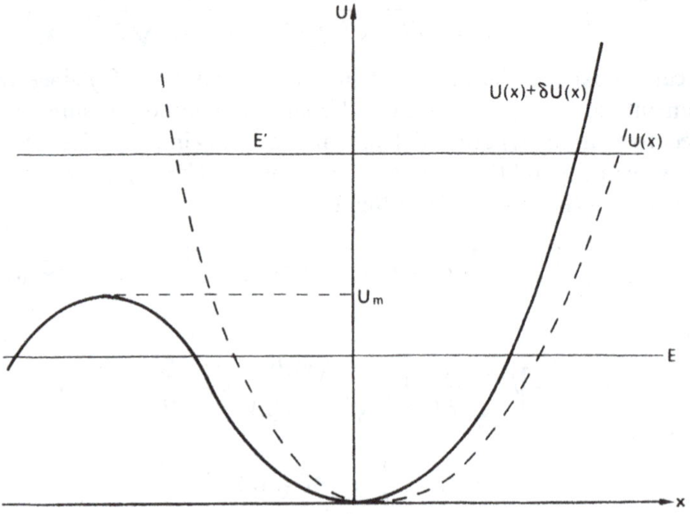

FIG. 49

When $E \ll U_m$ the correction to the period is $\delta T = 5\pi E/18\omega U_m$.

(c) $\delta T = 3\pi A\sqrt{m}/2\alpha E^{\frac{5}{2}}\sqrt{2}$; the formula is applicable when $|E| \gg |U_m| \approx \sqrt{8AV}$, $(E < 0)$.

2. Motion of a Particle in Three-dimensional Potentials

2.1. To study the orbits of the particle we use the energy and angular momentum conservation laws:

$$\tfrac{1}{2}m(\dot{\boldsymbol{r}}\cdot\dot{\boldsymbol{r}})+U(r) = E, \tag{1}$$

$$m[\boldsymbol{r}\wedge\dot{\boldsymbol{r}}] = \boldsymbol{M}. \tag{2}$$

It follows from (2) that the orbit lies in a plane. Introducing polar coordinates in that plane (see Fig. 50) we get

$$\tfrac{1}{2}m\dot{r}^2+\tfrac{1}{2}mr^2\dot{\varphi}^2+U(r) = E, \tag{3}$$

$$mr^2\dot{\varphi} = M. \tag{4}$$

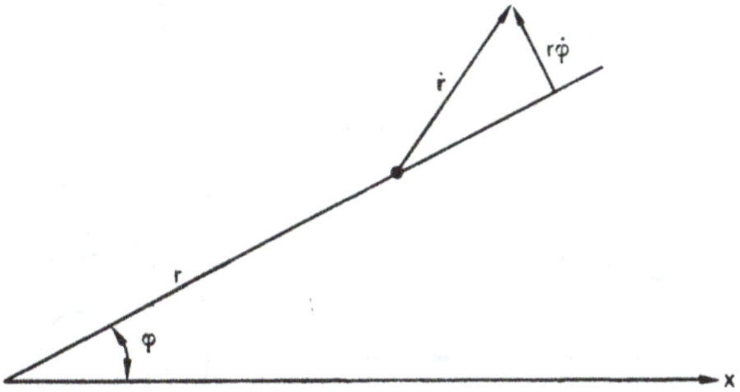

Fig. 50

Using (4) to eliminate $\dot{\varphi}$ from (3) we get

$$\tfrac{1}{2}m\dot{r}^2+U_{\text{eff}}(r) = E, \tag{5}$$

where

$$U_{\text{eff}}(r) = U(r)+\frac{M^2}{2mr^2}.$$

The radial motion can thus be considered as a one-dimensional motion in the potential $U_{\text{eff}}(r)$.

For a qualitative discussion of the character of the orbits we use diagrams of

$$U_{\text{eff}}(r) = -\frac{\alpha}{r} - \frac{\gamma}{r^3} + \frac{M^2}{2mr^2} \tag{6}$$

for different values of M (Fig. 51).

When $M^4 > 12m^2\alpha\gamma$, U_{eff} has two extrema (for $r_{1,2} = [M^2 \mp \sqrt{M^4 - 12m^2\alpha\gamma}]/2m\alpha$), where $U_{\text{eff}}(r_2) = U_{\text{min}} < 0$, while U_{max} can be either positive, when $M^4 > 16m^2\alpha\gamma$ (Fig. 51a), or negative, when $12m^2\alpha\gamma < M^4 < 16m^2\alpha\gamma$ (Fig. 51b). If $M^4 < 12m^2\alpha\gamma$, the function $U_{\text{eff}}(r)$ will be monotonic (Fig. 51c).

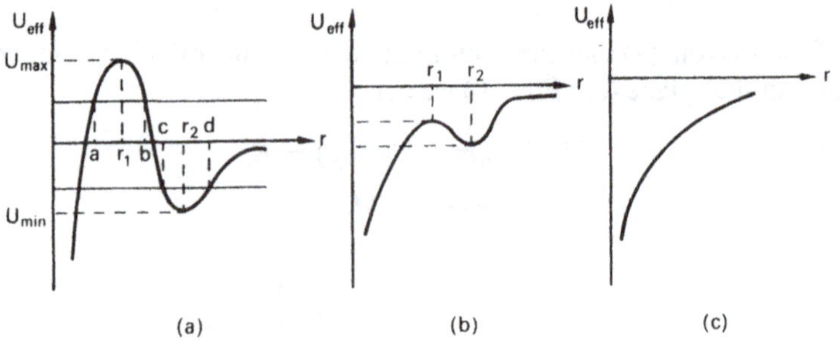

FIG. 51

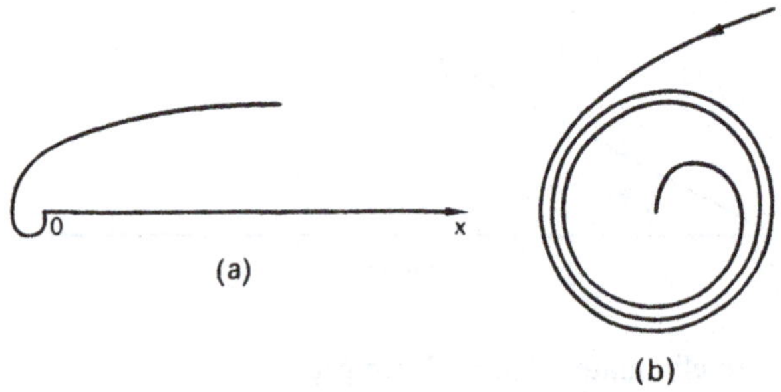

FIG. 52

Let us consider the case of Fig. 51a in somewhat more detail. If $E > U_{\text{max}}$ the particle coming from infinity falls into the centre of the potential. The quantity $\dot{\varphi}$ then increases according to (4). This is all we need to sketch the orbit (see Figs. 52a, b).

At large distances such that $\gamma r^{-3} \ll \alpha r^{-1}$, the main term in U is $-\alpha/r$ and the orbit differs little from a hyperbola. For the form of the orbit as $r \to 0$, we refer to problem 2.8. If the energy is close to U_{max}, the particle passes very slowly through the range of values of r which are close to r_1. At the same time the radius vector turns round with a velocity $\dot{\varphi} \approx M/mr_1^2$ so that the particle may perform many revolutions around the centre before it passes through this range of values (Fig. 52b).

If $E = U_{max}$ the particle approaches the point $r = r_1$ asymptotically during its radial motion (compare problem 1.3). The orbit is a spiral approaching the circle of radius r_1 and centre O (Fig. 53a). If, on the other hand, the particle starts in the region $r < r_1$ and is moving away from the centre, its orbit also approaches this circle, but this time from the inside (Fig. 53b). Finally, motion along the circle $r = r_1$ is possible when $E = U_{max}$.

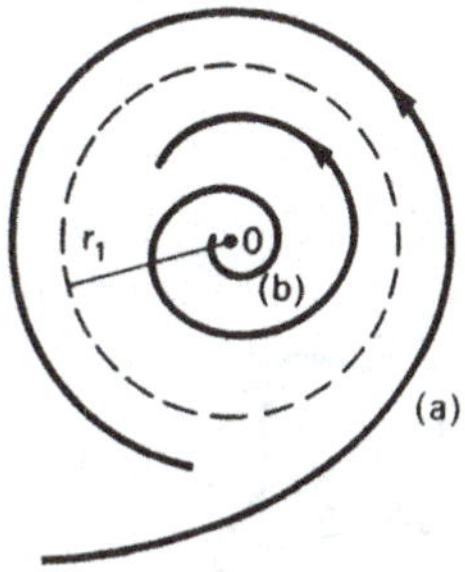

FIG. 53

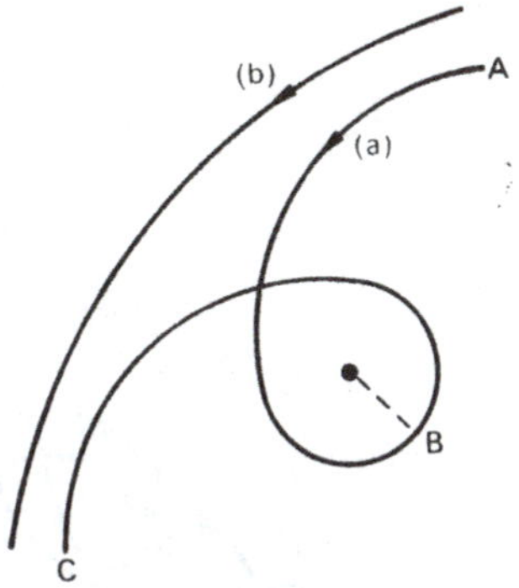

FIG. 54

The motion along this circle is an unstable one, as any change in E or M will bring the particle onto an orbit which moves away from the circle.

If $0 < E < U_{max}$ a particle coming from infinity will be reflected from the potential barrier U_{eff} and again move off to infinity. Examples of such orbits are given in Fig. 54a, b. If the energy is close to U_{max} the particle makes many revolutions around the centre before $\dot{r}$ changes sign. The closer the energy is to zero (for a fixed value of M this corresponds to larger values of the impact parameter) the less twisted the orbit of the particle.

When $E < U_{max}$, the case is also possible of the particle falling towards the centre, when it is moving in the region $r < a$. The orbit for that case is given in Fig. 55.

When $U_{min} < E < 0$ the particle can also perform radial oscillations in the range $c \leq r \leq d$. If the energy is close to zero, the amplitude of the radial oscillations will be large; their period can also become large and the radius vector may perform several revolutions during one radial oscillation (Fig. 56a). When the energy is close to U_{min} the orbit is close to a circle with radius r_2 (Fig. 56b) while the angle over which the radius vector turns during one period of the radial oscillation depends on the quantities

FIG. 55

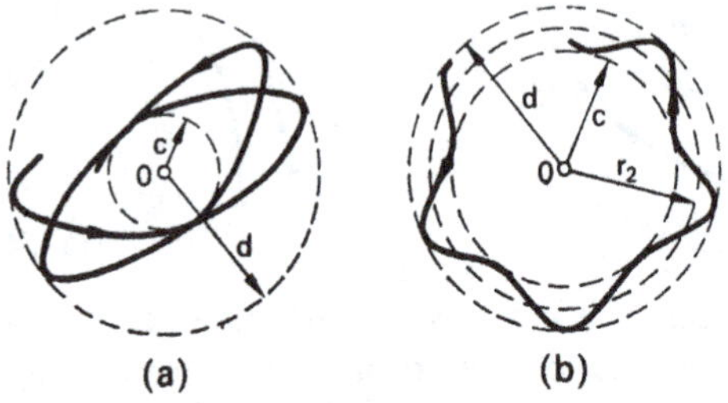

FIG. 56

α, γ, and M (compare problem 5.4). When $E = U_{min}$ the particle moves along the above-mentioned circle.

One can analyse the motion of the particle in a similar way for the other cases.

What are the particular features of the orbit when $M^4 = 12m^2\alpha\gamma$?

Let us now consider the orbits in more detail. One can obtain the equation for the orbit from equations (4) and (5). From (5) we get

$$\dot{r} = \pm\sqrt{\frac{2}{m}(E - U_{eff})}, \tag{7}$$

or

$$t = \pm\sqrt{\frac{m}{2}}\int^{r}\frac{dr}{\sqrt{E-U_{\text{eff}}(r)}}+C. \tag{8}$$

Using (4) to eliminate dt from (7) we find the equation of the orbit:

$$\varphi = \pm\frac{M}{\sqrt{2m}}\int^{r}\frac{dr}{r^2\sqrt{E-U_{\text{eff}}(r)}}+C'. \tag{9}$$

Let us consider the case $M^4 > 12m^2\alpha\gamma$. If the particle moves towards the centre we must take in (7), and of course also in (8), the lower sign. If at $t = 0$, $r = r_0$, we can rewrite (8) in the form

$$t = -\sqrt{\frac{m}{2}}\int_{r_0}^{r}\frac{dr}{\sqrt{E-U_{\text{eff}}(r)}}. \tag{10}$$

Equation (10) is an implicit equation for r as a function of t. If the orbit passes through the point $r = r_0$, $\varphi = \varphi_0$, the equation of the orbit becomes

$$\varphi = -M\int_{r_0}^{r}\frac{dr}{r^2|p_r|}+\varphi_0, \tag{11}$$

where we have taken once again the lower sign, and where $|p_r| = \sqrt{2m[E-U_{\text{eff}}(r)]}$. In particular, if the velocity of the particle at infinity makes an angle ψ with the x-axis, we must put $r_0 = \infty$, $\varphi_0 = \pi-\psi$.

If $E > U_{\max}$, equations (10) and (11) completely determine the orbit and the time when the particle passes through each point of the orbit. However, if $0 < E < U_{\max}$, these equations correspond only to the section AB of the orbit (see Fig. 54a). At B the radial component of the velocity $\dot{r}$ vanishes and then changes sign. The section BC of the orbit is thus described by equation (9) with the upper sign and we must redetermine the constant C'. It is convenient to write (9) in the form

$$\varphi = M\int_{r_{\min}}^{r}\frac{dr}{r^2|p_r|}+C'. \tag{12}$$

As long as C' is not determined, we can choose the lower limit of the integral arbitrarily. According to (12) we now have

$$C' = \varphi(r_{\min}). \tag{13}$$

Determining $\varphi(r_{\min})$ from (11) we get the following equation for the section BC of the orbit:

$$\varphi = M\int_{r_{\min}}^{r} \frac{dr}{r^2|p_r|} - M\int_{r_0}^{r_{\min}} \frac{dr}{r^2|p_r|} + \varphi_0. \tag{14}$$

Similarly we can determine the time dependence of r along BC:

$$t = \sqrt{\frac{m}{2}}\int_{r_{\min}}^{r} \frac{dr}{\sqrt{E-U_{\text{eff}}(r)}} - \sqrt{\frac{m}{2}}\int_{r_0}^{r_{\min}} \frac{dr}{\sqrt{E-U_{\text{eff}}(r)}}. \tag{15}$$

If $U_{\min} < E < 0$, $a < r_0 < b$, $\dot{r}(0) < 0$, $\varphi|_{t=0} = \varphi_0$, equation (11) describes the section AB of the orbit in Fig. 54b. The section BC is described by the equation

$$\varphi = M\int_{a}^{r} \frac{dr}{r^2|p_r|} + \varphi_1, \tag{16}$$

where the angle φ_1 can be obtained by putting $r = a$ in (16). The equation for the section CD is

$$\varphi = -M\int_{b}^{r} \frac{dr}{r^2|p_r|} + \varphi_2, \tag{17}$$

where φ_2 is determined from (16) with $r = b$, and so on. Substituting the values of φ_1 and φ_2 into (16) and (17) we get the equations for BC and CD in the form

$$\varphi = M\int_{a}^{r} \frac{dr}{r^2|p_r|} - M\int_{r_0}^{a} \frac{dr}{r^2|p_r|}, \tag{18}$$

$$\begin{aligned}\varphi &= -M\int_{b}^{r} \frac{dr}{r^2|p_r|} + M\int_{a}^{b} \frac{dr}{r^2|p_r|} - M\int_{r_0}^{a} \frac{dr}{r^2|p_r|} \\ &= -M\int_{a}^{r} \frac{dr}{r^2|p_r|} + 2M\int_{a}^{b} \frac{dr}{r^2|p_r|} - M\int_{r_0}^{a} \frac{dr}{r^2|p_r|}.\end{aligned} \tag{19}$$

One verifies easily that the equation for that section of the orbit which corresponds to the nth radial oscillation, taking the section BC to be the first, has the form†

$$\varphi = \pm M \int_a^r \frac{dr}{r^2 |p_r|} + 2(n-1)M \int_a^b \frac{dr}{r^2 |p_r|} - M \int_{r_0}^a \frac{dr}{r^2 |p_r|} + \varphi_0. \tag{20}$$

In the equations given here we have assumed that the angle φ changes continuously, and we have not introduced the limitation $0 \leqq \varphi < 2\pi$. There is an infinity of values of φ corresponding to a given value of r, corresponding to different values of n and different signs in equation (20): φ is a many-valued function of r; on the other had, r is a single-valued function of φ.

All other cases can be treated in a similar fashion.

2.2. Outside the sphere of radius R the particle moves with a speed $\sqrt{2E/m}$ and inside with a speed $\sqrt{2(E+V)/m}$. Depending on the values of E and M we get different kinds of orbits. When $(M^2/2mR^2) - V < E < M^2/2mR^2$, the particle can either move inside the sphere and be reflected at its surface (Fig. 57a); or, provided $E > 0$, we can have an infinite orbit

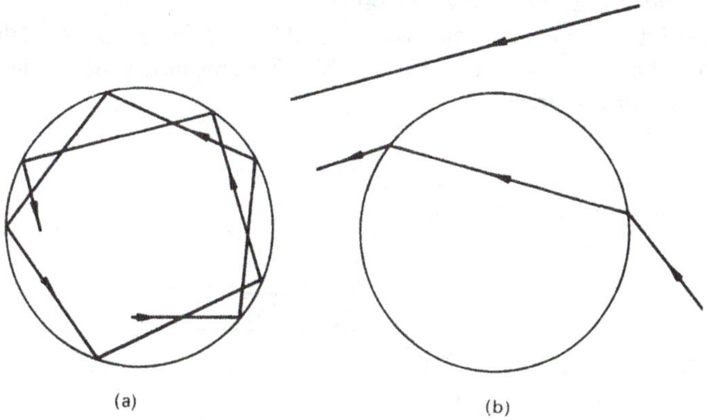

(a) (b)

FIG. 57

† The equation (20) for the orbit can be written in the form

$$\int_a^r \frac{dr}{r^2|p_r|} = \frac{\arccos \gamma(\varphi+\alpha)}{\gamma M}$$

(we bear in mind that $0 \leqq \arccos x < \pi$), where

$$\frac{\pi}{\gamma} = M \int_a^b \frac{dr}{r^2|p_r|}, \quad \alpha = M \int_{r_0}^a \frac{dr}{r^2|p_r|} - \varphi_0.$$

(which can be a straight line, see Fig. 57b). When $M^2/2mR^2 < E$, we can have a refracted orbit (Fig. 57b).

What is the shape of the orbit when $E = M^2/2mR^2 - V$?

2.3. To determine the equation of the orbit we use the equations

$$\left.\begin{aligned} \varphi &= \int \frac{M\,dr}{r^2\sqrt{2m(E-U_{\text{eff}}(r))}}, \\ U_{\text{eff}}(r) &= U(r)+\frac{M^2}{2mr^2}, \end{aligned}\right\} \tag{1}$$

and we then get†

$$r = \frac{p}{e\cos\gamma(\varphi-\psi)-1}, \tag{2}$$

where

$$p = \frac{2}{\alpha}\left(\beta+\frac{M^2}{2m}\right), \quad e = \sqrt{1+\frac{4E}{\alpha^2}\left(\beta+\frac{M^2}{2m}\right)}, \quad \gamma = \sqrt{1+\frac{2m\beta}{M^2}}, \tag{3}$$

$E > 0$, and ψ is an arbitrary constant.

The orbit is the curve which is obtained from a hyperbola by reducing the polar angles by a factor γ (Fig. 58). The constant ψ determines the orientation of the orbit.

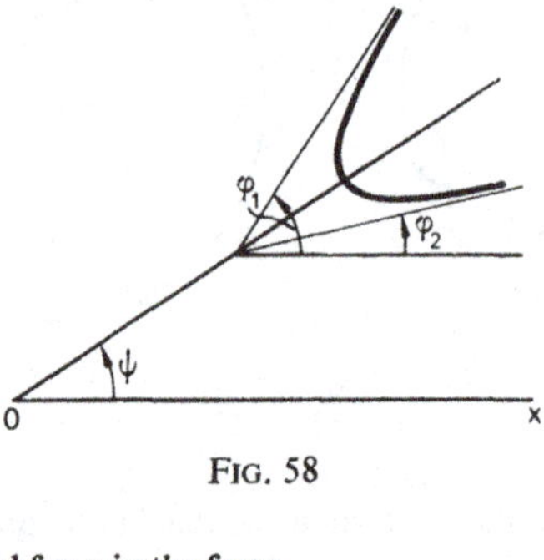

FIG. 58

† If we write the integral for φ in the form

$$\frac{\tilde{M}}{M}\varphi = \int \frac{\tilde{M}\,dr}{r^2\sqrt{2m(E-\tilde{M}^2/2mr^2-\alpha/r)}},$$

where $\tilde{M}^2 = M^2+2m\beta$, the integral is reduced to the corresponding integral in the Kepler problem (see, for instance, ter Haar, 1964, p. 9).

The direction of the asymptotes is determined by the condition $r \to \infty$, or $e \cos \gamma(\varphi_{1,2}-\psi) = 1$. The directions of the velocity before and after the scattering are at an angle

$$\pi-(\varphi_1-\varphi_2) = \pi-\frac{2}{\gamma}\arccos\frac{1}{e} = \pi-\frac{2}{\gamma}\arctan\sqrt{\frac{4E}{\alpha^2}\left(\beta+\frac{M^2}{2m}\right)}$$

to one another.

2.4. It is useful to study first of all the character of the orbit using a graph of $U_{\text{eff}}(r)$. This graph is given in Fig. 59 for the case where $\beta < M^2/2m$. In that case all orbits are infinite and lie in the region $r > r_m$, when $E > 0$.

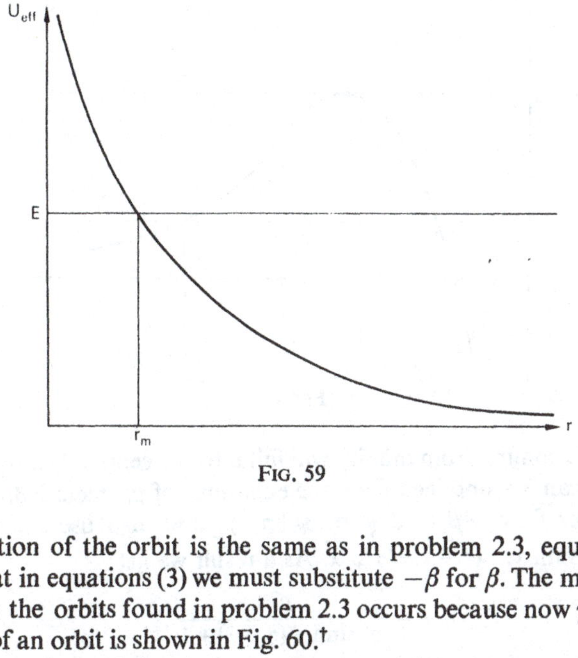

FIG. 59

The equation of the orbit is the same as in problem 2.3, equation (2), except that in equations (3) we must substitute $-\beta$ for β. The main difference with the orbits found in problem 2.3 occurs because now $\gamma < 1$. An example of an orbit is shown in Fig. 60.†

The form of $U_{\text{eff}}(r)$ for the case when $\beta > M^2/2m$ is shown in Fig. 61. If

$$E > U_m = \frac{\alpha^2}{4(\beta-M^2/2m)},$$

† The inflection point A is determined from the condition $dU/dr=0$, that is, $r=2\beta/\alpha$.

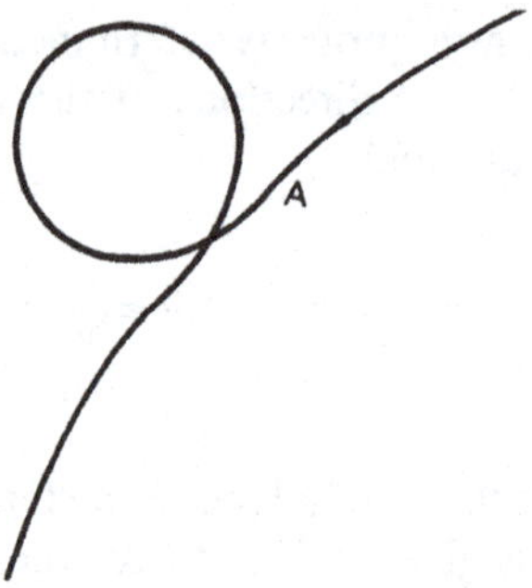

FIG. 60

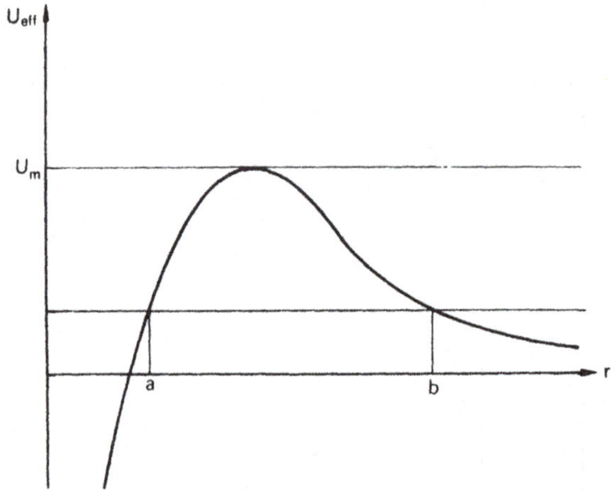

FIG. 61

the particle coming from infinity will fall into the centre. The equation of the orbit can be obtained from the equations of problem 2.3. We must then replace β by $-\beta$ and ψ by $\psi+\pi/2\gamma$, and also use the formulae $\sin ix = i \sinh x$, $\sqrt{-x} = i\sqrt{x}$. As a result we get

$$r = \frac{p'}{e' \sinh \gamma'(\varphi-\psi)+1}, \tag{1}$$

$$p' = \frac{2}{\alpha}\left(\beta-\frac{M^2}{2m}\right), \quad e' = \sqrt{\frac{4E}{\alpha^2}\left(\beta-\frac{M^2}{2m}\right)-1}, \quad \gamma' = \sqrt{\frac{2m\beta}{M^2}-1}. \tag{2}$$

The orbit for this case is shown in Fig. 62a. We note that as $r \to 0$, $\varphi \to \infty$. This means that a particle coming from infinity and falling into the centre makes an infinite number of revolutions around the centre.

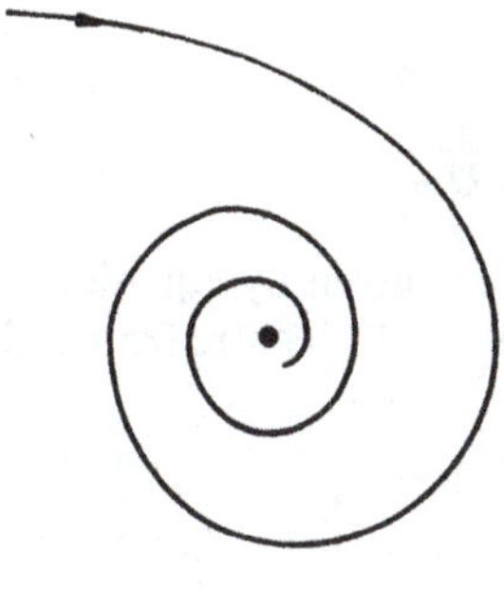

FIG. 62a

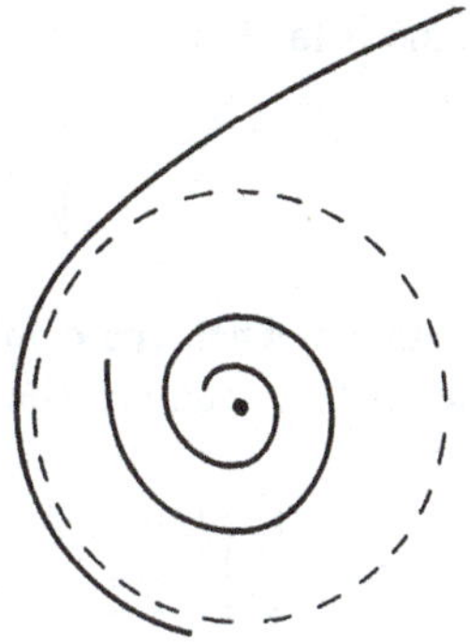

FIG. 62b

If $E < U_m$, we see from Fig. 61 that the particle can either move in the region $b \leqq r < \infty$ (scattering), or in the region $0 < r \leqq a$ (falling into the centre). We obtain the equation for the orbit, using the relation $\cos ix = \cosh x$, and for the second case again the substitution of $\psi + \pi/\gamma$ for ψ:

$$r = \frac{p'}{1 \mp e'' \cosh \gamma'(\varphi - \psi)}, \qquad e'' = \sqrt{1 - \frac{4E}{\alpha^2}\left(\beta - \frac{M^2}{2m}\right)}. \tag{3}$$

For the case $E = U_m$ it is not possible to use equation (2) of problem 2.3, as we have assumed in its derivation that $e \neq 0$ and we must start again from the integral (1) of problem 2.3. We find

$$r = \frac{p'}{1 + Ce^{-\gamma'\varphi}},$$

that is,

$$r = \frac{p'}{1 \pm \exp\left[-\gamma'(\varphi - \psi)\right]} \quad \text{or} \quad r = p'$$

depending on the initial value of r. The orbit is either a spiral starting at infinity and approaching asymptotically the circle with radius $r = p'$, or a spiral starting near the centre and approaching the same circle asymptotically, or it is this circle itself (Fig. 62b).

Finally, for the case $\beta = M^2/2m$ it is also simplest to start again from the original integral. In that case scattering occurs and the equation for the orbit is

$$r = \frac{2M^2\alpha}{2M^2E - m\alpha^2(\varphi - \psi)^2}.$$

The time it takes the particle to fall into the centre is found from the equation

$$t = \sqrt{\frac{m}{2}} \int_0^r \frac{dr}{\sqrt{E - U_{\text{eff}}(r)}}.$$

For instance, when the orbit has the form given by equations (1) and (2) of the present problem, the time to fall into the centre from a distance r is given by

$$t = \frac{1}{E}\sqrt{\frac{m}{2}}\left[\sqrt{Er^2 - \alpha r - \beta - \frac{M^2}{2m}} - \sqrt{\beta - \frac{M^2}{2m}}\right]$$
$$+ \frac{\alpha}{2E}\sqrt{\frac{m}{2E}}\left[\arcsin\frac{(2Er/\alpha) - 1}{e'} - \arcsin\frac{1}{e'}\right].$$

2.5. The equation of the orbit is

$$r = \frac{p}{1 + e\cos\gamma(\varphi - \psi)},$$

where p, e, and γ are defined in problem 2.3. When $E < 0$, the orbit is a finite one, and†

$$T_r = \frac{\pi\alpha\sqrt{m}}{(2|E|)^{3/2}}, \quad \Delta\varphi = \frac{2\pi}{\gamma}, \quad T_\varphi = \gamma T_r.$$

The orbit is closed, if γ is a rational number. In Fig. 63 we show the orbit for $\gamma \sim 4$.

2.6. When $\beta < M^2/2m$ we have

$$r = \frac{\tilde{p}}{1 - \tilde{e}\cos\tilde{\gamma}(\varphi - \psi)}, \quad \tilde{p} = \frac{2}{\alpha}\left(\frac{M^2}{2m} - \beta\right),$$
$$\tilde{\gamma} = \sqrt{1 - \frac{2m\beta}{M^2}}, \quad \tilde{e} = \sqrt{1 + \frac{4E}{\alpha^2}\left(\frac{M^2}{2m} - \beta\right)},$$

if $E < 0$, $\Delta\varphi = 2\pi/\tilde{\gamma}$, $T_\varphi = \tilde{\gamma}T_r$, and T_r will be the same as in the preceding problem.

† The period T_r is the same as in the potential $U_0 = -\alpha/r$. To determine T_r it is sufficient to note that adding a term β/r^2 to the potential U_0 has the same effect on the radial motion as increasing M. However, the period T_r is independent of M in the Coulomb potential U_0.

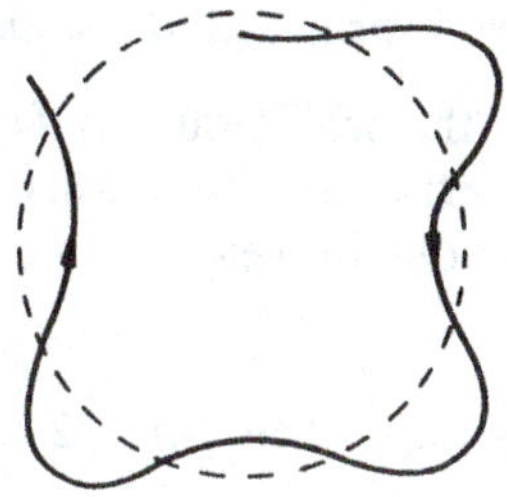

FIG. 63

When $\beta > M^2/2m$, we have (using the notation of problem 2.4)

$$r = \frac{p'}{e \sinh \gamma'(\varphi - \psi) + 1}, \quad \text{when} \quad E > 0;$$

$$r = \frac{p'}{e \cosh \gamma'(\varphi - \psi) + 1}, \quad \text{when} \quad E < 0.$$

2.7. (a) A finite orbit is possible if the function $U_{\text{eff}}(r)$ has a minimum. The equation $U'_{\text{eff}}(r) = 0$ can be reduced to the form $f(x) = \varkappa M^2/\alpha m$, where $f(x) = x(x+1)e^{-x}$, $x = \varkappa r$. Using a graph of $f(x)$ one sees easily that this equation has real roots only when $\varkappa M^2/\alpha m$ is less than the maximum value of $f(x)$, for $x > 0$. This maximum value is equal to $(2+\sqrt{5}) \exp[-\frac{1}{2}(1+\sqrt{5})] \approx 0{\cdot}84$. A finite orbit is thus possible, provided $M^2 < 0{\cdot}84\, \alpha m/\varkappa$.

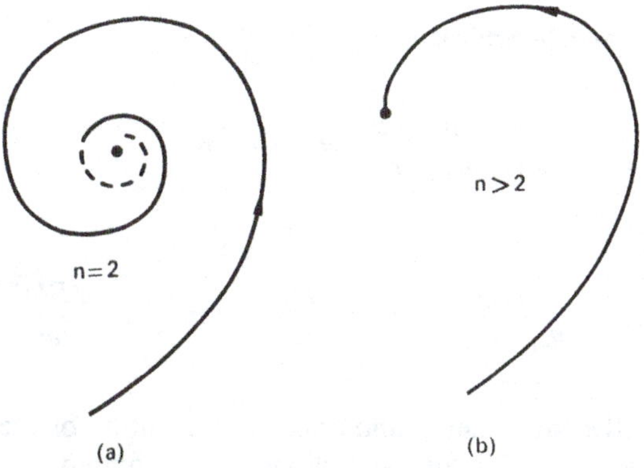

FIG. 64

(b) A finite orbit is possible provided $M^2 < 8mV/e^2\varkappa^2$.

2.8. In the equation for the orbit (equation (1) of problem 2.3) we can neglect for small values of r the quantity E, when $n = 2$, and also the term $M^2/2mr^2$, when $n > 2$. We obtain then

$$\varphi = -\frac{M \ln (r/r_0)}{\sqrt{2m\alpha - M^2}} + \varphi_0, \quad \text{when} \quad n = 2 \text{ (see Fig. 64a)},$$

$$\varphi = -\frac{2M}{\sqrt{2m\alpha}\,(2-n)} r^{-1+\frac{1}{2}n}, \quad \text{when} \quad n > 2 \text{ (see Fig. 64b)}.$$

It turns out that the number of revolutions is infinite only when $n = 2$.

The time it takes the particle to fall into the centre is finite as the radial velocity increases when the centre is approached.

2.9. The number of revolutions of the particle around the centre is infinite only in the case

(b) $E = 0, \quad n \leqq 2$.

2.10. The time it takes the particle to fall into the centre is $\pi\sqrt{mR^3/2\alpha}$.

2.11. The relative motion is characterised by the angular momentum $M = \mu v \varrho$ and the energy $E = \frac{1}{2}\mu v^2$, where $\mu = m_1 m_2/(m_1+m_2)$ is the reduced mass. The distance to be determined follows from the condition $U_{\text{eff}}(r_{\text{min}}) = E$. Solutions can be obtained easily for $n = 1, 2$, and 4.

2.12. The particle orbit is

$$\frac{\mu}{m_{1,2}} \frac{p}{r_{1,2}} = 1 \pm e \cos \varphi,$$

where

$$\mu = \frac{m_1 m_2}{m_1+m_2}, \quad p = \frac{M^2}{\mu\alpha}, \quad e = \sqrt{1+\frac{2EM^2}{\mu\alpha^2}},$$

E and M are the total energy and angular momentum of the system. The particles move in similar conical sections with a common focus and their radius vectors are at any moment in opposite directions (Fig. 65).

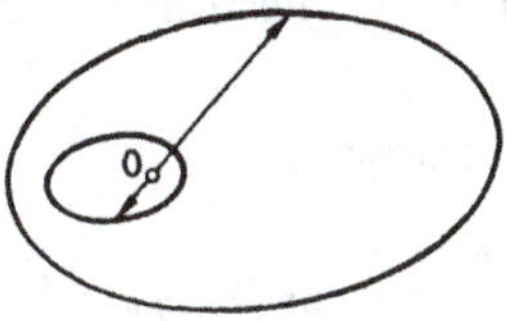

FIG. 65

2.13. One sees easily from Fig. 66 that

$$\mathrm{OS} = \varrho(\cot\varphi_0 - \cot 2\varphi_0). \tag{1}$$

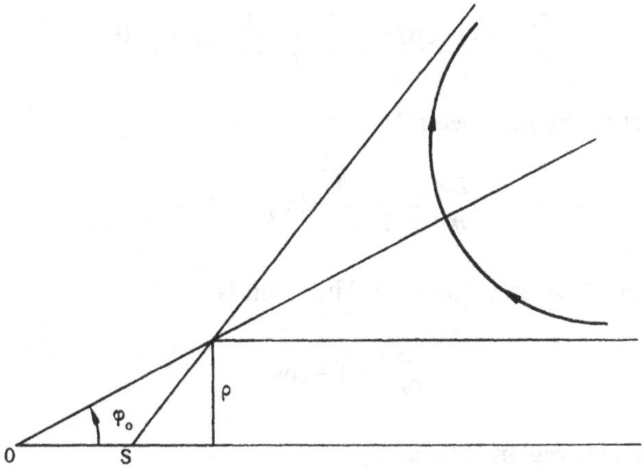

FIG. 66

Here

$$\varphi_0 = \varrho \int_{r_{\min}}^{\infty} \frac{dr}{r^2\sqrt{1-(U(r)/E)-(\varrho^2/r^2)}}. \tag{2}$$

As $\varrho \to 0$, $\varphi_0 \to 0$, and

$$\mathrm{OS} = \left\{2\int_{r_{\min}}^{\infty} \frac{dr}{r^2\sqrt{1-(U(r)/E)}}\right\}^{-1} + O(\varrho^2). \tag{3}$$

The point S is the virtual focus of the beam of scattered particles so that up to and including terms of first order in ϱ the position of the points where the asymptote of the orbit intersects the axis of the beam is independent of ϱ.

2.14. The equation of the orbit is

$$\frac{p}{r} = e\cos(\varphi-\varphi_0)-1,$$

where $p = M^2/m\alpha$, $e = \sqrt{1+2EM^2/m\alpha^2}$, while φ_0 is determined from the condition that $\varphi \to 0$, as $r \to \infty$, so that $\cos\varphi_0 = 1/e$. The region which cannot be reached by the particles is bounded by the envelope of the family of orbits. To find it we differentiate the equation for the orbit,

$$\frac{M^2}{m\alpha r}+1-\cos\varphi-\frac{M}{\alpha}\sqrt{\frac{2E}{m}}\sin\varphi = 0, \tag{1}$$

with respect to the parameter M:

$$\frac{2M}{mr}-\sqrt{\frac{2E}{m}}\sin\varphi = 0, \tag{2}$$

and eliminate M from (1) and (2). The result is

$$\frac{2\alpha}{Er} = 1+\cos\varphi.$$

The inaccessible region is thus

$$r < \frac{2\alpha}{E(1+\cos\varphi)}$$

which is bounded by a paraboloid of revolution (Fig. 67).

2.15.

$$\varrho < \frac{2a\delta}{1-\delta^2-(1-\delta)^2\cos\varphi},$$

where $\delta = mav^2/2\alpha$, OA $= a$.

2.16. We take the scalar product of the equation

$$[v \wedge M]-\alpha\frac{r}{r} = A$$

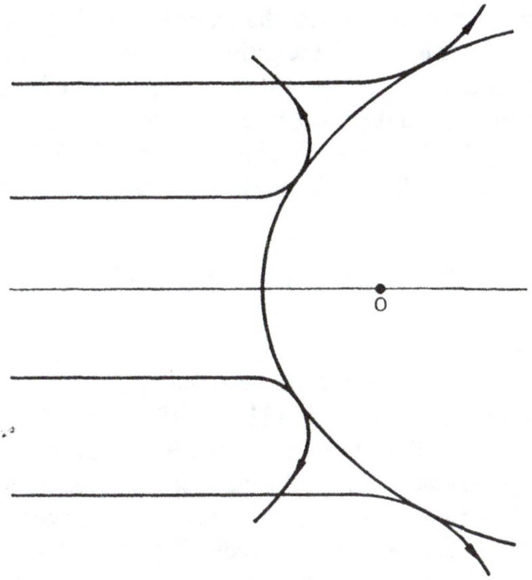

FIG. 67

with $\boldsymbol{r}$. Denoting by φ the angle between $\boldsymbol{r}$ and $\boldsymbol{A}$, we get

$$\frac{M^2}{m}-\alpha r = Ar\cos\varphi, \quad \text{or} \quad \frac{p}{r} = 1+e\cos\varphi,$$

where $p = M^2/m\alpha$, $e = A/\alpha$. We note that the vector $\boldsymbol{A}$ is directed from the centre of the potential field to the point $r = r_{\min}$.

2.17.

$$\delta T = -\frac{\partial \delta I}{\partial E}, \quad \text{where} \quad \delta I = T < \delta U > = 2\sqrt{\frac{m}{2}}\int_{r_1}^{r_2} \frac{\delta U(r)dr}{\sqrt{E-U_{\text{eff}}(r)}}$$

(compare problem 1.10).

Similarly we can write for the change in the angular distance between successive pericentre passages ($r = r_{\min}$) in the form $\delta\Delta\varphi = \partial I/\partial M$ (compare problem 3 of § 15 and § 49 of Landau and Lifshitz, 1960).

2.18. The potential $U(r)$ differs little from the Coulomb potential $U_0(r) = -\alpha/r$ in the region $r \ll D$. Therefore a finite orbit which is close to an ellipse with a parameter p and an eccentricity e determined by the integrals of motion E and M will retain its shape, but will change its orientation. The velocity of rotation Ω of the ellipse is determined by the displacement of the pericentre over a period $\Omega = \delta\Delta\varphi/T_0$ which we can evaluate using the equations from the preceding problem with $\delta U = \alpha/D - \alpha r/2D^2$,† while T_0 is the period in the Coulomb potential. The result is $\Omega = M/2mD^2$. We can write the equation for the orbit in the form

$$\frac{p}{r} = 1 + e\cos\gamma\varphi, \quad \gamma = 1 - \frac{\Omega T_0}{2\pi} \tag{1}$$

The deviation of the curve (1) from the actual orbit is of first order in δU, that is, during one period equation (1) describes the orbit with the same degree of accuracy as the equation for the fixed ellipse. However, equation (1) retains the same accuracy during many periods. It is therefore just this equation which we can call the "correct zeroth approximation".

In other words, only secular first order effects have been taken into account in equation (1).

2.19. The potential $U = -\alpha/r^{1+\varepsilon}$ differs little from the Coulomb potential so that the orbit of a particle in this potential will be a slowly precessing ellipse. Expanding U in terms of ε we can write it in the form $U = U_0 + \delta U$, where

$$U_0 = -\frac{\tilde{\alpha}}{r}, \quad \delta U = \frac{\varepsilon\tilde{\alpha}}{r}\ln\frac{r}{R}, \quad \tilde{\alpha} = \alpha R^{-\varepsilon},$$

while R is a constant which characterises the size of the orbit. We can evaluate the shift of the pericentre $\delta\Delta\varphi = (\partial/\partial M)\int_0^T \delta U dt$ (see problem 2.17) by making the substitution (see Landau and Lifshitz, 1960, § 15)

$$r = -\frac{\tilde{\alpha}}{2E}(1 - e\cos\xi), \quad t = \frac{T}{2\pi}(\xi - e\sin\xi),$$

$$e = \sqrt{1 + \frac{2EM^2}{m\tilde{\alpha}^2}}, \quad T = \pi\tilde{\alpha}\sqrt{\frac{m}{2|E|^3}}.$$

† It is convenient to change to an integration over the eccentric anomaly ξ, where $r = (\alpha/2|E|)(1 - e\cos\xi)$ (see ter Haar, 1964, p. 131).

The result is

$$\Omega = \frac{\delta\Delta\varphi}{T} = \frac{\varepsilon\tilde{\alpha}}{2\pi}\frac{\partial}{\partial M}\int_0^{2\pi} \ln \frac{\tilde{\alpha}(1-e\cos\xi)}{2|E|R}\, d\xi$$

$$= -\frac{\varepsilon\tilde{\alpha}}{2\pi}\frac{\partial e}{\partial M}\int_0^{2\pi}\frac{\cos\xi\, d\xi}{1-e\cos\xi} = \frac{\pi\varepsilon|E|}{M}.$$

The condition for the applicability of the calculations made, $\delta U \ll U_0$, can most easily be satisfied by taking $R = \sqrt{r_{\min}r_{\max}} \cong M/\sqrt{2|E|}$ (discuss why this is so). The condition that δU be small leads to $|\varepsilon \ln(1-e^2)| \ll 1$.

Simultaneously we must satisfy the condition $\delta\Delta\varphi \ll 2\pi$ leading to the requirement $|\varepsilon| \ll 1-e^2$, which is more restrictive.

2.20. We have the following expressions for the changes in the period of radial oscillations and in the period of revolution:

$$\delta T_r = -\frac{\partial\delta I}{\partial E}, \quad \delta T_\varphi = -\frac{2\pi}{\Delta\varphi}\left[\frac{\partial}{\partial E}+\frac{T_r}{\Delta_\varphi}\frac{\partial}{\partial M}\right]\delta I, \quad \delta\Delta\varphi = \frac{\partial\delta I}{\partial M}.$$

(a) $\delta I = -T_r\delta E$;

(b) $\delta I = T_r < \delta U > - T_r\delta U(r_0)$,

where r_0 is the distance of the particle from the centre at the moment δU is "switched on" (compare problem 2.17).

2.21. If we expand the integrand in the equation for the orbit,

$$\varphi = \int \frac{M\, dr}{r^2\sqrt{2m(E-M^2/2mr^2+\alpha/r-\gamma/r^3)}}, \tag{1}$$

in terms of $\delta U = \gamma/r^3$, we can write this equation in the form

$$\varphi = \varphi_0(r)+\delta\varphi(r), \tag{2}$$

where

$$\varphi_0(r) = \int \frac{M\, dr}{r^2\sqrt{2m(E-M^2/2mr^2+\alpha/r)}}, \tag{3}$$

$$\delta\varphi(r) = \int \frac{\gamma M\, dr}{r^5\sqrt{2m(E-M^2/2mr^2+\alpha/r)^3}}. \tag{4}$$

If we neglect in (2) the correction $\delta\varphi(r)$, we obviously get the equation of the orbit in a Coulomb potential (see Landau and Lifshitz, 1960, § 15)

$$\frac{p}{r} = 1+e\cos\varphi, \tag{5}$$

where $p = M^2/m\alpha$, $e = \sqrt{[1+(2EM^2/m\alpha^2)]}$. If we take into account the correction $\delta\varphi(r)$ in (2), we get, in place of (5),

$$\frac{p}{r} = 1+e\cos(\varphi-\delta\varphi(r)). \tag{6}$$

In the right-hand side of (6) we can expand in terms of $\delta\varphi(r)$ and use in $\delta\varphi(r)$ for r the relation $r = r_0(\varphi)$ which follows from (5). The result is

$$\frac{p}{r} = 1+e\cos\varphi+e\,\delta\varphi(r_0(\varphi))\sin\varphi. \tag{7}$$

Integrating (4), we find†

$$\delta\varphi(r_0(\varphi)) = \frac{m^2\alpha\gamma}{M^4}\left\{-3\varphi-\frac{2e^2+1}{e}\sin\varphi - \frac{1+e\cos\varphi}{e^2\sin\varphi}\,[2e+(e^2+1)\cos\varphi]\right\}. \tag{8}$$

Substituting (8) into (7) gives a result which is accurate up to and including first-order terms in $\zeta = m^2\alpha\gamma/M^4$:

$$\frac{p}{r} = 1+e\cos[(1+3\zeta)\varphi]+\zeta\,\frac{2e^2+1}{e}\sin^2\varphi - \zeta\,\frac{1+e\cos\varphi}{e}\,[2e+(e^2+1)\cos\varphi]. \tag{9}$$

† We can rewrite (4) in the form

$$\delta\varphi = \frac{\partial}{\partial M}\int\frac{\sqrt{2m}\,\gamma\,dr}{r^3\sqrt{E-M^2/2mr^2+\alpha/r}},$$

and use (5) to change the integration into one over φ:

$$\delta\varphi = \frac{\partial}{\partial M}\,\frac{m^2\gamma\alpha}{M^3}\int(1+e\cos\varphi)\,d\varphi$$

$$= -\frac{3m^2\gamma\alpha}{M^4}(\varphi+e\sin\varphi)+\frac{m^2\gamma\alpha}{M^3}\,\frac{\partial e}{\partial M}\sin\varphi+\frac{m^2\gamma\alpha}{M^3}(1+e\cos\varphi)\frac{\partial\varphi}{\partial M}. \tag{8'}$$

From (5) we find

$$\frac{2M}{m\alpha^2 r} = \frac{\partial e}{\partial M}\cos\varphi - e\frac{\partial\varphi}{\partial M}\sin\varphi, \qquad \frac{\partial e}{\partial M} = \frac{e^2-1}{eM},$$

and substituting this into (8′), we obtain (8).

In the vicinity of $\varphi = 0$ and $\varphi = \pi$, the expansion (2) can no longer be applied as $\delta\varphi$ increases indefinitely. Equation (9) for the orbit remains, however, valid also in those regions (compare problem 1.8).

In the case of an infinite orbit ($E \geqq 0$) equation (9) is the solution of the problem. If $E < 0$, equation (9) remains the equation for the orbit only during a few revolutions,† namely, as long as $3\zeta\varphi \ll 1$. Taking only the secular part $\delta\varphi = -3\zeta\varphi$ in (8) into account, we obtain the equation

$$\frac{p}{r} = 1+e\cos\lambda\varphi, \quad \lambda = 1+3\zeta, \tag{10}$$

which describes the path over a long section of the orbit; this is a "correct" zeroth approximation (as distinct from (5); compare problem 2.18). It is obviously easy to transform equation (9) also in such a way that it describes the orbit over a long stretch with an accuracy up to and including first-order terms, and we have

$$\frac{p}{r} = 1+e\cos\lambda\varphi+\zeta(2e^2+1)\sin^2\lambda\varphi$$
$$-\zeta\frac{1+e\cos\lambda\varphi}{e}[2e+(e^2+1)\cos\lambda\varphi]. \tag{11}$$

2.22. It is sufficient to prove that the Lagrangian can be split into two parts when expressed in terms of the centre of mass coordinates, $\boldsymbol{R} = (m_1\boldsymbol{r}_1+m_2\boldsymbol{r}_2)/(m_1+m_2)$, and the relative coordinates, $\boldsymbol{r} = \boldsymbol{r}_2-\boldsymbol{r}_1$:

$$L = L_1(\boldsymbol{R}, \dot{\boldsymbol{R}})+L_2(\boldsymbol{r}, \dot{\boldsymbol{r}}),$$

$$L_1(\boldsymbol{R}, \dot{\boldsymbol{R}}) = \tfrac{1}{2}(m_1+m_2)\dot{\boldsymbol{R}}^2+(e_1+e_2)(\boldsymbol{E}\cdot\boldsymbol{R}),$$

$$L_2(\boldsymbol{r}, \dot{\boldsymbol{r}}) = \frac{m_1m_2}{2(m_1+m_2)}\dot{\boldsymbol{r}}^2-\frac{e_1e_2}{r}+\frac{m_1m_2}{m_1+m_2}\left(\frac{e_1}{m_1}-\frac{e_2}{m_2}\right)(\boldsymbol{E}\cdot\boldsymbol{r}).$$

The function $L_1(\boldsymbol{R}, \dot{\boldsymbol{R}})$ determines the motion of the centre of mass which is the same as the motion of a particle of mass m_1+m_2 and charge e_1+e_2 in a uniform field $\boldsymbol{E}$. The relative motion, determined by $L_2(\boldsymbol{r}, \dot{\boldsymbol{r}})$, is the same as the motion of a particle of mass $m_1m_2/(m_1+m_2)$ (the reduced mass) in a Coulomb field as well as in a uniform field.

One could, of course, have obtained the same result starting from the equations of motion of the particles.

† In particular, the radius vector $\boldsymbol{r}$ must be a periodic function of φ.

2.23.

$$L = \frac{1}{2}(m_1\dot{r}_1^2+m_2\dot{r}_2^2)+\frac{e}{c}(A(r_1)\cdot\dot{r}_1)+\frac{e}{c}(A(r_2)\cdot\dot{r}_2).$$

The Lagrangian can be split into two parts depending only on R, $\dot{R}$ and r, $\dot{r}$ (using the notation of problem 2.22), if $e_1/m_1 = e_2/m_2$:

$$L = \frac{1}{2}(m_1+m_2)\dot{R}^2+\frac{e_1+e_2}{c}(A(R)\cdot\dot{R})+\frac{1}{4}m\dot{r}^2+\frac{e_1m_1^2+e_2m_2^2}{c(m_1+m_2)^2}(A(r)\cdot\dot{r}).$$

2.24.

$$T = \frac{1}{2}\sum_{n=1}^{N}\mu\dot{\xi}_n^2, \quad p = \mu_N\dot{\xi}_N, \quad M = \sum_{n=1}^{N}\mu_n[\xi_n \wedge \dot{\xi}_n],$$

where

$$\frac{1}{\mu_n} = \frac{1}{\sum_{k=1}^{n} m_k}+\frac{1}{m_{n+1}} \quad (n = 1, \ldots, N-1), \qquad \mu_N = \sum_{k=1}^{N} m_k.$$

2.25. Let the coordinates of the incident particle and of the particle initially at rest be x_1 and x_2, respectively, and let at $t = 0$, $x_1 = -R$, $x_2 = 0$. The centre of mass of the system moves according to the equation $X = -R/2+vt/2$. The relative motion ($x = x_2-x_1$) follows from the equation

$$t = -\sqrt{\frac{m}{4}}\int_R^x \frac{dx}{\sqrt{\frac{1}{4}mv^4-\alpha x^{-n}}}.$$

The first particle thus has the following position:

$$x_1 = X-\frac{x}{2} = -\frac{R}{2}+\frac{1}{2}\int_x^R \frac{dx}{\sqrt{1-(4\alpha/mv^2x^n)}}-\frac{x}{2}.$$

The distance between the particles decreases until it becomes $x_{\min} = (mv^2/4\alpha)^{1/n}$ and then increases again. When it is again equal to R, the first particle has come to the point

$$x_{1f} = x_{\min}\left\{\int_1^{R/x_{\min}}\left(\frac{1}{\sqrt{1-z^{-n}}}-1\right)dz-1\right\}. \tag{1}$$

The point where the first particle comes to rest is the limit of x_{1f}, as $R \to \infty$. If $n \leq 1$, $x_{1f} \to \infty$, as $R \to \infty$, that is, both particles go to infinity after the collision.

2.27. The motion of a charged particle in an electromagnetic field is determined by the Lagrangian

$$L = \frac{1}{2}mv^2 - e\varphi + \frac{e}{c}(v \cdot A), \tag{1}$$

where φ and A are the scalar and vector potentials (see, for instance, ter Haar, 1964, p. 113).

Using cylindrical coordinates we have

$$L = \frac{1}{2}m(\dot{r}^2 + r^2\dot{\varphi}^2 + \dot{z}^2) + \frac{e}{c}\frac{\mathcal{M}r^2\dot{\varphi}}{(r^2+z^2)^{3/2}}. \tag{2}$$

We see from the equation of motion for z,

$$m\ddot{z} + \frac{3e}{2c}\frac{\mathcal{M}r^2z\dot{\varphi}}{(r^2+z^2)^{5/2}} = 0, \tag{3}$$

that for $z = 0$ the component of the force along the z-axis vanishes. The orbit thus lies in the plane $z = 0$ when $z(0) = \dot{z}(0) = 0$.

As φ is a cyclic coordinate, we have

$$\frac{\partial L}{\partial \dot{\varphi}} = mr^2\dot{\varphi} + \frac{e\mathcal{M}}{cr} = p_\varphi = \text{const.} \tag{4}$$

From this equation it follows that p_φ is the value of $\mathcal{M}_z$ as $r \to \infty$, in the case of an infinite orbit. Moreover, the energy conservation law is satisfied (since $\partial L/\partial t = 0$):

$$\tfrac{1}{2}m(\dot{r}^2 + r^2\dot{\varphi}^2) = E. \tag{5}$$

Using (4) to eliminate $\dot{\varphi}$ from (5) we get

$$\tfrac{1}{2}m\dot{r}^2 + U_{\text{eff}}(r) = E, \tag{6}$$

where

$$U_{\text{eff}}(r) = \left(p_\varphi - \frac{e\mathcal{M}}{cr}\right)^2 / 2mr^2. \tag{7}$$

The radial motion thus takes place as in the one-dimensional potential $U_{\text{eff}}(r)$.

We have drawn $U_{\text{eff}}(r)$ given by (7) for the case $p_\varphi < 0$ and for the case $p_\varphi > 0$ in Figs. 68a and b.

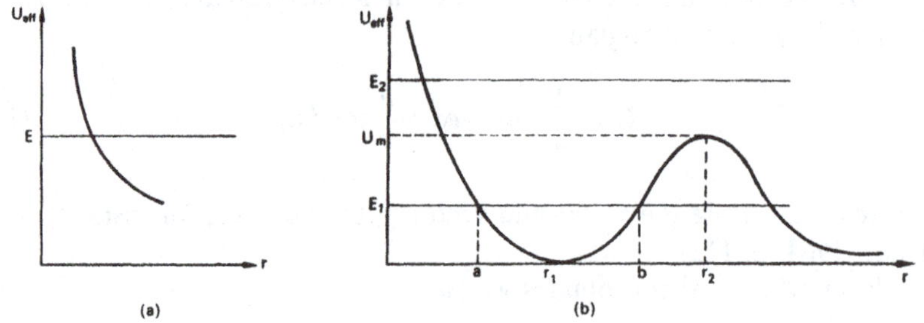

FIG. 68

In the case when $p_\varphi < 0$ the orbit is always infinite for $E > 0$. In order to give a qualitative description of the orbit it is useful to use (4) to write

$$\dot{\varphi} = -\frac{|p_\varphi|}{mr^2} - \frac{e\mathcal{M}}{mcr^3}. \tag{8}$$

The velocity with which the radius vector of the particle turns round has all the time the same direction and increases when the particle approaches the dipole. Curve 1 in Fig. 69 shows such an orbit. The orbit is symmetric with respect to the straight line connecting the centre of the field with the point $r = r_{\min}$.

When $p_\varphi > 0$, scattering can occur for any energy $E > 0$, but if $E < U_m = c^2p_\varphi^4/32\, me^2\mathcal{M}^2$ ($E = E_1$ in Fig. 68 b), there is also the possibility of finite orbits. From the equation

$$\dot{\varphi} = \frac{p_\varphi}{mr^2} - \frac{e\mathcal{M}}{mcr^3}$$

it follows that $\dot{\varphi} > 0$ when $r > r_1 = e\mathcal{M}/cp_\varphi$ and $\dot{\varphi} < 0$ when $r < r_1$. For $r = r_1$ there is a "sticking point" in φ. A particle with an energy $E > U_m$ ($E = E_2$ in Fig. 68b) is scattered while in two points (where $r = r_1$) its velocity is parallel to its radius vector (curve 2 in Fig. 69). When $E = E_3 < U_m$ there can occur scattering without sticking points (curve 3 of Fig. 69) or a finite orbit in the annulus $a \leqq r \leqq b$ (Fig. 70). In the latter case the particle can perform both a direct (section AB) and a "counter" (section BC) motion as far as φ is concerned.

2.28. (a) It is convenient to use cylindrical coordinates and to take the vector potential in the form $A_\varphi = \frac{1}{2}Hr$, $A_z = A_r = 0$. In the z-direction the

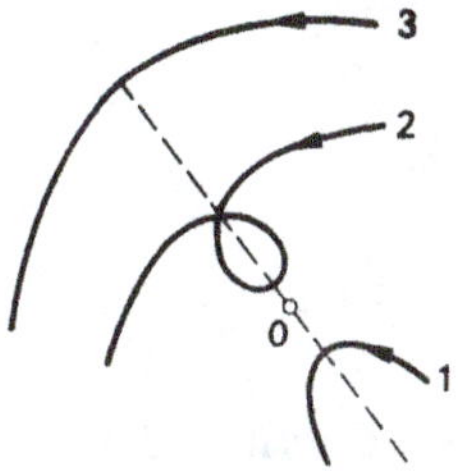

FIG. 69

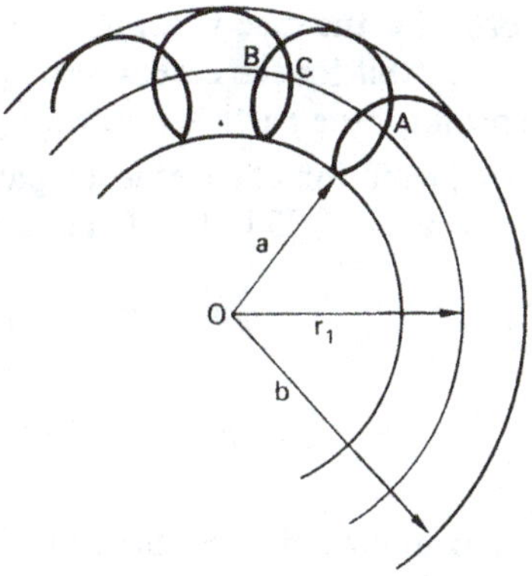

FIG. 70

motion is uniform, while in a plane perpendicular to the z-axis we have a finite motion. In Fig. 71 we show the projection of the orbit on this plane. The orbits (a), (b), and (c) correspond, respectively, to the cases $p_\varphi > 0$ (to fix our ideas we assume that $H > 0$; p_φ is the generalised momentum corresponding to the coordinate φ) and $U_1 < E_\perp < U_2, E_\perp = U_2$, and $U_2 < E_\perp$, where $E_\perp = E - \frac{1}{2}mv_z^2$, $U_1 = (\tilde{\Omega}-\Omega)p_\varphi$, $U_2 = \lambda p_\varphi/2\Omega$, $\Omega = eH/2mc$, $\tilde{\Omega} = \sqrt{\Omega^2+\lambda}$.

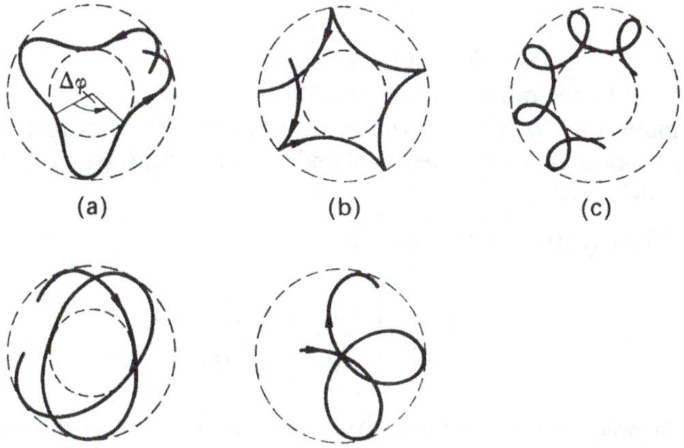

FIG. 71

An orbit for the case when $p_\varphi < 0$ is given in Fig. 71d, while Fig. 71e depicts the orbit for the case where $p_\varphi = 0$.

The orbit for the particle in the xy-plane can easily be determined once we know the motion of a free isotropic harmonic oscillator of frequency $\tilde{\Omega}$ (see problem 3 of § 23 in Landau and Lifshitz, 1960):†

$$r^2 = a^2 \cos^2 \tilde{\Omega}t + b^2 \sin^2 \tilde{\Omega}t,$$

$$\varphi = -\Omega t + \arctan\left(\frac{a}{b} \tan \tilde{\Omega}t\right).$$

The maximum and minimum radii (a and b) are determined by the energy $E = \frac{1}{2}m\tilde{\Omega}^2(a^2+b^2) - p_\varphi \Omega$ and the angular momentum $p_\varphi = m\tilde{\Omega}ab$; the origins for t and φ are chosen such that $\varphi(0) = 0$, $r(0) = a$.

Note that the period of the radial oscillations, $T = \pi/\tilde{\Omega}$ is independent of E and p_φ. The angle over which the radius vector turns during this period is

$$\Delta\varphi = \pi\left(\mp 1 - \frac{\Omega}{\tilde{\Omega}}\right), \quad p_\varphi \neq 0,$$

where the sign is the same as that of p_φ, and

$$\Delta\varphi = -\pi\frac{\Omega}{\tilde{\Omega}}, \quad \text{when} \quad p_\varphi = 0.$$

The angle $\Delta\varphi$ is independent of the energy E.‡

What will be the motion when $\lambda < 0$?

It is interesting to compare the motion of the particle in this problem with the motion in crossed electrical and magnetic fields (see Landau and Lifshitz, 1962, § 22).

2.29. The equation of the orbit is

$$\varphi = \sqrt{\frac{m}{2}} \int \frac{[p_\varphi^2/mr^2 - \Omega]dr}{\sqrt{E - U_{\text{eff}}(r)}}, \tag{1}$$

† The branches of $\arctan(a/b \tan \tilde{\Omega}t)$ should be chosen such that the angle φ is a continuous function of t.

‡ Another way to solve the problem is given in problem 6.23.

where $\Omega = eH/2mc$ and

$$U_{\text{eff}}(r) = -\frac{\alpha}{r}+\frac{1}{2}mr^2\left(\Omega-\frac{p_\varphi^2}{mr^2}\right)^2.$$

By looking at a graph of $U_{\text{eff}}(r)$ one can study the character of the motion qualitatively. One must then pay attention to the fact that $\dot{\varphi}$ changes sign when r passes through the value $r_0 = \sqrt{p_\varphi/m\Omega}$. The result is orbits such as the ones shown in Figs. 71a–e.† The different orbits occur when

(a) $p_\varphi > 0$, $U_{\min} < E < U_0$ where $U_{\min}$ is the minimum value of $U_{\text{eff}}(r)$ and $U_0 = U_{\text{eff}}(r_0)$;
(b) $p_\varphi > 0, E = U_0$;
(c) $p_\varphi > 0, E > U_0$;
(d) $p_\varphi < 0$;
(e) $p_\varphi = 0$.

In the last case the particle falls into the centre in the first loop.

Let us consider in somewhat more detail two limiting cases. Equation (1) can be written in the form

$$\varphi = \frac{p_\varphi}{\sqrt{2m}}\int\frac{dr}{r^2\sqrt{E+p_\varphi\Omega+\alpha/r-p_\varphi^2/2mr^2-m\Omega^2r^2/2}}-\Omega t. \tag{2}$$

We may thus describe the effect of the magnetic field as a change in the energy to $E' = E+p_\varphi\Omega$ and an extra term in the potential $U = -\alpha/r$ which is $\delta U = \frac{1}{2}m\Omega^2r^2$, each of which leads to a precession of the orbit, and also as an additional precession with an angular velocity $-\Omega$. If the magnetic field H is sufficiently small, the term δU can be considered to be a small correction to $U_0 = (p_\varphi^2/2mr^2)-\alpha/r$, provided the following condition is satisfied,

$$\delta U(r) \ll |U_0(r)|, \tag{3}$$

for the whole range of the motion. The precession velocity caused by δU can be found from

$$\Omega' = \frac{\delta\Delta\varphi}{T} = \frac{1}{T}\frac{\partial}{\partial p_\varphi}(T\langle\delta U\rangle), \tag{4}$$

where the averaging of δU is over the motion of the particle in the potential U_0 with an energy E' and an angular momentum p_φ, while T is the

† As we are only interested in a qualitative study, using the shape of $U_{\text{eff}}(r)$ we can use the same approximate treatment as in problem 2.28. Of course, the exact form of the orbits is different in the two problems.

period of that motion (compare problems 2.17 and 2.18). If we perform the calculation (to evaluate $\langle \delta U \rangle$ it is convenient to use the variables used in problems 2.18 and 2.19; since the period in the potential U_0 is independent of p_φ we can take T from under the differentiation sign in (4)), we get

$$\Omega' = -3\Omega^2 p_\varphi / 2|E'|; \tag{5}$$

we can assume δU to be a small correction if apart from (3) also the condition $\delta \Delta\varphi \ll 2\pi$ is satisfied, or

$$\Omega^2 p_\varphi \alpha \sqrt{m} |E'|^{-\frac{5}{2}} \ll 1. \tag{6}$$

It is, of course, impossible to consider δU to be a small correction when $E' \geqq 0$, as in that case neglecting δU may introduce a qualitative change in the character of the orbit. The quantity Ω' may turn out to be either small compared to Ω or large. The sign of Ω' is the opposite of that of p_φ, that is, the direction of this velocity is the opposite of that of the motion of the particle in its orbit. The direction of Ω, though, is determined by the magnetic field. The orbit is thus an ellipse precessing with the angular velocity

$$\Omega_{\text{prec}} = -\Omega + \Omega'. \tag{7}$$

To be more exact: the orbit is a fixed ellipse, if the system of reference rotates with an angular velocity Ω_{prec}, because it is possible that $\Omega T \gtrsim 1$.

It is interesting to compare the result obtained with the Larmor theorem (see Landau and Lifshitz, 1962, § 45, and also problem 9.14).

Is there a case when although E is positive we can consider δU to be a small correction?

Let us now consider the case when the field $U = -\alpha/r$ can be considered to be a small correction. If U were not present, the motion would be along a circle. Its radius a and the distance b of its centre from the centre of the potential field can be expressed in terms of the maximum and minimum distances of the particle from the centre of the potential,

$$r_{1,2}^2 = \frac{E + p_\varphi \Omega \pm \sqrt{(E + 2p_\varphi \Omega)E}}{m\Omega^2}. \tag{8}$$

There are now two possibilities (see Fig. 72), depending on how the circle is placed with respect to the origin. If $p_\varphi \Omega < 0$, case (a) occurs, and if $p_\varphi \Omega > 0$, case (b) occurs. In both cases we have

$$b^2 = (E + 2p_\varphi \Omega)/2m\Omega^2, \quad a^2 = E/2m\Omega^2. \tag{9}$$

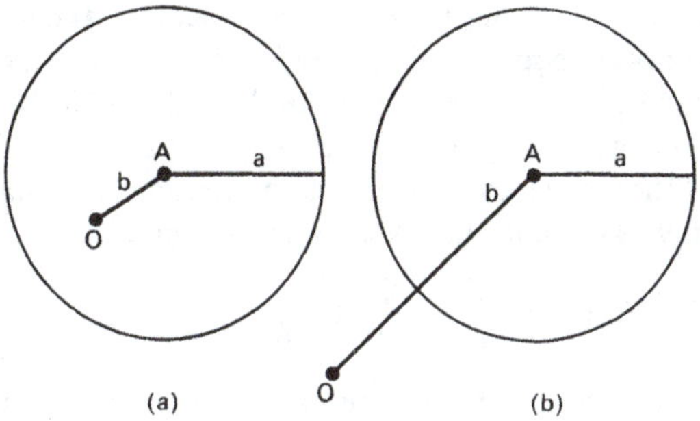

FIG. 72

Taking U into account leads to a systematic displacement of the circle (the so-called drift) while its radius and the distance from the origin which are determined by a and b do not change, that is, its centre moves along a circle of radius b. The angular velocity of the displacement of the centre of the circle is

$$\gamma = \frac{\partial}{\partial p_\varphi} \langle U \rangle,$$

where the averaging of U is over the uniform motion along the circle. Let us restrict ourselves to the case when $a \ll b$. In that case we may simply assume that

$$\langle U \rangle = -\alpha/b, \tag{10}$$

so that

$$\gamma = \alpha/2m\Omega b^3.$$

We note that in this case the linear drift velocity is equal to cE/H, where $eE = \alpha/b^2$ is the force acting upon the particle at a distance b (compare Landau and Lifshitz, 1962, § 22).

2.30. The problem of the motion of two identical charged particles in a uniform magnetic field can be reduced to the problem of the motion of the centre of mass and the problem of the relative motion (see problem 2.23).

For the centre of mass coordinates we have

$$X = R \cos \omega t, \tag{1}$$
$$Y = -R \sin \omega t,$$

where $\omega = eH/mc$.

The relative motion is the same as that of a motion of a particle of mass $m/2$ and charge $e/2$ in the potential $U = e^2/r$ and in a uniform magnetic field $\boldsymbol{H}$. This motion is similar to the one considered in the preceding problem (we need only change m to $m/2$, e to $e/2$, and α to $-e^2$ in the formulae). Let us restrict ourselves to the case where the radius a of the orbit is small compared to the distance b from the centre of the potential (Fig. 72b). We can easily find the frequency of the radial oscillations to a higher degree of accuracy than was done in the preceding problem, by expanding

$$U_{\text{eff}}(r) = \frac{e^2}{r} + \frac{p_\varphi^2}{mr^2} + \frac{1}{16}m\omega^2r^2 - \frac{1}{2}p_\varphi\omega$$

in a series in the vicinity of the minimum where $r = b$ (see Landau and Lifshitz, 1960, § 21).

From the condition $U'_{\text{eff}}(b) = 0$ we get

$$p_\varphi = \sqrt{\frac{1}{16}m^2\omega^2b^2 - \frac{1}{2}me^2b} \approx \frac{1}{2}mb^2\left(\frac{1}{2}\omega - \gamma\right), \quad \gamma = \frac{2e^2}{m\omega b^3}, \tag{2}$$

and we thus get finally for $\omega_r = \sqrt{2U''_{\text{eff}}(b)/m}$ the result $\omega_r = \omega - \frac{1}{2}\gamma$, and for the separation of the particles

$$r = b + a\cos(\omega_r t + \alpha). \tag{3}$$

To find $\varphi(t)$ we apply the principle of conservation of generalised momentum to $p_\varphi = \frac{1}{2}mr^2(\dot{\varphi} + \frac{1}{2}\omega)$. Using (2) and (3) we get

$$\varphi(t) = -\gamma t - \frac{a}{b}\sin(\omega_r t + \alpha) + \varphi_0. \tag{4}$$

Using (3) and (4) we get for the relative coordinates ($\beta = \alpha - \varphi_0$)

$$\begin{aligned} x &= r\cos\varphi = b\cos(\gamma t - \varphi_0) + a\cos(\omega t + \tfrac{1}{2}\gamma t + \beta), \\ y &= r\sin\varphi = -b\sin(\gamma t - \varphi_0) - a\sin(\omega t + \tfrac{1}{2}\gamma t + \beta). \end{aligned} \tag{5}$$

The first terms here correspond to the motion of the centre of the circle with a drift velocity $b\gamma$, and the second terms to the motion along this circle with an angular velocity $\omega + \frac{1}{2}\gamma$. The coordinates of the particles, $x_{1,2} = X \pm \frac{1}{2}x$, $y_{1,2} = Y \pm \frac{1}{2}y$ can be written in the form

$$\begin{aligned} x_{1,2} &= \pm\tfrac{1}{2}b\cos(\gamma t - \varphi_0) + \varrho_{1,2}\cos(\omega t + \psi_{1,2}), \\ y_{1,2} &= \mp\tfrac{1}{2}b\cos(\gamma t - \varphi_0) - \varrho_{1,2}\sin(\omega t + \psi_{1,2}), \end{aligned} \tag{6}$$

where

$$\varrho_{1,2} = \sqrt{R^2 + \tfrac{1}{4}a^2 \pm aR\cos(\tfrac{1}{2}\gamma t + \beta)},$$

$$\tan\psi_{1,2} = \frac{\pm a\sin(\frac{1}{2}\gamma t + \beta)}{2R \pm a\cos(\frac{1}{2}\gamma t + \beta)}.$$

The centres of the circles along which the particles move rotate thus around the origin with an angular velocity γ (a drift velocity $b\gamma/2$) while their radii oscillate with a frequency $\gamma/2$ (Fig. 73).

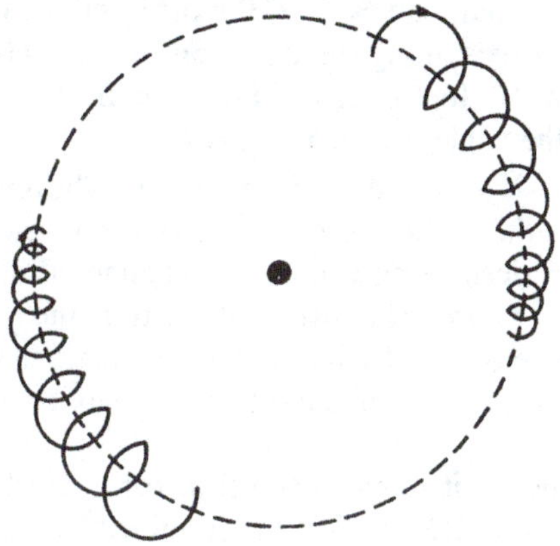

FIG. 73

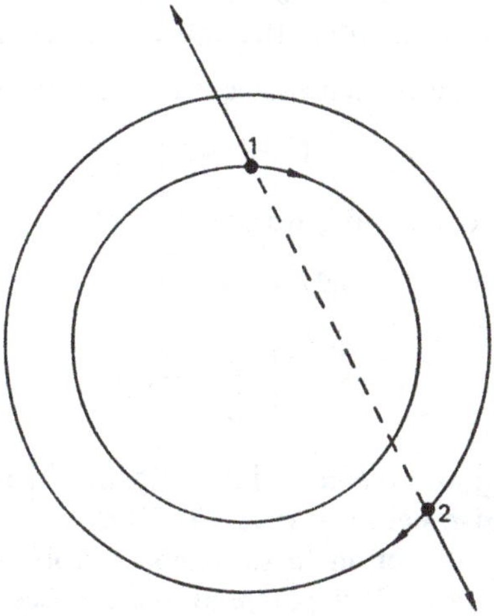

FIG. 74

Another limiting case when $a \gg b$ (distance of the centre of the orbits to the origin small compared to the radii of the orbits; Fig. 74) may give a clear insight into the mechanism of energy "exchange". The work carried out by the force of the interaction on the second particle is clearly positive, while the work carried out on the first particle is negative, when taken over many periods.

2.31. One can easily prove that the given quantity is a constant, by using the equation of motion (compare Landau and Lifshitz, 1960, § 15), and writing this quantity in the form $(\boldsymbol{A}\cdot\boldsymbol{F})+\frac{1}{2}([\boldsymbol{F}\wedge\boldsymbol{r}]\cdot[\boldsymbol{F}\wedge\boldsymbol{r}])$, where $\boldsymbol{A} = [\boldsymbol{v}\wedge\boldsymbol{M}]-\alpha\boldsymbol{r}/r$. For small values of $\boldsymbol{F}$ the orbit will be close to an ellipse with its semi-major axis along the direction of the vector $\boldsymbol{A}$ and with an eccentricity $e = |\boldsymbol{A}|/\alpha$. In this case $(\boldsymbol{A}\cdot\boldsymbol{F}) \cong$ constant, or $e \cos\psi \approx$ constant, where ψ is the angle between $\boldsymbol{A}$ and $\boldsymbol{F}$.

2.32. When there is a small extra term $\delta U(\boldsymbol{r})$ in the potential energy, the quantities characterising the motion of the particle, such as the angular momentum, the pericentre position, ..., change, although they do not change their values appreciably over a short time interval (a few periods of the unperturbed motion). However, these changes may add up over an extended time, so that some of the quantities may happen to change by large amounts.

In particular, the orbit remains elliptical for a short time interval. Its semi-major axis, $a = \alpha/2|E|$, which is determined by the energy, does not change over a long time, while the eccentricity $e = \sqrt{1-[M^2/m\alpha a]}$ and the orientation of the orbit are both liable to secular changes.

(a) The change in the angular momentum is determined by the equation

$$\dot{\boldsymbol{M}} = [\boldsymbol{r}\wedge\boldsymbol{F}]. \tag{1}$$

Averaging (1) over one period, we obtain

$$\langle\dot{\boldsymbol{M}}\rangle = [\langle\boldsymbol{r}\rangle\wedge\boldsymbol{F}], \tag{2}$$

where

$$\langle\boldsymbol{r}\rangle = \frac{1}{T}\int_0^T \boldsymbol{r}(t)\,dt. \tag{3}$$

For the averaging we use a coordinate system with the z-axis parallel to $\boldsymbol{M}$ and the x-axis parallel to $\boldsymbol{A}$ (Fig. 75). (Here $\boldsymbol{A} = [\boldsymbol{v}\wedge\boldsymbol{M}]-\alpha\boldsymbol{r}/r$ is an additional integral of motion in the Kepler problem. The vector $\boldsymbol{A}$ is directed from the centre of the potential to the pericentre, and $|\boldsymbol{A}| = \alpha e$.) Clearly, $-\langle\boldsymbol{r}\rangle$ is parallel to the positive x-axis.

Making the substitution $x = a(\cos\xi - e)$, $t = (T/2\pi)(\xi - e\sin\xi)$, we get

$$\langle x\rangle = \frac{a}{2\pi}\int_0^{2\pi}(\cos\xi - e)(1-\cos\xi)\,d\xi = -\frac{3}{2}ae. \tag{4}$$

Therefore

$$\langle\boldsymbol{r}\rangle = -\frac{3}{2}ae\frac{\boldsymbol{A}}{|\boldsymbol{A}|} = -\frac{3a\boldsymbol{A}}{2\alpha}. \tag{5}$$

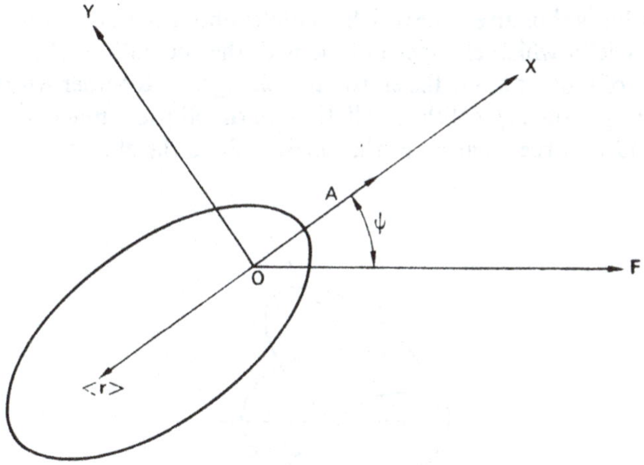

FIG. 75

(b) If $\boldsymbol{F}$ is at right angles to $\boldsymbol{M}$, it is obvious from symmetry considerations that the orbit lies in a plane and the vector $\boldsymbol{M}$ retains its direction — apart possibly from the sign.

Omitting the averaging sign we can write (2) and (5) in the form

$$\dot{M} = \tfrac{3}{2}ae\,F\sin\psi, \tag{6}$$

where ψ is the angle between $\boldsymbol{A}$ and $\boldsymbol{F}$. Using the fact that

$$e\cos\psi = \varepsilon = \text{constant} \tag{7}$$

(see problem 2.31) and eliminating e and ψ from (6) we find

$$\dot{M} = \frac{3}{2}aF\sqrt{1-\varepsilon^2-\frac{M^2}{m\alpha a}}. \tag{8}$$

Integrating equation (8) we get

$$\begin{aligned} M &= M_0\cos(\Omega t+\beta), \\ e &= \sqrt{1-(1-\varepsilon^2)\cos^2(\Omega t+\beta)}, \end{aligned} \tag{9}$$

where

$$\Omega = \tfrac{3}{2}F\sqrt{a/m\alpha}, \quad M_0 = \sqrt{m\alpha a(1-\varepsilon^2)}.$$

The orbit is thus an ellipse which oscillates about the direction of $\boldsymbol{F}$ with an eccentricity which changes in tune with the oscillations (Fig. 76). The direction of motion along the ellipse also changes — together with the sign of $\boldsymbol{M}$. The period $2\pi/\Omega$ of the oscillations of the ellipse is much longer than the period T of the rotation of the particle along the ellipse.

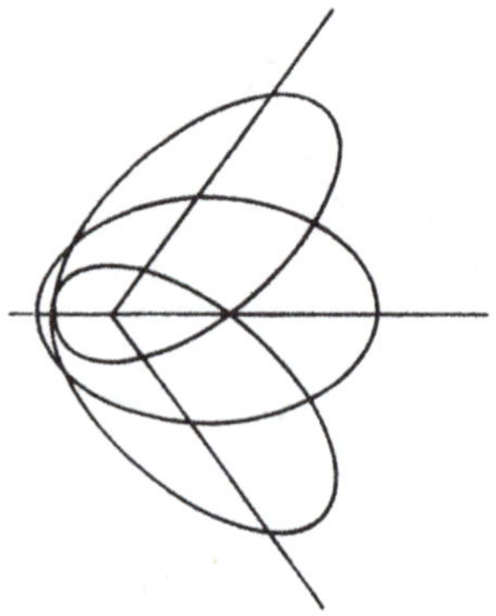

FIG. 76

(c) In the general case we consider also the change in the vector $\boldsymbol{A}$. Using the equations of motion, we easily get

$$\dot{\boldsymbol{A}} = \frac{1}{m}[\boldsymbol{F}\wedge\boldsymbol{M}]+[\boldsymbol{v}\wedge[\boldsymbol{r}\wedge\boldsymbol{F}]]. \tag{10}$$

For the averaging in (10) we use the equations

$$\left.\begin{aligned}\langle x\dot{x}\rangle &= \left\langle \frac{d}{dt}\frac{1}{2}x^2\right\rangle = 0,\\ \langle y\dot{y}\rangle &= \left\langle \frac{d}{dt}\frac{1}{2}y^2\right\rangle = 0,\\ \langle x\dot{y}\rangle+\langle y\dot{x}\rangle &= \left\langle \frac{d}{dt}xy\right\rangle = 0,\\ \langle x\dot{y}\rangle-\langle y\dot{x}\rangle &= \frac{M}{m}.\end{aligned}\right\} \tag{11}$$

As a result we get

$$\langle \dot{A} \rangle = \frac{3}{2m} [F \wedge M]. \tag{12}$$

We have thus for M and A, averaged over one period (in the following we omit the averaging sign), the following set of equations

$$\begin{aligned} \dot{A} &= \frac{3}{2m} [F \wedge M], \\ \dot{M} &= \frac{3a}{2\alpha} [F \wedge A]. \end{aligned} \tag{13}$$

The components of these vectors along the direction of F are conserved:

$$(M \cdot F) = \text{constant}, \quad (A \cdot F) = \text{constant}. \tag{14}$$

(The same result could also easily be obtained from other considerations.) For the transverse component of M,

$$M_\perp = M - \frac{F(F \cdot M)}{F^2}, \tag{15}$$

we obtain from (13)

$$\ddot{M}_\perp + \Omega^2 M_\perp = 0. \tag{16}$$

In a coordinate system $OX_1X_2X_3$ with the X_3-axis parallel to F we have for the solution of (13):

$$\left.\begin{aligned} M_1 &= B_1 \cos \Omega t + C_1 \sin \Omega t, \\ M_2 &= B_2 \cos \Omega t + C_2 \sin \Omega t. \end{aligned}\right\} \tag{17}$$

We then obtain from (13):

$$\left.\begin{aligned} A_1 &= -\frac{3F}{2m\Omega} (B_1 \sin \Omega t - C_1 \cos \Omega t), \\ A_2 &= \frac{3F}{2m\Omega} (B_2 \sin \Omega t - C_2 \cos \Omega t). \end{aligned}\right\} \tag{18}$$

As we should expect, the constants $B_{1,2}$ and $C_{1,2}$ are determined by the intitial values of the vectors M and A.

The end point of the vector M describes an ellipse with its centre on the X_3-axis and lying in a plane μ which is parallel to the X_1X_2-plane (Fig. 77).

The end point of the vector $\boldsymbol{A}$ also describes an ellipse with its centre on the X_3-axis and lying in a plane σ which is parallel to μ; this second ellipse is similar to the first one, but rotated over an angle $\pi/2$: $\boldsymbol{A}$ remains thus at right angles to $\boldsymbol{M}$ all the time. The plane of the orbit is perpendicular to $\boldsymbol{M}$, and the vector $\boldsymbol{A}$ determines the direction to the pericentre of the orbit.

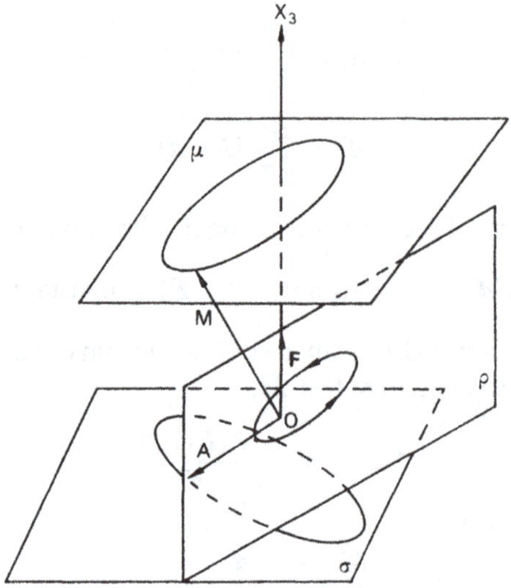

FIG. 77

The plane of the orbit thus rotates (precesses) around $\boldsymbol{F}$. The angle between the plane of the orbit ϱ and $\boldsymbol{F}$ oscillates about its mean value. The eccentricity and the angle between the projection of $\boldsymbol{F}$ upon the plane ϱ and the direction to the pericentre also oscillate about their mean values. All these motions occur with a frequency Ω.

We should bear in mind that we have neglected those corrections in $\boldsymbol{F}$ which are of first order but which do not lead to secular effects. Our solution is valid for a time interval of the order of several periods of the orbital precession.

The reader should check whether the inclusion of the next approximations will lead to a qualitative change in the character of the motion (for instance, to a possible departure of the particle to infinity).† The exact solution of the problem of the motion of a particle in the potential $U = -\alpha/r - (\boldsymbol{F} \cdot \boldsymbol{r})$, which can be given in parabolic coordinates (see

† Such a case is possible in quantum mechanics and is called "field emission".

problem 12.12b) shows that such effects do not take place if E is fixed and negative and if $\boldsymbol{F}$ is sufficiently small.

It should be emphasised that the appearance of secular changes of the orbit under the action of infinitesimal constant perturbations is connected with a degeneracy of the unperturbed motion.

See problem 12.12b for a solution of this problem for arbitrary $\boldsymbol{F}$.

2.33. The Lagrangian of the system,

$$L = \frac{1}{2} m\dot{r}^2 + \frac{\alpha}{r} + \frac{e}{c}\left(\dot{\boldsymbol{r}} \cdot \frac{[\mathcal{M} \wedge \boldsymbol{r}]}{r^3}\right), \tag{1}$$

is the same—apart from the notation—as the one considered in the problem of § 103 of Landau and Lifshitz (1962).

The equation of motion of $\boldsymbol{M}$ is the following one

$$\dot{\boldsymbol{M}} = \frac{e}{mcr^3} [\boldsymbol{M} \wedge \mathcal{M}]. \tag{2}$$

To average equation (2) over one period of the unperturbed motion, we introduce again the eccentric anomaly (ter Haar, 1964, p. 131):

$$r = a(1 - e\cos\xi), \quad t = \frac{T}{2\pi}(\xi - e\sin\xi),$$

where a and e are again the semi-major axis and the eccentricity of the unperturbed ellipse.

We then find

$$\langle r^{-3} \rangle = \frac{1}{T}\int_0^T \frac{dt}{r^3} = \frac{1}{2\pi a^3}\int_0^{2\pi} \frac{d\xi}{(1 - e\cos\xi)^2} = \frac{1}{a^3(1-e^2)^{\frac{3}{2}}},$$

and hence

$$\langle \dot{\boldsymbol{M}} \rangle = \frac{e[\boldsymbol{M} \wedge \mathcal{M}]}{mca^3(1-e^2)^{\frac{3}{2}}}, \tag{3}$$

that is, the vector $\boldsymbol{M}$ rotates with constant magnitude around the direction of the dipole.

A similar calculation for the vector $\boldsymbol{B}$ gives

$$\dot{\boldsymbol{B}} = \frac{e}{mcr^3}[\boldsymbol{B} \wedge \mathcal{M}] + \frac{3e}{m^2cr^5}(\boldsymbol{M} \cdot \mathcal{M})[\boldsymbol{M} \wedge \boldsymbol{r}], \tag{4}$$

and averaging this equation leads to

$$\langle \dot{\boldsymbol{B}} \rangle = [\boldsymbol{B} \wedge \boldsymbol{\Omega}], \tag{5}$$

where

$$\boldsymbol{\Omega} = \frac{e\mathcal{M}}{mca^3(1-e^2)^{\frac{3}{2}}} \{\boldsymbol{n}' - 3\boldsymbol{n}(\boldsymbol{n} \cdot \boldsymbol{n}')\} \tag{6}$$

with

$$\boldsymbol{n} = \boldsymbol{M}/|\boldsymbol{M}|, \quad \boldsymbol{n}' = \boldsymbol{\mathcal{M}}/|\boldsymbol{\mathcal{M}}|.$$

In deriving (5) we have used the fact that $\langle \boldsymbol{r}/r^5 \rangle$ will be along the major axis of the ellipse, that is, parallel to $\boldsymbol{B}$. From (5) we see that the vector $\boldsymbol{B}$ rotates with constant magnitude with an angular velocity $\boldsymbol{\Omega}$.

Equation (3) can be written in the form

$$\langle \dot{\boldsymbol{M}} \rangle = [\boldsymbol{M} \wedge \boldsymbol{\Omega}], \tag{7}$$

that is, $\boldsymbol{\Omega}$ is the precessional velocity of the orbit.

3. Scattering in a Given Field. Collisions between Particles

3.1.(a) It can be seen from Fig. 78 that the angle of deflection of a particle is twice the angle of the slope of the tangent to the surface of revolution at the point of collision. We have therefore

$$\tan \frac{1}{2}\theta = \frac{d\varrho}{dz} = \frac{b}{a}\cos\frac{z}{a}.$$

Hence we have

$$\varrho^2 = b^2 - a^2 \tan^2 \tfrac{1}{2}\theta,$$

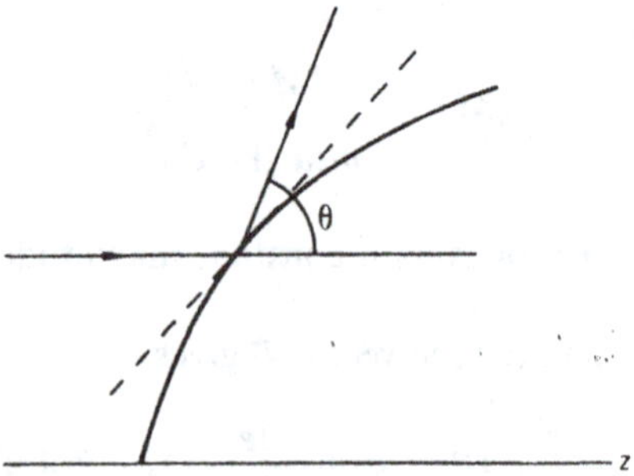

Fig. 78

and thus

$$d\sigma = \pi |d\varrho^2| = \pi a^2 \tan \tfrac{1}{2}\theta \frac{d\theta}{\cos^2 \frac{1}{2}\theta} = \frac{a^2 d^2\omega}{4\cos^4 \frac{1}{2}\theta}.$$

The possible deflections of the particle lie within the range of angles from zero, as $\varrho \to b$, to $\theta_m = \arctan(b/a)$, as $\varrho \to 0$. We have thus

$$d\sigma = \begin{cases} \frac{1}{4}a^2 \sec^4 \frac{1}{2}\theta \, d^2\omega, & \text{when} \quad 0 < \theta < \theta_m; \\ 0, & \text{when} \quad \theta_m < \theta. \end{cases}$$

(b)

$$d\sigma = \begin{cases} \frac{1}{4} b(a\sqrt{\tan(\theta/2)} - b)\, d^2\omega / \sin^2 \frac{1}{2}\theta \sin\theta, & \\ \qquad \text{when} \quad 0 < \theta < \theta_m = 2\arctan\left(\frac{b}{a}\right)^2; & \\ 0, \quad \text{when} \quad \theta_m < \theta. & \end{cases}$$

(c) $d\sigma = A^{-2/(n-1)}(n \tan \frac{1}{2}\theta)^{(n+1)/(n-1)}\, d^2\omega / 2(n-1) \sin\theta \cos^2 \frac{1}{2}\theta.$

3.2. It is the paraboloid of revolution $\varrho^2 = \alpha z/E$. The reader should check whether the trajectories of the particles scattered by the potential $U = -\alpha/r$ and those of the particles scattered by the paraboloid approximate one another as $r \to \infty$.

3.3.

$$d\sigma = \begin{cases} \left[\frac{a^2 n^2}{4\cos\frac{1}{2}\theta} \frac{(n\cos\frac{1}{2}\theta - 1)(n - \cos\frac{1}{2}\theta)}{(1 + n^2 - 2n\cos\frac{1}{2}\theta)^2} + \frac{1}{4}a^2\right] d^2\omega, & \\ \qquad \text{when} \quad 0 < \theta < \theta_m = 2\arccos n, & \\ 0, \qquad \text{when} \quad \theta_m < \theta < \pi, & \end{cases}$$

where $n = \sqrt{1 - (V/E)}$. Why is there a difference between this scattering cross-section and the one for scattering by a potential well (see Landau and Lifshitz, 1960, § 19, problem 2)?

3.4. (a)

$$\sigma = \begin{cases} \pi\left(\frac{\beta}{E} - \frac{\alpha^2}{4E^2}\right), & \text{when} \quad E > \alpha^2/2\beta; \\ 0, & \text{when} \quad E < \alpha^2/2\beta. \end{cases}$$

How does the cross-section change, when α changes sign?

(b)

$$\sigma = \begin{cases} \pi\left(2\sqrt{\dfrac{\gamma}{E}} - \dfrac{\beta}{E}\right), & \text{when} \quad E > \beta^2/4\gamma; \\ 0, & \text{when} \quad E < \beta^2/4\gamma. \end{cases}$$

3.5. (a) We first of all consider the motion of a particle in the potential $U = -\alpha/r^n$. The behaviour of $U_{\text{eff}}(r) = (E\varrho^2/r^2) - (\alpha/r^n)$ for different values of the impact parameter ϱ is shown in Fig. 79. The function $U_{\text{eff}}(r)$ reaches its maximum value,

$$U_m = \frac{1}{2}\alpha(n-2)\left(\frac{2E\varrho^2}{n\alpha}\right)^{n/(n-2)},$$

when

$$r = r_m = \left(\frac{n\alpha}{2E\varrho^2}\right)^{1/(n-2)}.$$

When $E < U_m$ (curve 1 in Fig. 79) the particles are scattered in the potential $U = -\alpha/r^n$, and the minimum distance from the centre $r_{\min}$ which is determined by the equation $U_{\text{eff}}(r) = E$ decreases with decreasing ϱ. When ϱ is further decreased the condition $U_m < E$ is satisfied (curve 3 in Fig. 79) and the particle can fall into the centre of the potential. This condition is

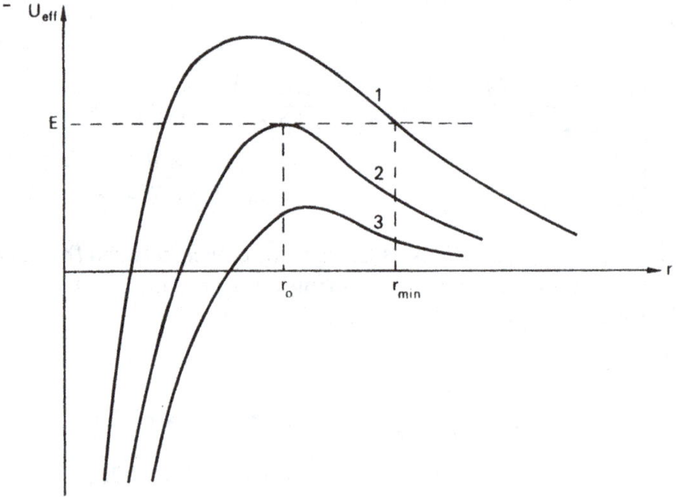

FIG. 79

satisfied when

$$\varrho^2 < \varrho_0^2 = n(n-2)^{(2-n)/n}(\alpha/2E)^{2/n}.$$

The cross-section for particles to hit a small sphere with its centre located in the centre of the potential is determined by different conditions, depending on the ratio of the radius of the sphere, R, and the value of $r_{\min}$ reached when $E = U_m$ (curve 2 in Fig. 79). This latter value, r_0, satisfies the equation

$$r_{\min} = r_0 = [2E(n-2)/\alpha]^{1/n}.$$

If $R < r_0$, only those particles which fall into the centre of the potential $U = -\alpha/r^n$ will hit the sphere, and the cross-section will be $\sigma = \pi\varrho_0^2$.

However, if $R > r_0$ all particles for which $r_{\min} \leqq R$ will hit the sphere and in that case

$$\sigma = \pi R^2 \left(1 + \frac{\alpha}{ER^n}\right).$$

(b) $\sigma = \pi\left[2\sqrt{\gamma/E} - (\beta/E)\right]$ provided both $2\sqrt{\gamma E} > \beta$ and $ER^4 > \gamma$; otherwise

$$\sigma = \pi R^2 \left(1 + \frac{\gamma}{ER^4} - \frac{\beta}{ER^2}\right).$$

3.6.

$$d\sigma = \frac{1}{4} R^2 \frac{(1+\lambda)\, d^2\omega}{(1+\lambda \sin^2 \frac{1}{2}\theta)^2},$$

where $\lambda = 4ER(RE+\alpha)/\alpha^2$. How can one explain the result which one obtains when $\alpha/RE = -2$?

3.7.

$$d\sigma = \frac{1}{2}\left(\frac{E}{V}\right)^2 \frac{d^2\omega}{\sqrt{1-(E\theta/V)^2}}, \quad 0 < \theta < \frac{V}{E}.$$

3.8. One can easily evaluate the angle of deflection of a particle, using a general formula (it is simplest to use the result of problem 2 in § 20 in Landau and Lifshitz, 1960), and we have

$$\theta = \left| \frac{3\pi\beta}{4E\varrho^4} - \frac{\pi\alpha}{2E\varrho^2} \right|. \tag{1}$$

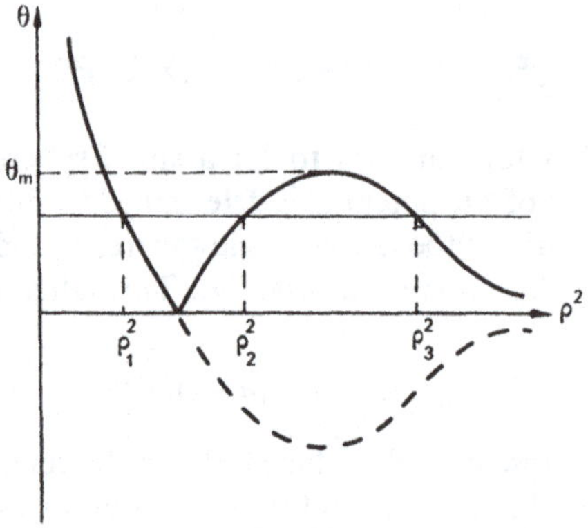

FIG. 80

The function $\theta(\varrho^2)$ is shown in Fig. 80. From (1) we find

$$\varrho_1^2 = \frac{\pi\alpha}{4E\theta}\left[\sqrt{1+\frac{\theta}{\theta_m}}-1\right],$$

$$\varrho_{2,3}^2 = \frac{\pi\alpha}{4E\theta}\left[1\mp\sqrt{1-\frac{\theta}{\theta_m}}\right],$$

where $\theta_m = \pi\alpha^2/12E\beta$.

For the cross-section we have

$$d\sigma = \pi(|d\varrho_1^2|+|d\varrho_2^2|+|d\varrho_3^2|) = \pi\, d(-\varrho_1^2+\varrho_2^2-\varrho_3^2)$$
$$= \frac{\pi\alpha}{4E\theta^3}\left\{\frac{1+\theta/2\theta_m}{\sqrt{1+\theta/\theta_m}}+\frac{2-\theta/\theta_m}{\sqrt{1-\theta/\theta_m}}-1\right\}d^2\omega. \qquad (2)$$

This result is valid provided each of the terms in (1) is much less than unity. An estimate shows that the condition $\theta \ll 1$ is sufficient for this. Equation (2) is obtained when $\theta < \theta_m$. If $\theta_m \ll 1$ and $\theta_m < \theta \ll 1$, we have for the cross-section

$$d\sigma = \pi\,|d\varrho_1^2| = \frac{\pi\alpha}{4E\theta^3}\left[\frac{1+\theta/2\theta_m}{\sqrt{1+\theta/\theta_m}}-1\right]d^2\omega.$$

Figure 81 shows how $d\sigma/d^2\omega$ depends on θ. The differential cross-section becomes infinite both as $\theta \to 0$ and as $\theta \to \theta_m$. The total cross-section for scattering into a range of angles adjoining $\theta = 0$ is infinite as the small-angle scattering corresponds to large impact parameters.

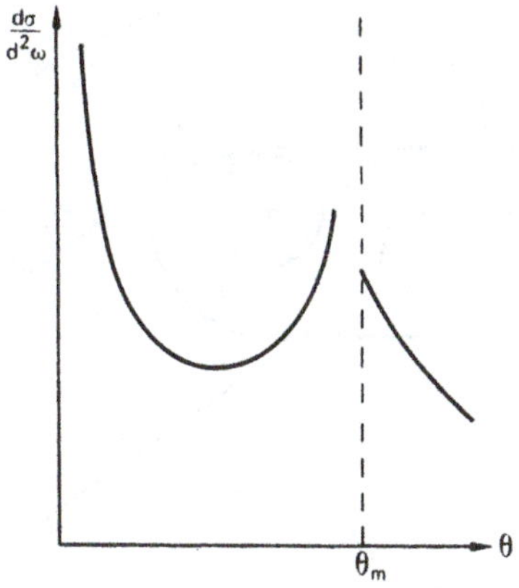

FIG. 81

The total cross-section for scattering into a range of angles $\theta_m - \delta \leqq \theta \leqq \theta_m$,

$$\int_{\theta_m-\delta}^{\theta_m} 2\pi \frac{d\sigma}{d^2\omega} \sin\theta \, d\theta = \frac{\pi^2 \alpha \delta^{\frac{1}{2}}}{2E\theta_m^{\frac{5}{2}}},$$

is finite, and tends to zero as $\delta \to 0$.

What is the relation between the number of scattered particles reaching a counter and its size, if the counter is located at an angle θ_m?

3.9. The velocity of the particle after scattering is at an angle

$$\theta = \pi - \frac{\pi}{\sqrt{1-a^2/\varrho^2}} \quad \left(a^2 = \frac{\alpha}{E}\right) \tag{1}$$

to its original direction. A counter registers particles scattered over an angle $|\theta| < \pi$ together with those particles which have made several revolutions around the scattering centre (Fig. 82a). The observed angle of deflection χ lies in the range $0 \leqq \chi \leqq \pi$ and satisfies the relation

$$-\theta = 2\pi l \pm \chi, \tag{2}$$

where $l = 0, 1, 2, 3, \ldots$ corresponds to the upper sign in (2) and $l = 1, 2, 3, \ldots$ to the lower sign in (2). From (1) and (2) we have (see Fig. 82b)

$$\varrho^2(\chi, l, \pm) = a^2 + \frac{\pi a^2}{2}\left(\frac{1}{2\pi l \pm \chi} - \frac{1}{2\pi l + 2\pi \pm \chi}\right).$$

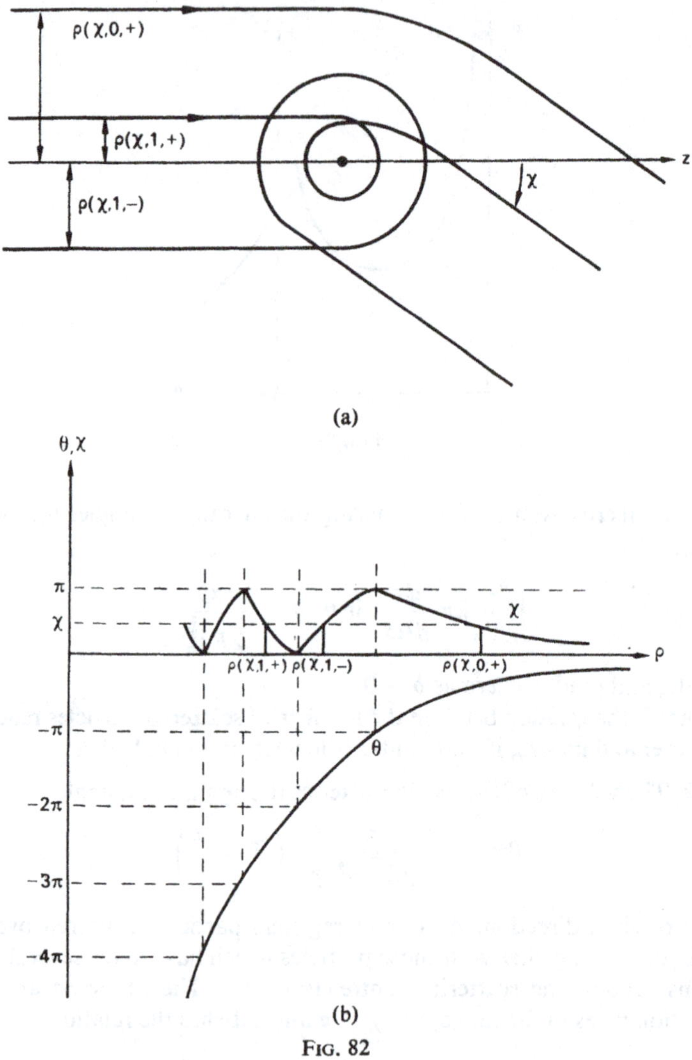

FIG. 82

The cross-section is

$$d\sigma = \pi \sum_{l=0}^{\infty} |d\varrho^2(\chi, l, +)| + \pi \sum_{l=1}^{\infty} |d\varrho^2(\chi, l, -)|.$$

Using the fact that

$$\frac{d\varrho^2(\chi, l, +)}{d\chi} < 0, \quad \frac{d\varrho^2(\chi, l, -)}{d\chi} > 0,$$

we find that

$$d\sigma = \pi d\left[-\sum_{l=0}^{\infty} \varrho^2(\chi, l, +)+\sum_{l=1}^{\infty} \varrho^2(\chi, l, -)\right] = \frac{\pi^2 a^2}{2} d\left(\frac{-1}{\chi}+\frac{1}{2\pi-\chi}\right)$$

$$= \frac{\pi a^2(2\pi^2-2\pi\chi+\chi^2)}{2\chi^2(2\pi-\chi)^2 \sin\chi} d^2\omega.$$

3.10. (a) One sees easily that the condition $E \gg V$ means that the angle over which the particle is deflected during the scattering is small. The change in momentum is

$$\Delta p = -\frac{\partial}{\partial\varrho}\int_{-\infty}^{+\infty} U(|\boldsymbol{\rho}+\boldsymbol{v}t|)\, dt = \frac{2V\sqrt{\pi}}{v}\, xe^{-x^2},$$

where $x = \varkappa\varrho$. The angle of deflection is

$$\theta = \frac{\Delta p}{p} = \frac{V\sqrt{\pi}}{E}\, xe^{-x^2} \tag{1}$$

We cannot solve equation (1) for x in analytical form. However, from the graph of the function xe^{-x^2} (Fig. 83) we see that equation (1) has two

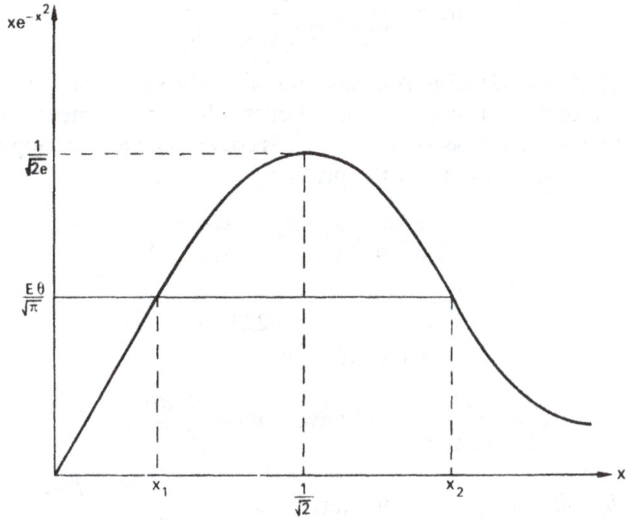

FIG. 83

roots when

$$\theta < \theta_m = \frac{V}{E}\sqrt{\frac{\pi}{2e}}.$$

Using equation (1) and the relation

$$d\theta = \frac{V\sqrt{\pi}}{E}(1-2x^2)e^{-x^2}\,dx$$

we can write the expression for the cross-section

$$d\sigma = \pi(|d\varrho_1^2|+|d\varrho_2^2|) = \frac{2\pi}{\varkappa^2}(x_1\,dx_1 - x_2\,dx_2),$$

in the form

$$d\sigma = \frac{d^2\omega}{\varkappa^2\theta^2}\left(\frac{x_2^2}{2x_2^2-1} - \frac{x_1^2}{1-2x_1^2}\right).$$

When $\theta \ll \theta_m$, it turns out that $x_1 \ll 1$ and $x_2 \ll 1$, so that $d\sigma = d^2\omega/2\varkappa^2\theta^2$.

When $\theta_m - \theta \ll \theta_m$ we can solve (1) by expanding xe^{-x^2} in a series near the maximum. We then get

$$x_{1,2} = \frac{1 \mp \sqrt{\theta_m - \theta}}{\sqrt{2}},$$

and hence

$$d\sigma = \frac{d^2\omega}{2\sqrt{2}\varkappa^2\theta_m^2\sqrt{\theta_m-\theta}}.$$

Figure 84 shows $d\sigma/d^2\omega$ as a function of θ. The singularity at $\theta = \theta_m$ is integrable (compare problem 3.8). Discuss whether the presence of the singularity in the cross-section at $\theta = \theta_m$ is connected with the approximations made in the solution of the problem.

(b)
$$d\sigma = \frac{d^2\omega}{\pi\varkappa^2\theta^3}\left(\frac{x_1+x_1^2}{1-2x_1} + \frac{x_2+x_2^2}{2x_2-1}\right),$$

where

$$\frac{x_{1,2}}{(1+x_{1,2})^3} = \left(\frac{2E\theta}{\pi V}\right)^2.$$

When $\theta \ll \theta_m = \dfrac{\pi V}{3E\sqrt{3}}$ we have $d\sigma = \dfrac{V\,d^2\omega}{4\varkappa^2 E\theta^3}$.

When $\theta_m - \theta \ll \theta_m$, we have $d\sigma = \dfrac{\sqrt{7}\,d^2\omega}{\pi\varkappa^2\theta_m^3\sqrt{1-(\theta^2/\theta_m^2)}}$.

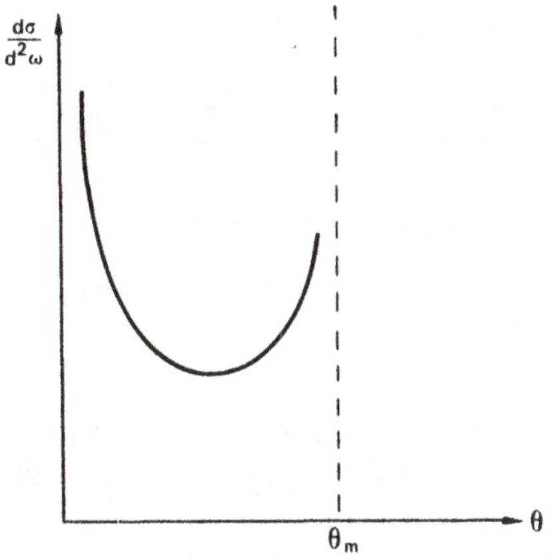

FIG. 84

3.11. (a) A particle with a velocity $\boldsymbol{V}$ before the collision will have a velocity $\boldsymbol{V}' = \boldsymbol{V}-2\boldsymbol{n}(\boldsymbol{n}\cdot\boldsymbol{V})$ after the collision, where $\boldsymbol{n}$ is a unit vector which is normal to the surface of the ellipsoid. Using the relations† $\boldsymbol{V} = V(0, 0, 1)$, $\boldsymbol{n} = N^{-1}([x/a^2], [y/b^2], [z/c^2])$ we get

$$\boldsymbol{V}' = V\left(\frac{-2xz}{N^2a^2c^2}, \frac{-2yz}{N^2b^2c^2}, 1-\frac{2z^2}{N^2c^4}\right). \tag{1}$$

Introducing polar coordinates with the axis along $\boldsymbol{V}$ we can write $\boldsymbol{V}' = V(\sin\theta\cos\varphi, \sin\theta\sin\varphi, \cos\theta)$, and from (1) we then have

$$\tan\varphi = \frac{a^2y}{b^2x}, \quad \cos\theta = 1-\frac{2z^2}{N^2c^4}, \quad \sin^2\theta = \left(\frac{2z}{N^2c^2}\right)^2\left(\frac{x^2}{a^4}+\frac{y^2}{b^4}\right). \tag{2}$$

For the cross-section we have

$$d\sigma = dx\,dy = \left|\frac{\partial(x, y)}{\partial(\theta, \varphi)}\right| d\theta\,d\varphi,$$

where the dependence of x and y on θ and φ follows from (2) and from the equation for the ellipsoid.

To evaluate the Jacobian it is convenient to introduce an auxiliary variable U such that

$$x = a^2U\cos\varphi, \qquad y = b^2U\sin\varphi.$$

† We know from differential geometry that $\boldsymbol{n} \propto \nabla(x^2/a^2+y^2/b^2+z^2/c^2-1)$, while N is determined by the relation $\boldsymbol{n}^2 = 1$.

From (1) and (2) it then follows that

$$\sin\theta = \frac{2zU}{Nc^2}, \quad 1-\cos\theta = \frac{2z^2}{Nc^4}, \quad \tan\frac{\theta}{2} = \frac{z}{Uc^2},$$

and from the equation of the ellipsoid we find

$$U^{-2} = a^2\cos^2\varphi + b^2\sin^2\varphi + c^2\tan^2\tfrac{1}{2}\theta.$$

Moreover, we have

$$\frac{\partial(x, y)}{\partial(\theta, \varphi)} = \frac{\partial(x, y)}{\partial(U, \varphi)}\frac{\partial(U, \varphi)}{\partial(\theta, \varphi)} = \frac{a^2b^2}{2}\frac{\partial U^2}{\partial\theta}.$$

We thus get, finally,

$$d\sigma = \frac{a^2b^2c^2\, d^2\omega}{4\sin^4\frac{1}{2}\theta[a^2\cos^2\varphi + b^2\sin^2\varphi + c^2\tan^2\frac{1}{2}\theta]^2}.$$

What is the limit which we must take to obtain from this result the cross-section for scattering by a paraboloid?

(b)

$$d\sigma = \frac{a^2b^2c^2\, d^2\omega}{\cos^3\theta\,[a^2\cos^2\varphi + b^2\sin^2\varphi + c^2\tan^2\theta]^2}.$$

(c)

$$d\sigma = \frac{\cos\theta\; a^2b^2c^2\, d^2\omega}{\sin^4\theta\,[a^2\cos^2\varphi + b^2\sin^2\varphi + c^2\cot^2\theta]^2}.$$

3.12. (a) The change in momentum due to scattering is

$$\Delta \boldsymbol{p} = -\int_{-\infty}^{+\infty} \frac{\partial U(\boldsymbol{r}(t))}{\partial \boldsymbol{r}}\, dt. \tag{1}$$

For small angle scattering we can substitute in the right-hand side of (1): $\boldsymbol{r}(t) = \boldsymbol{\rho} + \boldsymbol{v}t$ $(\varrho \perp \boldsymbol{v})$ and thus we have†

$$\Delta \boldsymbol{p} = -\frac{\partial}{\partial \boldsymbol{\rho}}\int_{-\infty}^{+\infty} U(\boldsymbol{\rho} + \boldsymbol{v}t)\, dt = -\frac{\partial}{\partial \boldsymbol{\rho}}\frac{\pi(\boldsymbol{a}\cdot\boldsymbol{\rho})}{v\varrho}. \tag{2}$$

† Differentiation with respect to $\boldsymbol{\rho}$ rather than with respect to $\boldsymbol{r}$ (where $\boldsymbol{\rho} \perp \boldsymbol{v}_\infty$) means that the formula obtained for $\Delta \boldsymbol{p}$ determines only its components perpendicular to $\boldsymbol{v}_\infty$.

Let the z-axis be parallel to $\boldsymbol{v}$ and the y-axis at right angles to $\boldsymbol{a}$. We then have

$$\Delta p_x = \frac{-\pi a_x}{v}\frac{\varrho_y^2}{\varrho^3}, \quad \Delta p_y = \frac{\pi a_x}{v}\frac{\varrho_x \varrho_y}{\varrho^3}. \tag{3}$$

The direction of the velocity after the scattering can be characterised by two spherical polar angles:

$$\tan\varphi = \frac{\Delta p_y}{\Delta p_x}, \quad \theta = \frac{\Delta p}{p}. \tag{4}$$

It is clear from (3) that scattering only occurs when $\frac{1}{2}\pi < \varphi < \frac{3}{2}\pi$. From (3) and (4) we then have

$$\varrho_x = \pm\frac{\pi a_x}{2E}\frac{\sin\varphi\cos\varphi}{\theta}, \quad \varrho_y = \mp\frac{\pi a_x}{2E}\frac{\cos^2\varphi}{\theta}. \tag{5}$$

For the cross-section we find

$$d\sigma = \sum d\varrho_x\, d\varrho_y = \sum \left|\frac{\partial(\varrho_x, \varrho_y)}{\partial(\theta, \varphi)}\right| d\theta\, d\varphi$$

$$= \left(\frac{\pi a_x}{E}\right)^2 \frac{\cos^2\varphi}{2\theta^4}\, d^2\omega. \tag{6}$$

The summation in (6) is over the two possible values of $\boldsymbol{\rho}$ (see (5)).

(b)

$$d\sigma = \frac{|\boldsymbol{a}_\perp|}{E}\frac{d^2\omega}{\theta^3}.$$

The cross-section turns out to be symmetrical with respect to $\boldsymbol{v}_\infty$, although the potential is by no means symmetric with respect to this direction; $\boldsymbol{a}_\perp$ is the component of $\boldsymbol{a}$ at right angles to $\boldsymbol{v}_\infty$.

3.13. The change in the angle of deflection of the particle is given by the equation (see problem 2.17)

$$\delta\theta(\varrho) = -\frac{1}{E}\frac{\partial}{\partial\varrho}\int_{r_{\min}}^{\infty}\frac{\delta U(r)\, dr}{\sqrt{1-\varrho^2/r^2-U(r)/E}}. \tag{1}$$

We then find from the equation $\theta = \theta_0(\varrho)+\delta\theta(\varrho)$:

$$\varrho = \varrho_0(\theta) - \delta\theta(\varrho_0(\theta))\frac{d\varrho_0(\theta)}{d\theta}$$

(see problem 1.8). The function $\theta_0(\varrho)$ and hence the function $\varrho_0(\theta)$ are the expressions obtained when $\delta U = 0$. We then get for the cross-section:

$$\frac{d\sigma}{d\theta} = \pi\left|\frac{d\varrho^2}{d\theta}\right| = \pi\left|\frac{d\varrho_0^2(\theta)}{d\theta} - \frac{d}{d\theta}\left(2\varrho_0(\theta)\,\delta\theta(\varrho_0(\theta))\,\frac{d\varrho_0(\theta)}{d\theta}\right)\right|$$

$$= \frac{d\sigma_0}{d\theta} \mp \frac{d}{d\theta}\left(\delta\theta(\varrho_0(\theta))\,\frac{d\sigma_0}{d^2\omega}\right). \tag{2}$$

The sign in (2) is the opposite of that of $d\varrho_0(\theta)/d\theta$.

(a)

$$\delta\frac{d\sigma}{d\theta} = \frac{\pi\beta}{E}\frac{d}{d\theta}\left\{\frac{\pi-\theta+2\cos\frac{1}{2}\theta}{\sin\theta}\right\};$$

(c)

$$\delta\frac{d\sigma}{d\theta} = \frac{2\gamma}{\pi^3\sqrt{\beta E}}\frac{d}{d\theta}\left\{\frac{(\pi-\theta)^2}{\sqrt{\theta(2\pi-\theta)}}\right\}.$$

3.14. The energy acquired by the particle,

$$\varepsilon = \frac{(\boldsymbol{p}+\Delta\boldsymbol{p})^2}{2m} - \frac{p^2}{2m} \approx (\boldsymbol{v}\cdot\Delta\boldsymbol{p}),$$

is to first order determined solely by the change in the longitudinal component of the momentum. As we assume that the deflection of the particle is small, we can (after differentiating) put $\boldsymbol{r} = \boldsymbol{\varrho}+\boldsymbol{v}(t-\tau)$ in the expression for the force $\boldsymbol{F}$ acting upon the particle,

$$\boldsymbol{F} = -\nabla U(\boldsymbol{r}, t).$$

Here ϱ is the impact parameter and τ the time when the particle is at its smallest distance from the centre. Therefore we have

$$\varepsilon = \left(\boldsymbol{v}\cdot\int_{-\infty}^{+\infty}\boldsymbol{F}(t)\,dt\right) = \varepsilon_m e^{-\varkappa^2\varrho^2}\cos\varrho,$$

$$\varepsilon_m = \sqrt{\pi}\,V_2\frac{\omega}{\varkappa v}\,e^{-\omega^2/4\varkappa^2v^2},\ \varphi = \omega\tau,$$

and the scattering cross-section for particles with a given value of τ is when $\cos\varphi > 0$ ($\cos\varphi < 0$)

$$\frac{d\sigma}{d\varepsilon} = \begin{cases}\pi/\varkappa^2|\varepsilon|, & \text{when}\quad 0<\varepsilon<\varepsilon_m\cos\varphi \quad (0>\varepsilon>\varepsilon_m\cos\varphi);\\ 0, & \text{when}\quad |\varepsilon|>\varepsilon_m|\cos\varphi|.\end{cases}$$

In the incident beam there are particles with different values of τ. If we average the cross-section over the phase φ, using, for example, for $\varepsilon > 0$ the formula $\left\langle \frac{d\sigma}{d\varepsilon} \right\rangle = \frac{1}{2\pi} \int_{-\alpha}^{\alpha} \frac{d\sigma}{d\varepsilon} d\varepsilon$, $\alpha = \arccos \frac{\varepsilon}{\varepsilon_m}$, we get

$$\left\langle \frac{d\sigma}{d\varepsilon} \right\rangle = \begin{cases} \arccos (|\varepsilon|/\varepsilon_m)/\varkappa^2 |\varepsilon|, & \text{when} \quad |\varepsilon| < \varepsilon_m; \\ 0, & \text{when} \quad |\varepsilon| > \varepsilon_m. \end{cases}$$

3.15.

$$\frac{dN}{N} = \frac{\lambda^2 \sin \theta \, d\theta}{\cos^3 \theta \sqrt{1-\lambda^2 \tan^2 \theta}}, \quad \lambda = \frac{V^2 - V_0^2}{2VV_0},$$

$0 \leqq \theta \leqq \arctan \lambda^{-1}$, if $V > V_0$; $\pi - \arctan |\lambda|^{-1} \leqq \theta \leqq \pi$, if $V < V_0$.

3.16.

$$\frac{dN}{N} = \frac{3(T_{\max} - T)(T - T_{\min})}{(T_{\max} - T_{\min})^3} \, dT, \quad T_{\min} \leqq T \leqq T_{\max},$$

$$T_{\min} = \tfrac{1}{2} m(V_0 - V)^2, \quad T_{\max} = \tfrac{1}{2} m(V_0 + V)^2.$$

3.17. $\tan \theta_1 = \cot \theta_2 = \alpha / E\varrho$; $E = \frac{1}{2} mV^2$ (see the problem in § 17 of Landau and Lifshitz, 1960).

3.18.

$$\begin{aligned} \tfrac{1}{2}\pi &\leqq \theta \leqq \pi, & &\text{when} \quad m_1 < m_2; \\ \theta &= \tfrac{1}{2}\pi, & &\text{when} \quad m_1 = m_2; \\ 0 &\leqq \theta < \tfrac{1}{2}\pi, & &\text{when} \quad m_1 > m_2. \end{aligned}$$

3.19. The velocity component normal to the sphere's surface at the point of impact becomes zero in the centre-of-mass system while the tangential component V_0' is conserved (see Fig. 85). The scattering cross-section as function of the angle of deflection χ of the particle in the centre-of-mass system is

$$d\sigma = \pi |d\varrho^2| = 4\pi a^2 |d \cos^2 \chi| = 4a^2 \cos \chi \, d^2\omega.$$

To transform to the laboratory system we use the equation

$$\tan \theta = \frac{V_0' \sin \chi}{V_0' \cos \chi + V_0} = \frac{\sin \chi \cos \chi}{1 + \cos^2 \chi}$$

to find the equation

$$\cos^2 \chi_{1,2} = \tfrac{3}{2} \cos^2 \theta - 1 \pm \tfrac{1}{2} \cos \theta \sqrt{9 \cos^2 \theta - 8}.$$

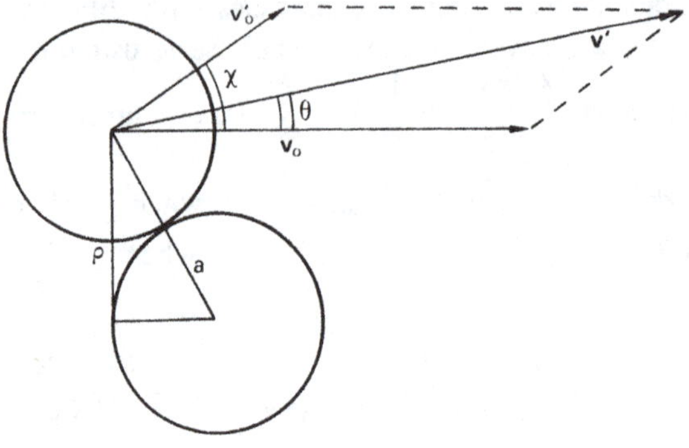

FIG. 85

Taking into account the fact that there are two possible connections between χ and θ, we get

$$d\sigma = 4\pi a^2(|d\cos^2\chi_1|+|d\cos^2\chi_2|) = 4\pi a^2\, d(\cos^2\chi_1-\cos^2\chi_2)$$
$$= 4a^2 \frac{5-9\sin^2\theta}{\sqrt{1-9\sin^2\theta}}\, d^2\boldsymbol{\omega}, \quad \text{where} \quad 0<\theta<\arcsin\tfrac{1}{9}.$$

If the spheres impinging upon those at rest are identical with them so that there are no means of distinguishing between them after the collision, we must add to the cross-section which we have just obtained the cross-section

$$d\sigma' = 4a^2\cos\theta d^2\boldsymbol{\omega}, \quad 0<\theta<\tfrac{1}{2}\pi,$$

which refers to the spheres which were originally at rest flying off at an angle θ.

3.20. $I = I_0 e^{-n\sigma x}$.

3.21. $dN = \sigma n_1 n_2 |\boldsymbol{V}_1-\boldsymbol{V}_2|\, d^3\boldsymbol{r}\, dt.$

3.22. (a) $F_{\text{fr}} = 2\pi m v^2 n \int_0^\pi f(\theta)(1-\cos\theta)\sin\theta\, d\theta$;†

(b) $\overline{\theta^2} = 2\pi\left(\frac{m}{M}\right)^2 nl \int_0^\pi f(\theta)\sin^3\theta\, d\theta,$

where l is the path travelled by M, v its velocity, and n the concentration of light particles.

† The quantity $\int (d\sigma/d^2\boldsymbol{\omega})(1-\cos\theta)\, d^2\boldsymbol{\omega}$ is called the transport cross-section — as distinct from the total cross-section $\int (d\sigma/d^2\boldsymbol{\omega})\, d^2\boldsymbol{\omega}$.

4. Lagrangian Equations of Motion. Conservation Laws

4.1. Assuming that $t = 0$ when the particle is at $x = 0$, we find $C = 0$, and from the condition that $x = a$ at $t = \tau$ we find that $B = (a/\tau) - A\tau$. Substituting the function $x(t) = At^2 + (a/\tau - A\tau)t$ into the action, we find

$$S = \int_0^\tau L(x, \dot{x})\,dt = \int_0^\tau \left(\tfrac{1}{2}m\dot{x}^2 + Fx\right) dt$$
$$= \frac{1}{6}mA^2\tau^3 + \frac{1}{2}\frac{ma^2}{\tau} - \frac{1}{6}FA\tau^3 + \frac{1}{2}Fa\tau.$$

From the condition that the action be a minimum, $\partial S/\partial A = 0$, it follows that $A = F/2m$. It is clear that in the present case the orbit

$$x = \frac{Ft^2}{2m} + \left(\frac{a}{\tau} - \frac{F\tau}{2m}\right)t$$

is exact. However, the only thing the solution given here allows us to state is that this orbit in some sense is the best one among all possible orbits of this kind.

In order that we can be certain that this orbit indeed gives a smaller value for S than any other $x(t)$, that is, that it is the true orbit, we must verify that it satisfies the Lagrangian equations of motion.

4.2.

$$x = v_x t - a, \quad 0 < t < t_0 = a/v_x;$$
$$x = \sqrt{v_x^2 - 2V/m}\,(t - \tau) + a, \quad t_0 < t < \tau;$$
$$y = at/\tau;$$

where $v_x = (2aV/m\tau)^{\frac{1}{3}}$.

4.3. From the relation

$$\tilde{L}(Q, \dot{Q}, t) = L(q(Q, t), \dot{q}(Q, \dot{Q}, t), t) = L\left(q(Q, t); \frac{\partial q}{\partial Q}\dot{Q} + \frac{\partial q}{\partial t}, t\right)$$

we get

$$\frac{d}{dt}\frac{d\tilde{L}}{d\dot{Q}} = \frac{\partial q}{\partial Q}\frac{d}{dt}\frac{\partial L}{\partial \dot{q}} + \frac{\partial L}{\partial \dot{q}}\frac{d}{dt}\frac{\partial q}{\partial Q}, \qquad \frac{\partial \tilde{L}}{\partial Q} = \frac{\partial L}{\partial q}\frac{\partial q}{\partial Q} + \frac{\partial L}{\partial \dot{q}}\frac{\partial \dot{q}}{\partial Q}.$$

Bearing in mind that

$$\frac{\partial \dot{q}}{\partial Q} = \frac{d}{dt}\frac{\partial q}{\partial Q},$$

we get

$$\frac{d}{dt}\frac{\partial \mathcal{L}}{\partial \dot{Q}} - \frac{\partial \mathcal{L}}{\partial Q} = \frac{\partial q}{\partial Q}\left(\frac{d}{dt}\frac{\partial L}{\partial \dot{q}} - \frac{\partial L}{\partial q}\right). \tag{1}$$

The validity of the equation

$$\frac{d}{dt}\frac{\partial L}{\partial \dot{q}} - \frac{\partial L}{\partial q} = 0$$

thus leads to the validity of the analogous equation

$$\frac{d}{dt}\frac{\partial \mathcal{L}}{\partial \dot{Q}} - \frac{\partial \mathcal{L}}{\partial Q} = 0.$$

If there are several degrees of freedom, we get instead of (1) the following equation:

$$\frac{d}{dt}\frac{\partial \mathcal{L}}{\partial \dot{Q}_i} - \frac{\partial \mathcal{L}}{\partial Q_i} = \sum_k \frac{\partial q_k}{\partial Q_i}\left(\frac{d}{dt}\frac{\partial L}{\partial \dot{q}_k} - \frac{\partial L}{\partial q_k}\right).$$

4.4.

$$\mathcal{L}\left(Q, \frac{dQ}{d\tau}, \tau\right) = L\left(q, \frac{dq}{dt}, t\right)\frac{dt}{d\tau}.$$

Here

$$q = q(Q, \tau), \quad \frac{dq}{dt} = \frac{dq}{d\tau}\frac{d\tau}{dt}, \quad \frac{dq}{d\tau} = \frac{\partial q}{\partial Q}\frac{dQ}{d\tau} + \frac{\partial q}{\partial \tau},$$

$$\frac{dt}{d\tau} = \frac{\partial t}{\partial Q}\frac{dQ}{d\tau} + \frac{\partial t}{\partial \tau}.$$

4.5.

$$L = \frac{1}{2}m\frac{\dot{x}^2}{1+\lambda\dot{x}} - (1+\lambda\dot{x})U(x), \quad \dot{x} = \frac{dx}{d\tau}.$$

4.6.

$$L = -\sqrt{1-\left(\frac{dq}{d\tau}\right)^2}.$$

This problem is a purely formal one. However, both this Lagrangian and the transformation considered ("improved" by the introduction of dimensional factors) have a simple physical meaning in the theory of relativity (see, for instance, Landau and Lifshitz, 1962, §§ 4 and 8).

4.7. From

$$P_l = \frac{\partial L}{\partial \dot{Q}_l}, \quad E' = \sum_l P_l \dot{Q}_l - L,$$

we find

$$P_l = \sum_k \frac{\partial f_k}{\partial Q_k} p_k, \quad E' = E - \sum_k p_k \frac{\partial f_k}{\partial t}.$$

4.8. Applying the formulae of the preceding problem, we obtain

(a) $p'_r = m\dot{r}' = p_r, \quad p'_\varphi = mr'^2(\dot{\varphi}' + \Omega) = p_\varphi, \quad E' = E - \Omega p_\varphi;$

(b) $p'_x = p_x \cos \Omega t - p_y \sin \Omega t,$ (1)

$p'_y = p_x \sin \Omega t + p_y \cos \Omega t.$

It follows from (1) that $\boldsymbol{p}' = \boldsymbol{p}$, while (1) also gives the rules for the transformation of vector components when we are changing to a coordinate system which is rotated over an angle Ωt. Note that $\boldsymbol{p}' \neq m\boldsymbol{v}'$ (compare Landau and Lifshitz, 1960, § 39).

4.9.

(a) $E'_1 = E - (\boldsymbol{V} \cdot \boldsymbol{P})$, where $\boldsymbol{P}'_1 = \boldsymbol{P}_1 = \sum_a \boldsymbol{p}_a;$

(b) $E'_2 = E - (\boldsymbol{V} \cdot \boldsymbol{P}) - \frac{1}{2} V^2 \sum_a m_a, \quad \boldsymbol{P}'_2 = \boldsymbol{P} - \boldsymbol{V} \sum_a m_a.$

The two expressions for the energy differ by a constant. Usually, we employ the second formula, as it agrees with the definition of the energy in the theory of relativity.

4.10. Let $q_i = \varphi_i(t)$ describe the motion of the system (trajectory AB in Fig. 85a). As the form of the action is invariant when we change to the variables q'_i, t', the motion is also described by the equations $q'_i = \varphi_i(t')$. If we express these equations in terms of the variables q_i, t, we have up to first order in ε:

$$q_i(t - \delta t) = \varphi_i(t) - \delta q_i,$$

with

$$\delta q_i = \varepsilon \Psi_i(\varphi(t), t), \qquad \delta t = \varepsilon X(\varphi(t), t)$$

(trajectory A′B′ in Fig. 85a). Small changes in the coordinates and the time at the beginning and the end of the motion, when we change from the orbit AB to the orbit A′B′, lead to the following change in the action:

$$S_{A'B'} - S_{AB} = \left[\frac{\partial S}{\partial t}(-\delta t) + \sum_i \frac{\partial S}{\partial q_i}(-\delta q_i)\right]_A^B.$$

Here we have (see Landau and Lifshitz 1960, § 43)

$$\frac{\partial S}{\partial t} = L - \sum_i \frac{\partial L}{\partial \dot{q}_i}\dot{q}_i = -E(t), \quad \frac{\partial S}{\partial q_i} = \frac{\partial L}{\partial \dot{q}_i} = p_i(t).$$

On the other hand, according to the conditions of the problem $S_{AB} = S_{A'B'}$, so that

$$E(t_A)\,\varepsilon X(q_A, t_A) - \sum_i p_i(t_A)\,\varepsilon \Psi_i(q_A, t_A)$$
$$= E(t_B)\,\varepsilon X(q_B, t_B) - \sum_i p_i(t_B)\,\varepsilon \Psi_i(q_B, t_B),$$

or,

$$EX - \sum_i p_i \Psi_i = \text{constant}.$$

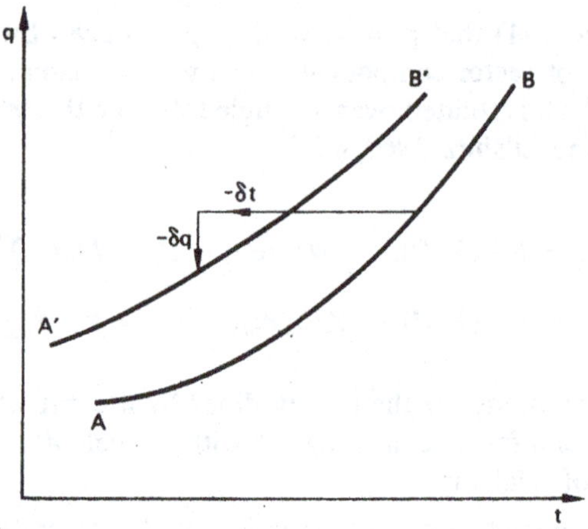

FIG. 85a

4.11.

$$\sum_i \frac{\partial L}{\partial \dot{q}_i}(\dot{q}_i X - \Psi_i) - LX + f = \text{constant}.$$

4.12. (a) The linear momentum;
(b) the angular momentum;
(c) the energy;
(d) $M_z + h/2\pi p_z$ = constant, where h is the pitch of the screw;
(e) $Ex - p_x t$ = constant: the integral of motion of the centre of inertia of the system (see Landau and Lifshitz, 1962, § 14).

4.13. (a) The potential energy is $U = -(\boldsymbol{F}\cdot\boldsymbol{r})$, and this energy and at the same time the action remain unchanged under translations in directions at right angles to $\boldsymbol{F}$ or under rotations around axes parallel to $\boldsymbol{F}$. Integrals of motion are thus the linear momentum components at right angles to $\boldsymbol{F}$ and the angular momentum component parallel to $\boldsymbol{F}$. As the Lagrangian is independent of the time, the energy is an integral of motion.

The statement that different points in some region of space are "interchangeable" means that the value of the potential energy (but not of the force) is the same in all those points. The space in which there is a uniform field is by no means itself uniform.

(b) The similarity transformation leaves the form of the action invariant when $n = 2$. In that case

$$(\boldsymbol{p}\cdot\boldsymbol{r}) - 2Et = \text{constant},$$

For instance, in the central force potential $U = \alpha/r^2$, if we write this integral in the form $mr\dot{r} - 2Et = \text{constant}$, and take the relation

$$\dot{r} = \sqrt{\frac{2}{m}\left[E - \frac{\alpha}{r^2} - \frac{M^2}{2mr^2}\right]}$$

into account, we obtain the functional dependence $r(t)$ (compare Landau and Lifshitz, 1960, § 15, problem 2);

(c) $E - (\boldsymbol{V}\cdot\boldsymbol{p}) = \text{constant};$
(d) $(\boldsymbol{r}\cdot\boldsymbol{P}) - 2Et = \text{constant}$, where $\boldsymbol{P} = m\boldsymbol{v} + e/c\boldsymbol{A}$, if $\boldsymbol{A}(\alpha\boldsymbol{r}) = \alpha^{-1}\boldsymbol{A}(\boldsymbol{r})$;
(e) $E - p_\varphi\Omega = \text{constant}.$

4.14. (Compare problem 4.12 (e).) $m\boldsymbol{r} - \boldsymbol{p}t = \text{constant}$. Is this integral of motion the eighth independent integral for a closed system (apart from E, $\boldsymbol{M}$, and $\boldsymbol{p}$)?

4.15. (a) Let the z-axis be parallel to $\boldsymbol{H}$. A translation along the z-axis or a rotation around it leaves the form of $\boldsymbol{A}$, and hence also the form of the action, invariant. We have thus the following integrals of motion: $p_z = \partial L/\partial \dot{z} = m\dot{z}$ and $M_z = xP_y - yP_x = m(x\dot{y} - y\dot{x}) + (e/2c)H(x^2+y^2)$. Moreover, the energy, $E = \frac{1}{2}m(\dot{x}^2+\dot{y}^2+\dot{z}^2)$ is an integral of motion.

(b) $E = \frac{1}{2}m(\dot{x}^2+\dot{y}^2+\dot{z}^2)$, $P'_y = m\dot{y} + eHx/c$, $p'_z = m\dot{z}$ (compare problem 10.7).

Symmetry considerations allow us to determine various integrals of motion depending on the choice of a vector potential for a given field $\boldsymbol{H}$. However, the quantities E, $p_z = p'_z$, M_z, and P'_y are all integrals of motion, independent of the choice of $\boldsymbol{A}$.

4.16. (a) $E = \frac{1}{2}m(\dot{x}^2+\dot{y}^2+\dot{z}^2)$,

$$M_z = m(x\dot{y}-y\dot{x})+\frac{e\mathcal{M}}{e\sqrt{x^2+y^2}},$$ where the z-axis is taken parallel to $\mathcal{M}$ (compare problem 2.27).

(b) From the symmetry properties of the given field we can obtain the following integrals of motion:

$$p_z = m\dot{z}, \quad M_z \equiv p_\varphi = mr^2\dot{\varphi}+e\mu/c, \quad E = \tfrac{1}{2}m(\dot{r}^2+r^2\dot{\varphi}^2+\dot{z}^2).$$

However, the motion in this "field" is free-particle motion. Indeed, the Lagrangian, $L = \frac{1}{2}mv^2+e\mu\dot{\varphi}/c$, differs from the Lagrangian of a free particle only by the total derivative with respect to time of the function $e\mu\varphi/c$.†

We note that in the case when μ is a function of the time, p_z and M_z remain integrals of motion.

4.17. (a) $\ddot{x}+x = 0$. The same equation could have obtained from the Lagrangian $L_1(x, \dot{x}) = \dot{x}^2-x^2$. It is well known that if two Lagrangians differ by a total derivative of a function of the coordinates and the time, they lead to the same Lagrangian equations of motion. The reverse statement is incorrect.

(b) $\ddot{x}+\alpha\dot{x}+\omega^2x = 0$.

4.18. (a) In spherical polars the Lagrangian equations of motion for a particle moving in a potential U are:

$$m(\ddot{r}-r\dot{\varphi}^2\sin^2\theta-r\dot{\theta}^2)+\frac{\partial U}{\partial r} = 0,$$

$$m(r^2\ddot{\theta}+2r\dot{r}\dot{\theta}-r^2\dot{\varphi}^2\sin\theta\cos\theta)+\frac{\partial U}{\partial\theta} = 0,$$

$$m(r^2\ddot{\varphi}\sin^2\theta+2r\dot{r}\dot{\varphi}\sin^2\theta+2r^2\dot{\theta}\dot{\varphi}\sin\theta\cos\theta)+\frac{\partial U}{\partial\varphi} = 0.$$

We can easily write them in the form

$$m\dot{v}_i = F_i$$

where the components of the force are the components of $-\nabla U$:

$$F_r = -\frac{\partial U}{\partial r}, \quad F_\theta = -\frac{1}{r}\frac{\partial U}{\partial\theta}, \quad F_\varphi = -\frac{1}{r\sin\theta}\frac{\partial U}{\partial\varphi}.$$

† Of course, in this case we have $\boldsymbol{H} = \text{curl}\,\boldsymbol{A} = 0$.

Hence we have

$$\dot{v}_r = \ddot{r} - r\dot{\varphi}^2 \sin^2\theta - r\dot{\theta}^2,$$
$$\dot{v}_\theta = r\ddot{\theta} + 2\dot{r}\dot{\theta} - r\dot{\varphi}^2 \sin\theta\cos\theta,$$
$$\dot{v}_\varphi = r\ddot{\varphi}\sin\theta + 2\dot{r}\dot{\varphi}\sin\theta + 2r\dot{\theta}\dot{\varphi}\cos\theta.$$

(b)

$$\dot{v}_i = \frac{1}{2h_i}\left(\frac{d}{dt}\frac{\partial}{\partial \dot{q}_i} - \frac{\partial}{\partial q_i}\right)\frac{d^2 s}{dt^2}$$
$$= h_i\ddot{q}_i + 2\sum_l \frac{\partial h_i}{\partial q_l}\dot{q}_i\dot{q}_l - \frac{1}{h_i}\sum_l h_l \frac{\partial h_l}{\partial q_i}\dot{q}_l^2.$$

4.19. (a) The Lagrangian

$$L = \tfrac{1}{2}m \sum_{i,j=1}^{3} g_{ij}\dot{q}_i\dot{q}_j - U(q),$$

with

$$g_{ij} = \sum_{k=1}^{3} \frac{\partial x_k}{\partial q_i}\frac{\partial x_k}{\partial q_j}, \qquad x_1 \equiv x,\ x_2 \equiv y,\ x_3 \equiv z,$$

leads to the equations

$$m\sum_{k=1}^{3} g_{sk}\ddot{q}_k + m\sum_{k,l=1}^{3} \Gamma_{s,kl}\dot{q}_k\dot{q}_l = -\frac{\partial U}{\partial q_s} \quad (s = 1, 2, 3), \tag{1}$$

where the

$$\Gamma_{s,kl} = \frac{1}{2}\left(\frac{\partial g_{sk}}{\partial q_l} + \frac{\partial g_{ls}}{\partial q_k} - \frac{\partial g_{kl}}{\partial q_s}\right)$$

are the so-called Christoffel symbols of the first kind.

(b) Using the notation $q_4(x, t) = t$ we can proceed as under (a) and obtain the same formulae, merely replacing $\sum_1^3$ by $\sum_1^4$.

What is the meaning of the terms in (1) which contain $\Gamma_{1,k4}$ $(k = 1, 2, 3, 4)$, if the q_i are Cartesian coordinates in a rotating frame of reference (see problem 4.8)?

4.20. The equations of motion are

$$-\mathcal{L}\dot{I} = \varphi_A - \varphi_B, \quad \dot{q}_2/C = \varphi_B - \varphi_A.$$

We shall assume that the potential source is a capacitor with a very large capacitance C_0 and that its charge at the time when $q_1 = 0$ is Q. The energy of the system including the potential source and the inductance is

$$E_0 = \frac{(Q+q_1)^2}{2C_0} + \frac{1}{2}\mathcal{L}\dot{q}_1^2.$$

Shifting the zero of the energy and considering the limit as $C_0 \to \infty$, $\lim_{C_0 \to \infty} Q/C_0 = U$, we get

$$E = E_0 - Q^2/2C_0 = Uq_1 + \tfrac{1}{2}\mathcal{L}\dot{q}_1^2.$$

This is the form of the energy which leads to the Lagrangian given in the problem.

Similar to this, the energy of a particle of mass m in a uniform force field $-F(t)$ is $\frac{1}{2}m\dot{x}^2 + Fx$.

The same Lagrangian may be obtained from that of an electromagnetic field including interactions between potentials and charges (Landau and Lifshitz, 1962, §§ 27, 28):

$$L = \frac{1}{8\pi}\int (E^2 - H^2)d^3r + \frac{1}{c}\int (A \cdot j)d^3r - \int \varphi\varrho d^3r = \frac{1}{8\pi}\int (H^2 - E^2)d^3r.$$

(using Gaussian units).

Generally speaking the electromagnetic field is a system with an infinite number of degrees of freedom. However, the fields inside the capacitor and inductance are specified by the charge q_2 or the current q_1. Therefore the Lagrangian can be expressed in terms of the electric field energy inside the capacitor as

$$\frac{1}{8\pi}\int E^2 d^3r = \frac{q_2^2}{2C},$$

and in terms of the magnetic field energy inside the inductance as

$$\frac{1}{8\pi}\int H^2 d^3r = \frac{1}{2}\mathcal{L}\dot{q}_1^2$$

(Landau and Lifshitz, 1960a, §§ 2, 32).

4.21. (a) $L = \frac{1}{2}\mathcal{L}\dot{q}_1^2 - (q_2^2/2C) + U(q_2 - q_1)$;

(b) $L = \frac{1}{2}\mathcal{L}\dot{q}^2 - q^2/2C$;

(c) $L = \dfrac{1}{2}\mathcal{L}_1\dot{q}_1^2 + \dfrac{1}{2}\mathcal{L}_2\dot{q}_2^2 - \dfrac{q_1^2}{2C_1} - \dfrac{q_2^2}{2C_2} - \dfrac{(q_1+q_2)^2}{2C}$.

4.22.

(a) $L = \dfrac{1}{2}ml^2\dot{\varphi}^2 + \dfrac{1}{2}\mathcal{L}\dot{q}^2 + mgl\cos\varphi - \dfrac{q^2}{2C(\varphi)}$;

(b) $L = \dfrac{1}{2}m\dot{x}^2 + \dfrac{1}{2}\mathcal{L}(x)\dot{q}^2 - \dfrac{1}{2}\varkappa x^2 + mgx - \dfrac{q^2}{2C}$.

4.23. Let φ be the angle of rotation of the frame around the AB-axis, such that $\varphi = 0$ gives the direction of the magnetic field; let $\dot{q}$ be the current in the frame (the positive direction is the one from A to D). The Lagrangian for the system is

$$L = \tfrac{1}{2}ma^2\dot{\varphi}^2 + \tfrac{1}{2}\mathscr{L}\dot{q}^2 + Ha^2\dot{q}\sin\varphi.$$

The integrals of motion are the energy,

$$E = \tfrac{1}{2}ma^2\dot{\varphi}^2 + \tfrac{1}{2}\mathscr{L}\dot{q}^2, \tag{1}$$

and the momentum conjugate to the cyclic coordinate q which is associated with the total magnetic flux through the frame,

$$\frac{\partial L}{\partial \dot{q}} = \mathscr{L}\dot{q} + Ha^2\sin\varphi = \Phi_0.$$

The current through the frame is thus uniquely determined by its position:

$$\dot{q} = (\Phi_0 - Ha^2\sin\varphi)/\mathscr{L}.$$

Substituting $\dot{q}$ into (1) we obtain

$$E = \tfrac{1}{2}ma^2\dot{\varphi}^2 + U_{\text{eff}}(\varphi), \quad U_{\text{eff}}(\varphi) = (\Phi_0 - Ha^2\sin\varphi)^2/2\mathscr{L}. \tag{2}$$

The problem of the system's motion is thus reduced to a one-dimensional one.

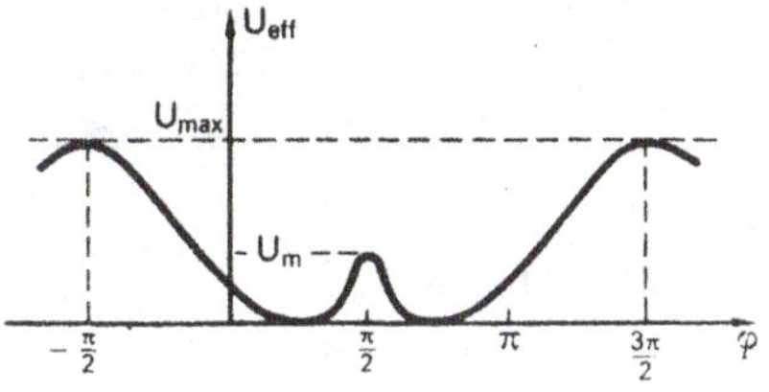

FIG. 86

Let us consider the case $0 < \Phi_0 < Ha^2$ in more detail. The function $U_{\text{eff}}(r)$ for this case is given in Fig. 86. One sees that when $E > U_{\max} = (\Phi_0 + Ha^2)^2/2\mathscr{L}$ the frame rotates and $\dot{\varphi}$ is a periodic function with period

$$T = \sqrt{2m}\,a\int_{-\pi/2}^{\pi/2}\frac{d\varphi}{\sqrt{E - U_{\text{eff}}(\varphi)}}.$$

When $U_{\max} > E > (\Phi_0 - Ha^2)^2/2\mathscr{L} = U_m$, the frame performs periodic oscillations within the angular interval $\varphi_1 < \varphi < \pi - \varphi_1$, where

$$\varphi_1 = \arcsin\frac{\Phi_0 - \sqrt{2\mathscr{L}E}}{Ha^2};$$

the period tends to infinity as $E \to U_{max}$ (see problem 1.5). When $0 < E < U_m$ one can have oscillations either in the interval $\varphi_1 < \varphi < \varphi_2$ or in the interval $\pi - \varphi_2 < \varphi < \pi - \varphi_1$, where

$$\varphi_2 = \arcsin \frac{\Phi_0 + \sqrt{2\mathcal{Q}E}}{Ha^2}.$$

How will the character of the frame's rotation change if one assumes it to have a small resistance?

4.24. (a) The equation of motion for the system can be obtained using a Lagrangian with an additional term responsible for the constraints (Goldstein, 1950, §§ 2–4)

$$L^* = \tfrac{1}{2}m(\dot{x}^2 + \dot{z}^2) - mgz + \lambda(z - ax^2),$$

where λ is a time-dependent Lagrangian multiplier. The equations of motion

$$m\ddot{x} = -2\lambda ax, \qquad (1)$$

$$m\ddot{z} - mg = \lambda, \qquad (2)$$

together with the equation of constraint $z = ax^2$, completely determine the motion of the particle.

On the right-hand side of equations (1) and (2) there are the components of the reaction force along the two axes: $R_x = -2\lambda ax$ and $R_z = \lambda$. They can be rewritten in terms of the coordinate and velocity of the particle with the help of the equation of constraint as follows:

$$R_x = -2axR_z, \quad R_z = \frac{(2a\dot{x}^2 - mg)m}{m + 4a^2x^2}.$$

(b)
$$\left.\begin{aligned} &m\ddot{r} - mg\cos\varphi - mr\dot{\varphi}^2 = \lambda, \\ &mr^2\ddot{\varphi} + 2mr\dot{r}\dot{\varphi} + mgr\sin\varphi = 0, \\ &r = l. \end{aligned}\right\}$$

The reaction force, $\lambda = mg\cos\varphi + ml\dot{\varphi}^2$ lies along $\boldsymbol{r}$.

4.25.

$$L^* = \tfrac{1}{2}m(r^2\dot{\varphi}^2 + \dot{r}^2) + mgr\cos\varphi + \lambda(\varphi - \Omega t);$$

$\lambda = 2mr\dot{r}\Omega + mgr\sin\Omega t$ is the generalised force (torque) corresponding to the coordinate φ.

4.26. (a) $\dot{E} = -\dfrac{\partial L}{\partial t} + \sum\limits_{i=1}^{s} \dot{q}_i R_i.$

(b) Using the transformation which is the inverse of the one for the velocities

$$\dot{q}_i = \sum_{k=1}^{s} \frac{\partial q_i}{\partial Q_k} \dot{Q}_k,$$

we obtain

$$R_i' = \sum_{k=1}^{s} \frac{\partial q_i}{\partial Q_k} R_k.$$

Therefore one can find the forces R_i in terms of any generalised coordinates if the constraint and friction forces are known in Cartesian coordinates. In particular, if the friction forces are given in terms of a dissipative function, $R_i = -\partial F/\partial \dot{q}_i$, the transformation of F is reduced to a change of variables.

4.27. The equations stated in this problem can be obtained by eliminating the λ_β from the following equations:

$$\frac{d}{dt}\frac{\partial L}{\partial \dot{q}_\beta} - \frac{\partial L}{\partial q_\beta} = \lambda_\beta, \quad \beta = 1, \ldots, r;$$

$$\frac{d}{dt}\frac{\partial L}{\partial \dot{q}_n} - \frac{\partial L}{\partial q_n} = -\sum_{\beta=1}^{r} \lambda_\beta b_{\beta n}, \quad n = r+1, \ldots, s.$$

The following relations must be taken into account:

$$\frac{\partial \tilde{L}}{\partial \dot{q}_n} = \frac{\partial L}{\partial \dot{q}_n} + \sum_{\beta=1}^{r} \frac{\partial L}{\partial \dot{q}_\beta} b_{\beta n},$$

$$\frac{\partial \tilde{L}}{\partial q_n} = \frac{\partial L}{\partial q_n} + \sum_{\beta=1}^{r} \sum_{m=r+1}^{s} \frac{\partial L}{\partial \dot{q}_\beta} \frac{\partial b_{\beta m}}{\partial q_n} \dot{q}_m.$$

Thus, the equations of motion for a system with non-holonomous constraints differ from the Lagrangian equations of motion although the constraint equations permit one to eliminate certain coordinates and velocities from the Lagrangian.

4.28. (a) Taking into account that q_n occurs both in L_n and in L_{n+1}, we obtain the Lagrangian equations of motion

$$\frac{d}{dt}\frac{\partial L}{\partial \dot{q}_n} = \frac{\partial L_n}{\partial q_n} + \frac{\partial L_n}{\partial(\Delta q_n)} - \frac{\partial L_{n+1}}{\partial(\Delta q_{n+1})}, \quad \Delta q_n = q_n - q_{n-1}, \qquad (1)$$

whence we find as $a \to 0$

$$\frac{1}{a}\frac{\partial L_n}{\partial \dot{q}_n} \to \frac{\partial \mathcal{L}}{\partial(\partial q/\partial t)}, \quad \frac{1}{a}\frac{\partial L_n}{\partial q_n} \to \frac{\partial \mathcal{L}}{\partial q},$$

$$\frac{1}{a}\left[\frac{\partial L_n}{\partial(\Delta q_n)} - \frac{\partial L_{n+1}}{\partial(\Delta q_{n+1})}\right] \to -\frac{\partial}{\partial x}\frac{\partial \mathcal{L}}{\partial(\partial q/\partial x)},$$

so that the equations (1) are reduced to the following equations:

$$\frac{\partial}{\partial t}\frac{\partial \mathcal{L}}{\partial(\partial q/\partial t)}+\frac{\partial}{\partial x}\frac{\partial \mathcal{L}}{\partial(\partial q/\partial x)}=\frac{\partial \mathcal{L}}{\partial q}. \tag{2}$$

Here $\partial/\partial t$ and $\partial/\partial x$ should be applied to the function $q(x, t)$ and its derivatives. For a continuous system the variable x indicates a fixed point on the string.

We do not consider the physical consequences of the equations (2) since systems with an infinite number of degrees of freedom are the subject of field theory, but not of mechanics (see ter Haar, 1964, Ch. 8; Landau and Lifshitz, 1962, § 32).

(b) $E = \int\left\{\frac{\partial \mathcal{L}}{\partial(\partial q/\partial t)}\frac{\partial q}{\partial t}-\mathcal{L}\right\}\partial x.$

4.29. The Lagrangian is

$$L=\frac{1}{2}mv^2-U(\boldsymbol{r})+\frac{e}{c}(\boldsymbol{A}(\boldsymbol{r})\cdot\boldsymbol{v}),$$

where $\boldsymbol{A}(\boldsymbol{r})$ is the vector potential of the magnetic field, $\boldsymbol{H} = \operatorname{curl}\boldsymbol{A}$ (of course, $\boldsymbol{A}(\boldsymbol{r})$ can always be taken as a homogeneous function of the coordinates of degree $n+1$). If as a result of the similarity transformation, $\boldsymbol{r}\to\alpha\boldsymbol{r}$, $t\to\alpha^{1-\frac{1}{2}k}t$, the transformation of the vector potential is the same as that for the velocity, that is, $n=\frac{1}{2}k$, we have $L\to\alpha^k L$. Therefore, the equations of motion remain invariant after this transformation and the principle of mechanical similarity holds (see Landau and Lifshitz, 1960, § 10).

It is clear that the principle of mechanical similarity remains valid for a magnetic field if it is constant in space and if its value changes by a factor $\alpha^{\frac{1}{2}k-1}$ under a similarity transformation (see, for example, the following problems about an oscillator in a magnetic field: 2.27–2.29, 6.23).

4.30. The kinetic energy of the system is

$$T=\sum_a \tfrac{1}{2}m_a v_a^2,$$

so that

$$2T=\sum\left(\frac{\partial T}{\partial \boldsymbol{v}_a}\cdot\boldsymbol{v}_a\right)=\frac{d}{dt}\left(\sum m_a(\boldsymbol{v}_a\cdot\boldsymbol{r}_a)\right)-\sum(\boldsymbol{r}_a\cdot m_a\dot{\boldsymbol{v}}_a).$$

The term $(d/dt)(\sum m_a(\boldsymbol{v}_a \cdot \boldsymbol{r}_a))$ which is the total time derivative with respect of time of a bounded function becomes zero after averaging over large time interval (Landau and Lifshitz, 1960, § 10). Substituting

$$m_a \dot{\boldsymbol{v}}_a = -\frac{\partial U}{\partial \boldsymbol{r}_a} + \frac{e_a}{c}[\boldsymbol{v}_a \wedge \boldsymbol{H}]$$

into the second term and averaging over the time we obtain

$$\left\langle 2T + \left(\boldsymbol{H} \cdot \sum \frac{e_a}{c}[\boldsymbol{r}_a \wedge \boldsymbol{v}_a]\right)\right\rangle = k\langle U\rangle,$$

where the pointed brackets indicate the time averaging. In particular, if the magnetic field $\boldsymbol{H}$ does not change with time and $e_a/m_a = e/m$, we have

$$2\langle T\rangle + \frac{e}{mc}(\boldsymbol{H} \cdot \langle \boldsymbol{M}\rangle) = k\langle U\rangle,$$

where

$$\boldsymbol{M} = \sum m[\boldsymbol{r}_a \wedge \boldsymbol{v}_a]$$

is the angular momentum of the system.

5. Small Oscillations of Systems with One Degree of Freedom

5.1.

(a)
$$\omega^2 = \frac{V\alpha^2}{m}\sqrt{1-\left(\frac{F}{V\alpha}\right)^2};$$

a minimum in U occurs when $F < V\alpha$.

(b)
$$\omega^2 = \frac{8\pi}{3}\frac{V\alpha^4}{m}x_0^2\left(\frac{\Gamma(3/4)}{\Gamma(1/4)}\right)^2,$$

where the amplitude x_0 is determined from the equation

$$E = \tfrac{1}{2}m\dot{x}^2 + \tfrac{1}{3}V\alpha^4 x^4 = \tfrac{1}{3}V\alpha^4 x_0^4.$$

5.2. The Lagrangian of the system is (see Landau and Lifshitz, 1960, § 5, problem 4):

$$L = ma^2[\dot{\theta}^2(1+2\sin^2\theta) + \Omega^2\sin^2\theta + 2\Omega_0^2\cos^2\theta],$$

where we have introduced $\Omega_0^2 = 2g/a$.

When $\Omega > \Omega_0$ the potential energy of the system, $U = -ma^2(\Omega^2 \sin^2\theta + 2\Omega_0^2 \cos\theta)$ has a minimum when $\cos\theta_0 = \Omega_0^2/\Omega^2$. Expanding U in the neighbourhood of θ_0, and in the kinetic energy putting

$$1+2\sin^2\theta = 1+2\sin^2\theta_0 = 3-2(\Omega_0/\Omega)^4 \equiv M/2ma^2,$$

we get

$$L = \tfrac{1}{2}M\dot{x}^2 - \tfrac{1}{2}\varkappa x^2,$$

where $\varkappa = U''(\theta_0)$, $x = \theta-\theta_0$. Hence we get

$$\omega^2 = \frac{\varkappa}{M} = \Omega^2 \frac{1-\Omega_0^4/\Omega^4}{3-2\Omega_0^4/\Omega^4}.$$

When $\Omega \gg \Omega_0$, the oscillation frequency is proportional to the angular velocity, $\omega \approx \Omega/\sqrt{3}$ and $\theta_0 \approx \pi/2$; when $\Omega \to \Omega_0$, small oscillations occur with a frequency $\omega \to 0$ and $\theta_0 \to 0$.

If $\Omega < \Omega_0$, one can consider oscillations near $\theta_0 = 0$ for elastic collisions of the lateral particles; $\omega^2 = \Omega_0^2 - \Omega^2$ $(\Omega < \Omega_0)$.

If $\Omega = \Omega_0$, U has a minimum at $\theta_0 = 0$ and in the neighbourhood of it, we can write $U = ma^2\Omega_0^2(-2+\frac{1}{4}\theta^4)$, that is the oscillations are non-linear in an essential way. Retaining also in the kinetic energy terms up to the fourth order, we get

$$\frac{2\pi}{\omega} = T = 8\int_0^{\theta_m} \frac{\sqrt{1+2\theta^2}\,d\theta}{\sqrt{\Omega_0^2(\theta_m^4-\theta^4)}}.$$

Here θ_m is the amplitude of the oscillations (see Landau and Lifshitz, 1960, § 11, problem 2a).

5.3. $\omega^2 = (3g/R)(1-x_0^2)$, where $x_0 = \sqrt[3]{(q^2/8mgR)^2}$. When $x_0 > 1$, the point A is a position of stable equilibrium, but for $x_0 < 1$, it is unstable. The position of stable equilibrium φ_0 for $x_0 < 1$ is determined by the condition $\sin\frac{1}{2}\varphi_0 = x_0$.

5.4. $r = r_0 + a\cos\omega(t-t_0)$,

$$\varphi = \varphi_0 + \Omega(t-t_0) - (2a/r_0)(\Omega/\omega)\sin\omega(t-t_0),$$

where r_0, φ_0, a, and t_0 are integration constants ($a \ll r_0$), and

$$\Omega = \sqrt{\frac{n\alpha}{m}}\, r_0^{-\frac{1}{2}(n+2)}, \qquad \omega = \Omega\sqrt{2-n}.$$

5.5. At the point $\theta = \theta_0$ the effective potential energy

$$U_{\text{eff}}(\theta) = \frac{M_z^2}{2ml^2 \sin^2 \theta} - mgl \cos \theta$$

(Landau and Lifshitz, 1960, § 14, problem 1) has a minimum, so that $U'_{\text{eff}}(\theta_0) = 0$.

We thus obtain

$$M_z^2 = \frac{m^2 l^3 g \sin^4 \theta_0}{\cos \theta_0},$$

and the frequency of small oscillations is

$$\omega(\theta_0) = \sqrt{\frac{U''_{\text{eff}}(\theta_0)}{ml^2}} = \sqrt{\frac{g}{l} \frac{1+3\cos^2\theta_0}{\cos\theta_0}}.$$

For this calculation to be applicable the condition

$$\tfrac{1}{2} U''_{\text{eff}}(\theta_0)\,(\Delta\theta)^2 \gg \tfrac{1}{6} |U'''_{\text{eff}}(\theta_0)|\,(\Delta\theta)^3,$$

with $\Delta\theta$ the oscillation amplitude, must be satisfied. If $\theta_0 \sim 1$, it is satisfied for $\Delta\theta \ll 1$. If, however, $\theta_0 \ll 1$, we have $U'''_{\text{eff}}(\theta_0) \propto 1/\theta_0$, and the oscillations in θ can be considered to be small only when $\Delta\theta \ll \theta_0$. The result obtained, $\omega = 2\sqrt{g/l}$, is nevertheless valid also for $\Delta\theta \sim \theta_0$, when the oscillations in x and y are no longer harmonic. Indeed, in this case small oscillations with frequency $\sqrt{g/l}$ occur along the x- and y-axes, that is, the pendulum moves along an ellipse executing two oscillations in θ for each revolution (Landau and Lifshitz, 1960, § 23, problem 3).

5.6. The effective potential energy for radial oscillations of the molecule is

$$U_{\text{eff}} = \tfrac{1}{2} m\omega_0^2 (r - r_0)^2 + M^2/2mr^2,$$

where r is the distance between the atoms and m the reduced mass. The extra term which is assumed to be a small correction leads to a small shift in the equilibrium position $\delta r_0 = M^2/m^2\omega_0^2 r_0^3$. We determine the shift in the frequency by expanding U_{eff} in a series near $r_0 + \delta r_0$:

$$U_{\text{eff}} = \frac{1}{2} m\omega_0^2 (r - r_0 - \delta r_0)^2 + \frac{M^2}{2mr_0^2} + \frac{3M^2}{2mr_0^4}(r - r_0 - \delta r_0)^2.$$

We get from this a correction to the frequency:

$$\delta\omega = 3M^2/2m^2\omega_0 r_0^4.$$

5.7. (a) We get for the displacement from the equilibrium position: $x = x_0 \cos \omega t + (\dot{x}_0/\omega) \sin \omega t = \sqrt{[x_0^2 + (\dot{x}_0/\omega)^2]} \cos(\omega t + \varphi)$, $\tan \varphi = -\dot{x}_0/\omega x_0$, $\omega^2 = 2\varkappa/m$.

(b) Let the tension in each spring be f. For small displacements $|y| \ll \sqrt{fl/\varkappa}$, where l is the separation between the points where the springs are fixed, the oscillations are harmonic, $y = A \cos(\omega t + \varphi)$, and $\omega^2 = 2f/ml$. When $f = \varkappa l$, the oscillation frequency is equal to that in part (a). In the case of springs in which there is no tension ($f = 0$) the oscillations are non-linear, the restoring force is $F = -\varkappa y^3/l^2$, and the frequency (compare problem 5.1b) is $\omega = [\sqrt{\pi}\Gamma(\frac{3}{4})/\Gamma(\frac{1}{4})]\sqrt{2\varkappa/m}\,(y_m/l)$, where y_m is the amplitude of the oscillations.

If the mass can move in the xy-plane, its motion—for the case when $f \neq 0$ and x and y are small—consists of harmonic oscillations along the x- and y-axes with frequencies $\omega_x^2 = 2\varkappa/m$ and $\omega_y^2 = 2f/ml$, respectively (see problem 6.3).

5.8. Let y be the coordinate of the mass reckoned from the upper suspension point, and $2l$ the distance between the two suspension points. The Lagrangian of the system,

$$L = \frac{1}{2} m\dot{y}^2 - \varkappa(y-l)^2 + mgy = \frac{1}{2} m\dot{y}^2 - \varkappa\left(y - l - \frac{mg}{2\varkappa}\right)^2 + \text{constant},$$

describes a harmonic oscillator with frequency $\omega^2 = 2\varkappa/m$ and equilibrium position $y_0 = l + mg/2\varkappa$, so that $y = y_0 + A\cos(\omega t + \varphi)$. If we take the displacement from the equilibrium position as coordinate, we can eliminate the gravity potential from the Lagrangian.

5.9. For the angle between the pendulum and the vertical we have

$$\varphi = \frac{a\Omega^2 \cos \Omega t}{g - l\Omega^2}, \quad a\Omega^2 \ll |g - l\Omega^2|.$$

5.10. The result

$$I = \frac{dq}{dt} = \frac{U_0 \sin(\omega t - \varphi)}{\sqrt{R^2 + (\omega\mathcal{L} - 1/\omega C)^2}}, \quad \tan \varphi = \frac{\omega\mathcal{L} - 1/\omega C}{R},$$

can be obtained by solving the Lagrangian equations of motion for q. The Lagrangian of the system is (see problem 4.21) $L = \frac{1}{2}\mathcal{L}\dot{q}^2 - q^2/2C$, and the dissipative function is equal to $\frac{1}{2}R\dot{q}^2$ (compare Landau and Lifshitz, 1960a, §§ 48, 32).

5.11. The general solution of the equation of motion (see Landau and Lifshitz, 1960, § 26)

$$\ddot{x}+2\lambda\dot{x}+\omega_0^2 x = \frac{F}{m}\cos\gamma t,$$

under such conditions that $\omega^2 = \omega_0^2-\lambda^2 > 0$, has the form

$$x(t) = e^{-\lambda t}(a\cos\omega t+b\sin\omega t)$$
$$+\frac{F}{m[(\omega_0^2-\gamma^2)^2+4\lambda^2\gamma^2]}[(\omega_0^2-\gamma^2)\cos\gamma t-2\lambda\gamma\sin\gamma t],$$

where a and b are constants to be determined from the initial conditions. If we put $x(0) = \dot{x}(0) = 0$, we find finally

$$x(t) = \frac{F}{m[(\omega_0^2-\gamma^2)^2+4\lambda^2\gamma^2]}\Big\{(\omega_0^2-\gamma^2)(\cos\gamma t-e^{-\lambda t}\cos\omega t)$$
$$+2\lambda\gamma[\sin\gamma t-\frac{\omega_0^2+\gamma^2}{2\gamma\omega}e^{-\lambda t}\sin\omega t]\Big\}. \qquad (1)$$

Let us study this solution in the region near resonance, $\gamma = \omega+\varepsilon$, $|\varepsilon| \ll \omega$. If there is no friction at all, that is, $\lambda = 0$, the motion of the oscillator near resonance will show beats:

$$x = -\frac{F}{m\omega_0\varepsilon}\sin\tfrac{1}{2}\varepsilon t\sin\omega_0 t, \qquad (2)$$

where the amplitude and the frequency of the beats are determined by how near resonance we are (Fig. 87a). However, when $\gamma = \omega_0$, that is, at exact resonance, we get by letting $\varepsilon \to 0$:

$$x = -(F/2m\omega_0)t\sin\omega_0 t, \qquad (3)$$

that is, we get oscillations with an amplitude $a(t)$ which increases indefinitely as $a(t) = (F/2m\omega_0)t$ (see Fig. 87b).

When there is even a small amount of friction ($\lambda \ll \omega_0$) the character of the motion changes qualitatively. From (1) we get easily in the case when $\lambda \ll |\varepsilon|$ instead of (2)

$$x(t) = -\frac{F}{2m\omega_0\varepsilon}\sqrt{1-2e^{-\lambda t}\cos\varepsilon t-e^{-2\lambda t}}\cos(\omega_0 t+\varphi_1(t)). \qquad (4)$$

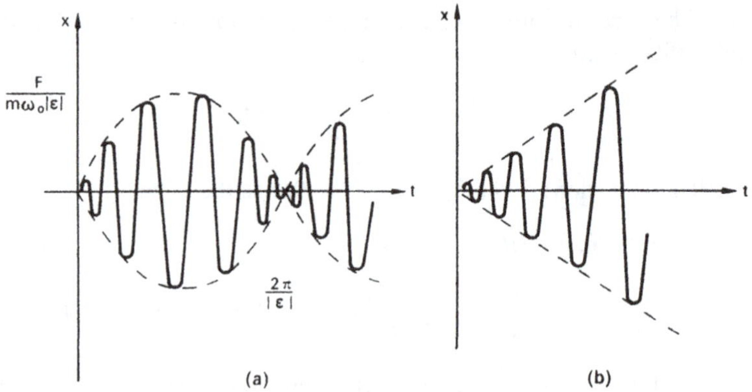

FIG. 87

Here $\varphi_1(t)$ is the phase of the oscillations which changes slowly with time. The amplitude of the oscillations oscillates slowly with a frequency $|\varepsilon|$ about the value $F/2m\omega_0|\varepsilon|$, gradually approaching that value (see Fig. 88a). It is interesting that during the transient stage the amplitude may reach twice the value of the amplitude of the steady-state oscillations.

When $|\varepsilon| \ll \lambda \ll \omega_0$,

$$x(t) = \frac{F}{2m\omega_0\lambda}(1-e^{-\lambda t})\cos(\omega_0 t+\varphi_2(t)). \tag{5}$$

In that case we have a transient process with a smoothly increasing amplitude which asymptotically approaches the value $F/2m\omega_0\lambda$ which is determined by the friction coefficient λ (see Fig. 88b). Finally, if the quantities ε and λ are of the same order of magnitude, $|\varepsilon| \approx \lambda < \omega_0$, we get oscillations of the amplitude around the value $F/2m\omega_0|\varepsilon|\sqrt{2}$ which corresponds to the steady-state oscillations which are reached very

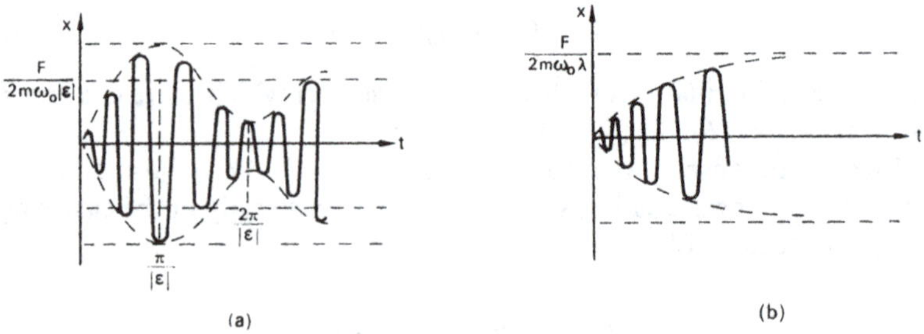

FIG. 88

slowly (see Fig. 89 for the case when $\varepsilon = \lambda$). The system thus proceeds to steady-state oscillations for these three cases (Figs. 88 and 89) over a time of the order of $t \sim 1/\lambda$, as is clear from (1).

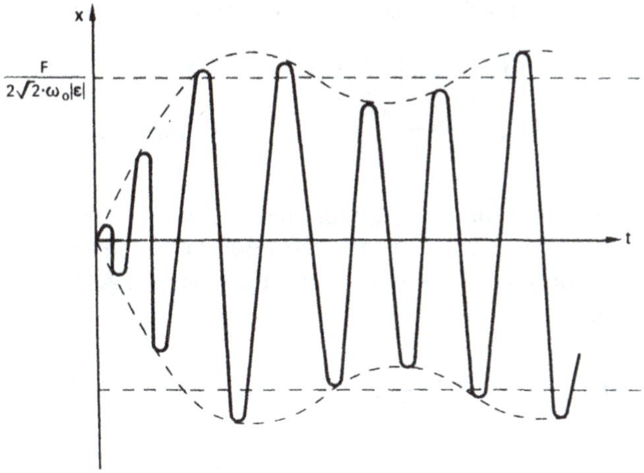

FIG. 89

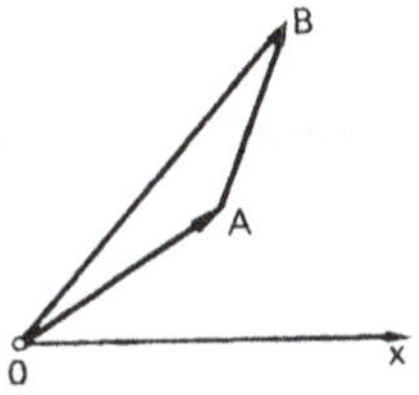

FIG. 90

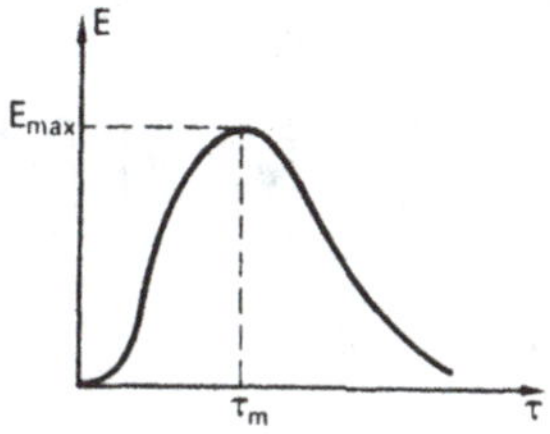

FIG. 91

One can use a vector diagram (see Fig. 90) to study qualitatively how the oscillations proceed to a steady state (transient process). The forced oscillation is depicted by the component of the vector $\boldsymbol{OA}$, which rotates with an angular velocity γ, onto the x-axis. The vector of the free oscillation, $\boldsymbol{AB}$, rotates with angular velocity ω, and its length decreases as $e^{-\lambda t}$. At $t = 0$, $\boldsymbol{OA}+\boldsymbol{AB} \approx 0$.

What is the nature of the transient process, if $x(0) = 0$, $\dot{x}(0) \neq 0$?

5.12. (a) The energy acquired by the oscillator,

$$E = \frac{\pi F^2}{2m}\tau^2 e^{-\frac{1}{2}(\omega\tau)^2},$$

depends on how fast the force is switched on (that is, on the parameter $\omega\tau$). For an instantaneous impact, $\omega\tau \ll 1$, or a very slow switching on, $\omega\tau \gg 1$, the energy transfer is small, while the maximum energy transfer, $E_m = \pi F^2/me\omega^2$, is reached when $\tau_m = \sqrt{2}/\omega$ (see Fig. 91).

(b) If $x \to a\cos(\omega t+\varphi)$, as $t \to \infty$,† we have

$$\Delta E = E(+\infty)-E(-\infty) = \frac{\pi F^2}{2m}\tau^2 e^{-\frac{1}{2}(\omega\tau)^2} - a\omega\tau F\sqrt{\pi}\, e^{-\frac{1}{4}(\omega\tau)^2}\sin\varphi.$$

Depending on the value of φ, the oscillator gains or loses energy. This change in energy is similar to the absorption or stimulated emission of light by an atom. When we average over the phase φ we get the same result as under (a).

5.13. (a)
$$x(t) = \frac{1}{2\mu}[\xi_1(t)+\xi_2(t)],$$

where

$$\xi_{1,2} = e^{\pm\mu t}\left[\int_0^t \frac{F(\tau)}{m}e^{\mp\mu\tau}d\tau+\dot{x}_0\mp\mu x_0\right].$$

(b)
$$x(t) = \frac{1}{\omega}\,\mathrm{Im}\left\{e^{i\omega t-\lambda t}\left[\int_0^t \frac{F(\tau)}{m}e^{\lambda\tau-i\omega\tau}d\tau+\dot{x}_0+(i\omega+\lambda)x_0\right]\right\},$$

where $\omega = \sqrt{\omega_0^2-\lambda^2}$.

5.14. The force

$$F(t) = -\nabla U(|r-r_0(t)|) \tag{1}$$

is acting upon the oscillator; here $r(t)$ is the deflection of the mass of the oscillator and $r_0(t)$ the radius vector of the impinging particle. Assuming that the particle is little deflected, we can put $r_0(t) = \rho+vt$ with ρ being the impact parameter ($\rho \perp v$). Assuming also that the amplitude of the vibrations of the oscillator is small we can put $r=0$ in (1) (after differentiating) and then

$$F(t) = 2\varkappa^2 V(\rho+vt)e^{-\varkappa^2\rho^2-\varkappa^2 v^2 t^2}. \tag{2}$$

† The meaning of φ is that of the "impact phase", that is, the phase which the oscillator would have had at $t = 0$, if there were no force acting upon it.

The oscillations along ρ and v are independent and the corresponding energy excitations are equal to

$$\frac{1}{2m}\left|\int_{-\infty}^{+\infty} F_{\varrho}(t)^{-i\omega t}\,dt\right|^2 \quad \text{and} \quad \frac{1}{2m}\left|\int_{-\infty}^{+\infty} F_{v}(t)e^{-i\omega t}\,dt\right|^2,$$

where F_{ϱ} and F_{v} are the components of F in the directions of ρ and v. The total energy excitation of the oscillator is†

$$\varepsilon = \frac{\pi V^2}{2E}(x+a)e^{-(x+a)}, \tag{3}$$

where

$$a = \frac{1}{2}\left(\frac{\omega}{\varkappa v}\right)^2, \quad x = 2(\varkappa\varrho)^2, \quad E = \tfrac{1}{2}mv^2.$$

The cross-section for exciting the oscillator to an energy between ε and $\varepsilon + d\varepsilon$ is

$$d\sigma = \pi\sum_k |d\varrho_k^2| = \frac{\pi}{2\varkappa^2}\frac{d\varepsilon}{\varepsilon}\sum_k\left|\frac{a+x_k(\varepsilon)}{1-a-x_k(\varepsilon)}\right|, \tag{4}$$

where the $x_k(\varepsilon)$ are the roots of equation (3). For a further consideration it is most convenient to solve (3) graphically, in the same way as was done in problem 3.10(a). When $\varepsilon \ll \varepsilon_1 = (\pi V^2/2E)ae^{-a}$, we get $d\sigma = (\pi/2\varkappa^2)(d\varepsilon/\varepsilon)$ (in equation (4) we assume that $x_k(\varepsilon) \gg 1, a$). For large ε the result depends on the value of a. If $a > 1$, we can only have $\varepsilon < \varepsilon_1$ (see Fig. 92a;

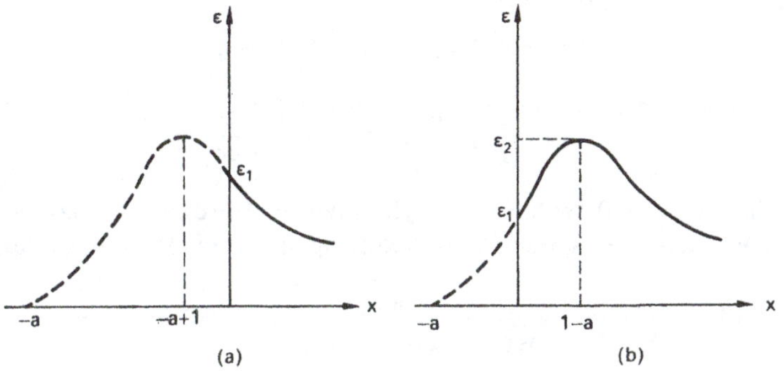

FIG. 92

† It is interesting to note that $\varepsilon(\omega)$ is the same function of ω as the spectral radiation density of a fast electron in a potential $U(r)$.

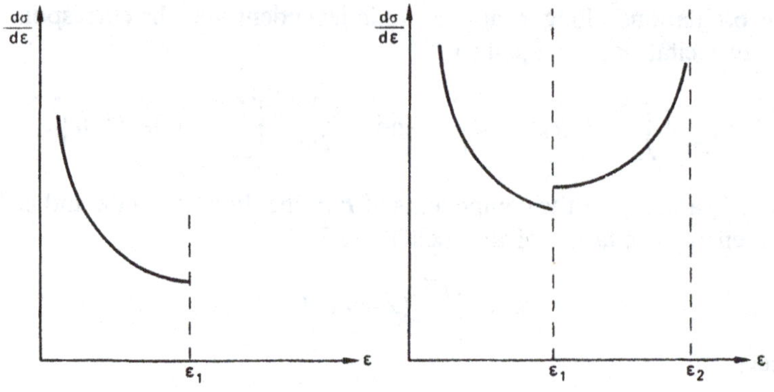

(a) (b)

FIG. 93

for the cross-section see Fig. 93a). However, if $a < 1$ we can have $\varepsilon < \varepsilon_2 = (\pi V^2/2Ee)$ (see Fig. 92b) and at $\varepsilon = \varepsilon_1$ the function $d\sigma/d\varepsilon$ will have a discontinuity while for $\varepsilon_2 - \varepsilon \ll \varepsilon_2$ it has an integrable singularity,

$$d\sigma = \frac{\pi}{\varkappa^2\sqrt{2}} \frac{d\varepsilon}{\varepsilon_2} \frac{1}{\sqrt{1-\varepsilon/\varepsilon_2}}$$

(see Fig. 93b).

5.15. If the oscillator has an "impact phase" φ (see problem 5.12(b)), we get, by repeating the calculations of the preceding problem, for the energy of the oscillator the expression (ε_0 is the initial energy of the oscillator)

$$\varepsilon = \varepsilon_1 e^{-2(\varkappa\varrho)^2} + 2\sqrt{\varepsilon_1\varepsilon_0}\, e^{-(\varkappa\varrho)^2}\cos\varphi + \varepsilon_0, \tag{1}$$

where

$$\varepsilon_1 = \frac{\pi}{4E}\left(\frac{V\omega}{\varkappa v}\right)^2 \exp\left[-\frac{1}{2}\left(\frac{\omega}{\varkappa v}\right)^2\right]$$

When $\cos\varphi > 0$, we have $\varepsilon > \varepsilon_0$ for all ϱ, while we can also have values $\varrho_{1,2}$ such that $\varepsilon < \varepsilon_0$, if $\cos\varphi < 0$. Solving equation (1) for ϱ^2 we find

$$\varrho^2 = \frac{1}{\varkappa^2}\ln\left[\frac{\sqrt{\varepsilon_1/\varepsilon_0}}{-\cos\varphi + \sqrt{\varepsilon/\varepsilon_0 - \sin^2\varphi}}\right], \quad \text{when} \quad \varepsilon > \varepsilon_0;$$

$$\varrho_{1,2}^2 = \frac{1}{\varkappa^2}\ln\left[\frac{\sqrt{\varepsilon_1/\varepsilon_0}}{|\cos\varphi| \pm \sqrt{\varepsilon/\varepsilon_0 - \sin^2\varphi}}\right],$$

when $\cos\varphi < 0$ and $\varepsilon_0 > \varepsilon > \varepsilon_{min} = \varepsilon_0 \sin^2\varphi$.

Hence we have

$$d\sigma = \pi \left| \frac{d\varrho^2}{d\varepsilon} \right| d\varepsilon = \frac{\pi}{2\varkappa^2} \frac{d\varepsilon}{\varepsilon_0} \frac{1}{\varepsilon/\varepsilon_0 - \sin^2\varphi - \cos\varphi\sqrt{\varepsilon/\varepsilon_0 - \sin^2\varphi}}, \quad (2)$$

when $\varepsilon > \varepsilon_0$, and

$$d\sigma = \pi \frac{d(-\varrho_1^2 + \varrho_2^2)}{d\varepsilon} d\varepsilon = \frac{\pi}{\varkappa^2} \frac{d\varepsilon}{\varepsilon_0} \frac{|\cos\varphi|}{(1-\varepsilon/\varepsilon_0)\sqrt{\varepsilon/\varepsilon_0 - \sin^2\varphi}}, \quad (3)$$

when $\varepsilon_0 > \varepsilon > \varepsilon_0 \sin^2\varphi$ and $\cos\varphi < 0$.

Averaging over all possible phases φ for a given ε, we get

$$\left\langle \frac{d\sigma}{d\varepsilon} \right\rangle = \frac{\pi}{2\varkappa^2} \frac{d\varepsilon}{|\varepsilon_0 - \varepsilon|} \quad (4)$$

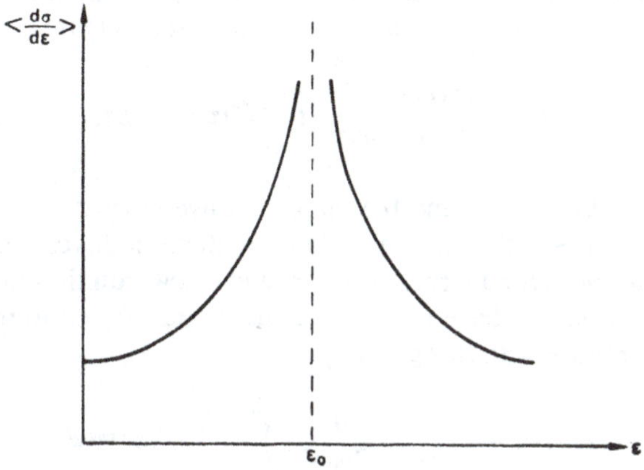

FIG. 94

(see Fig. 94). The averaging is performed, using the formulae

$$\left\langle \frac{d\sigma}{d\varepsilon} \right\rangle = \frac{1}{2\pi} \int_0^{2\pi} \frac{d\sigma}{d\varepsilon} d\varphi, \quad \text{when} \quad \varepsilon > \varepsilon_0;$$

$$\left\langle \frac{d\sigma}{d\varepsilon} \right\rangle = \frac{1}{2\pi} \int_{-\alpha}^{+\alpha} \frac{d\sigma}{d\varepsilon} d\varphi, \quad \text{when} \quad \varepsilon < \varepsilon_0. \quad \text{Here} \quad \alpha = \arcsin \sqrt{\frac{\varepsilon}{\varepsilon_0}}.$$

The singularity of the cross-sections (2), (3), and (4), as $\varepsilon \to \varepsilon_0$, is connected with the fact that the oscillator is excited for any, however large, ϱ. What is the cause of the additional singularity in (3) and why does it not appear in (4)?

5.16. We have the Lagrangian

$$L = \tfrac{1}{2}m\dot{x}^2 - \tfrac{1}{2}m\omega^2x^2 + xF(t).$$

We then have for the energy of the system

$$E(t) = \tfrac{1}{2}m(\mathrm{Re}\,\xi)^2 + \tfrac{1}{2}m(\mathrm{Im}\,\xi)^2 - \frac{F(t)}{\omega}\,\mathrm{Im}\,\xi = \tfrac{1}{2}m\left|\xi - \frac{iF(t)}{m\omega}\right|^2 - \frac{F^2(t)}{2m\omega^2}$$

where

$$\xi = \dot{x} + i\omega x = e^{i\omega t}\int_{-\infty}^{t} e^{-i\omega\tau}(F(\tau)/m)\,d\tau \tag{1}$$

(see Landau and Lifshitz, 1960, § 22). Although the expression for the energy has a well-defined limit as $t \to \infty$, the integral defining $\xi(t)$ has no limit as $t \to \infty$ (since $F(\tau) \to F_0$ as $\tau \to \infty$). Integrating (1) by parts, we get

$$\xi(t) = \frac{iF(t)}{m\omega_0} - \frac{ie^{i\omega t}}{m\omega}\int_{-\infty}^{t} F'(\tau)e^{-i\omega\tau}\,d\tau, \tag{2}$$

where $F'(\tau) \to 0$, as $\tau \to \infty$ and the integral converges as $t \to \infty$. It is clear from (2) that as $t \to \infty$ the motion of the oscillator is in this case a harmonic oscillation (the second term in (2)), around a new equilibrium position $x_0 = F_0/m\omega^2$ (the first term in (2)). The energy transferred to the oscillator is in accordance with this given by

$$E(+\infty) = -\frac{F_0^2}{2m\omega^2} + \frac{1}{2m\omega^2}\left|\int_{-\infty}^{+\infty} F'(\tau)e^{-i\omega\tau}\,d\tau\right|^2.$$

5.17.

$$\Delta E = E(\infty) + -E(-\infty) = -\frac{F_0^2}{2m\omega^2} + \frac{\lambda^4F_0^2}{2m\omega^2(\lambda^2+\omega^2)^2} - \frac{a\lambda^2F_0\cos\varphi}{\lambda^2+\omega^2},$$

$$E_0 = \tfrac{1}{2}m\omega^2a^2,$$

φ is the impact phase.

5.18. If in the formula (see Landau and Lifshitz, 1960, § 22)

$$\xi(\tau) = \xi(0)e^{i\omega\tau} + \frac{e^{i\omega\tau}}{m}\int_0^{\tau} F(t)e^{-i\omega\tau}\,dt$$

we integrate by parts n times, we get

$$\xi(\tau) = \xi(0)e^{i\omega\tau} + \frac{iF_0}{m\omega} + \frac{F^{(n)}(+0)e^{i\omega\tau} - F^{(n)}(\tau-0)}{m(i\omega)^{n+1}}$$
$$+ \frac{e^{i\omega\tau}}{m(i\omega)^{n+1}} \int_0^\tau F^{(n+1)}(t)e^{-i\omega\tau}\,dt.$$

Here $|\xi(0)| = a_0\omega$, where a_0 is the amplitude of the oscillations at the moment the force is switched on. The penultimate term in this formula is of order of magnitude $(F_0/m\omega)(\omega\tau)^{-n}$, while the last term is, generally speaking, considerably smaller—provided $F^{(n+1)}(t)$ changes smoothly. The square of the amplitude of the oscillations $|\xi-(iF_0/m\omega)|^2/\omega^2$ is for $t > \tau$ of order of magnitude $[a_0+\{F_0(\omega\tau)^{-n}/m\omega^2\}]^2$. If the force $F(t)$ is switched on slowly and smoothly, the energy transferred is thus very small.

5.19. (a) During the time interval $0 \leqq t \leqq \tau$ the oscillations have the form

$$x(t) = \frac{F}{m\omega^2}\,\frac{t}{\tau} + B\sin\omega t + C\cos\omega t.$$

The oscillations will be stable if $x(\tau) = x(0)$ and $\dot{x}(\tau) = \dot{x}(0)$. This condition leads to the following set of equations

$$\frac{F}{m\omega^2} + B\sin\omega\tau + C(\cos\omega\tau - 1) = 0,$$
$$B(\cos\omega\tau - 1) - C\sin\omega\tau = 0, \tag{1}$$

which determines the constants B and C. Thus we have for $0 \leqq t \leqq \tau$

$$x(t) = \frac{F}{m\omega^2}\left[\frac{t}{\tau} - \frac{\sin(\omega t - \frac{1}{2}\omega\tau)}{2\sin\frac{1}{2}\omega\tau}\right]. \tag{2}$$

However, if t lies in the interval $n\tau \leqq t \leqq (n+1)\tau$, where n is an integer, we must replace t on the right-hand side of (2) by $t' = t - n\tau$ $(0 \leqq t' \leqq \tau)$.

When $\omega\tau$ is close to an integral number times 2π the second term in (2) turns out to be very large—a case which is close to resonance. When $\omega\tau = 2\pi l$ (l an integer), there can be no stable oscillations—the set (1) is inconsistent.†

† If we write the force as a Fourier series

$$F(t) = \tfrac{1}{2}F - \sum_{l=1}^{\infty} \frac{F}{\pi l}\sin\frac{2\pi l t}{\tau}$$

we see that each harmonic term in the force which is acting can cause a resonance build-up. When $\tau = 2\pi l/\omega$ we have for sufficiently large t (how large?), $x(t) \sim -(Ft/2\pi m\omega l)\sin\omega t$.

(b)

$$x(t) = \frac{1}{\omega}\,\mathrm{Im}\left[\frac{iF}{m\omega} + \frac{F}{m(\lambda+i\omega)}\,e^{-\lambda t} + Ae^{i\omega t}\right],$$

$$A = -\frac{F}{m(\lambda+i\omega)}\,\frac{1-e^{-\lambda\tau}}{1-e^{i\omega\tau}},$$

when $0 \leqq t \leqq \tau$, while for $n\tau \leqq t \leqq (n+1)\tau$ we must replace on the right-hand side t by $t' = t-n\tau$.

(c) When $\omega_0 = 1/\sqrt{\mathscr{L}C} > \lambda = R/2\mathscr{L}$ the stable current is

$$I(t) = \frac{-1}{\sqrt{\omega_0^2-\lambda^2}}\,\frac{V}{\mathscr{L}}\,\mathrm{Im}\left[\frac{e^{\alpha t}}{1-e^{\alpha t}} + \frac{1}{\alpha\tau}\right],$$

$$\alpha = -\lambda + i\sqrt{\omega_0^2-\lambda^2}, \qquad (1)$$

for $0 \leqq t \leqq \tau$. When $n \leqq t/\tau \leqq n+1$, we must in the formula for the current replace t by $t' = t-n\tau$.

Can one use (1) to obtain an expression for the stable current when $\omega_0 < \lambda$ or when $\omega_0 = \lambda$?

5.20. (a)

$$A = \frac{\omega}{2\pi}\int_0^{2\pi/\omega} F(t)\,\dot{x}(t)\,dt$$

$$= \frac{\lambda\omega^2}{m}\left[\frac{f_1^2}{(\omega^2-\omega_0^2)^2+4\lambda^2\omega^2} + \frac{4f_2^2}{(\omega_0^2-4\omega^2)^2+16\lambda^2\omega^2}\right],$$

that is, the two harmonics in the force both transfer energy, independently of one another (the period T is equal to $2\pi/\omega$).

(b)

$$A = \frac{4\lambda\omega^2}{m}\sum_{n=1}^{\infty}\frac{n^2\,|\,a\,|^2}{(\omega_0^2-n^2\omega^2)^2+4\lambda^2n^2\omega^2}.$$

(c)

$$\langle A\rangle = \frac{\lambda}{m}\left[\frac{f_1^2\omega_1^2}{(\omega_0^2-\omega_1^2)^2+4\lambda^2\omega_1^2} + \frac{f_2^2\omega_2^2}{(\omega_0^2-\omega_2^2)^2+4\lambda^2\omega_2^2}\right].$$

When we average over a large time interval, $T \gg 2\pi/\omega_{1,\,2}$, it turns out that each of the two forces $f_1 \cos\omega_1 t$ and $f_2 \cos\omega_2 t$ acts independently on the oscillator. This is connected with the fact that only the squares of trigonometric functions have non-vanishing averages,

$$\frac{1}{T}\int_0^T \sin^2 \omega_1 t\, dt = \frac{1}{2}+\frac{1}{4T\omega_1}(1-\sin 2\omega_1 T) \to \frac{1}{2},$$

as $T \to \infty$, while the averages of cross-products such as $\sin \omega_1 t \cos \omega_1 t$, $\sin \omega_1 t \cos \omega_2 t, \ldots$, vanish: for instance,

$$\frac{1}{T}\int_0^T \sin \omega_1 t \cos \omega_2 t\, dt = \frac{1-\cos(\omega_1-\omega_2)T}{2(\omega_1-\omega_2)T}+\frac{1-\cos(\omega_1+\omega_2)T}{2(\omega_1+\omega_2)T} \to 0,$$

as $T \to \infty$.

(d) The displacement of the oscillator is

$$x(t) = \int_{-\infty}^{+\infty} \frac{\psi(\omega)e^{i\omega t}\, d\omega}{\omega_0^2-\omega^2+2i\lambda\omega},$$

so that the total work done by the force $F(t)$ is equal to

$$A = \int_{-\infty}^{+\infty} \dot{x}(t)F(t)\, dt = \frac{8\pi\lambda}{m}\int_0^\infty \frac{\omega^2 |\psi(\omega)|^2\, d\omega}{(\omega_0^2-\omega^2)^2+4\lambda^2\omega^2}. \qquad (1)$$

To prove this equation one uses the inverse Fourier transform

$$\int_{-\infty}^{+\infty} F(t)e^{i\omega t}\, dt = 2\pi\psi^*(\omega).$$

When $\lambda \ll \omega_0$ the main contribution to the integral (1) comes from the vicinity of the eigen-frequency of the oscillator $\omega = \omega_0$. We have thus

$$A \approx \frac{4\pi |\psi(\omega_0)|^2\omega_0}{m}\left[\lambda\int_0^\infty \frac{d\omega^2}{(\omega_0^2-\omega^2)^2+4\lambda^2\omega^2}\right].$$

The factor inside the square brackets can easily be evaluated and turns out to be independent of λ:

$$A = \frac{|2\pi\psi(\omega_0)|^2}{2m}$$

(compare Landau and Lifshitz, 1960, equation (22.12)).

6. Small Oscillations of Systems with Several Degrees of Freedom

6.1. Two normal vibrations are possible in the system, namely oscillations where the two masses move with the same frequency in phase or in antiphase (x_i are the displacements from the equilibrium position; compare problem 5.8):

$$(1)\ x_1 = A\cos(\omega_1 t+\varphi), \quad x_2 = \frac{2A}{\sqrt{5}-1}\cos(\omega_1 t+\varphi);$$

$$(2)\ x_1 = B\cos(\omega_2 t+\varphi), \quad x_2 = \frac{-2B}{\sqrt{5}+1}\cos(\omega_2 t+\varphi).$$

The eigen-frequencies are here given by

$$\omega_{1,2}^2 = \frac{3\mp\sqrt{5}}{2}\,\frac{\varkappa}{m} \quad \text{(compare problem 7.2).}$$

6.2. Let x_i $(i = 1, 2, 3)$ be the displacement of the ith mass along the circle. The Lagrangian of the system is

$$L = \tfrac{1}{2}m(\dot{x}_1^2+\dot{x}_2^2+\dot{x}_3^2)-\tfrac{1}{2}\varkappa(x_1^2+(x_2-x_1)^2+(x_3-x_2)^2+x_3^2).$$

The equations of motion,

$$\begin{aligned} m\ddot{x}_1+\varkappa(2x_1-x_2) &= 0,\\ m\ddot{x}_2+\varkappa(2x_2-x_3-x_1) &= 0,\\ m\ddot{x}_3+\varkappa(2x_3-x_2) &= 0, \end{aligned} \tag{1}$$

can be reduced to a set of algebraic equations through the substitution $x_i = A_i\cos(\omega t+\varphi)$:

$$\begin{aligned} (-m\omega^2+2\varkappa)A_1-\varkappa A_2 &= 0,\\ -\varkappa A_1+(-m\omega^2+2\varkappa)A_2-\varkappa A_3 &= 0,\\ -\varkappa A_2+(-m\omega^2+2\varkappa)A_3 &= 0. \end{aligned} \tag{2}$$

The set of equations (2) has a non-trivial solution only when its determinant vanishes:

$$\left(-\omega^2+\frac{2\varkappa}{m}\right)\left[\left(-\omega^2+\frac{2\varkappa}{m}\right)^2-\frac{2\varkappa^2}{m^2}\right] = 0. \tag{3}$$

We get thus for the eigen-frequencies

$$\omega_{1,3}^2 = \left(2\mp\sqrt{2}\right)\frac{\varkappa}{m}, \quad \omega_2^2 = \frac{2\varkappa}{m}. \tag{4}$$

Of the three equations (2) only two are independent, because of (3) and (4). Substituting the values of $\omega_s^2 (s = 1, 2, 3)$ from (4) into (2) we get the ratios of the amplitudes:

$$A_1 = \frac{1}{\sqrt{2}} A_2 = A_3 = A \quad \text{for} \quad \omega = \omega_1;$$

$$A_1 = -A_3 = B, \quad A_2 = 0 \quad \text{for} \quad \omega = \omega_2;$$

$$A_1 = -\frac{1}{\sqrt{2}} A_2 = A_3 = C \quad \text{for} \quad \omega = \omega_3.$$

The eigen-vibrations of the system are thus:

$$\begin{aligned} x_1 &= A\cos(\omega_1 t+\varphi_1)+B\cos(\omega_2 t+\varphi_2)+C\cos(\omega_3 t+\varphi_3),\\ x_2 &= \sqrt{2}\,A\cos(\omega_1 t+\varphi_1)-\sqrt{2}\,C\cos(\omega_3 t+\varphi_3), \qquad (5)\\ x_3 &= A\cos(\omega_1 t+\varphi_1)-B\cos(\omega_2 t+\varphi_2)+C\cos(\omega_3 t+\varphi_3). \end{aligned}$$

The constants $A, B, C, \varphi_1, \varphi_2$, and φ_3 are determined by the initial conditions. The eigen-vibrations (5) describe the motion of the system completely. However, for solving many problems (for instance, problems with extra forces (see problems 6.26(b), and 6.27) or when developing perturbation theory or quantising the system) it is more convenient to use normal coordinates. This is connected with the fact that the normal coordinates,

$$q_{1,3} = \tfrac{1}{2}(x_1 \pm \sqrt{2}\,x_2 + x_3),$$

$$q_2 = \frac{1}{\sqrt{2}}(x_1 - x_3),$$

reduce the Lagrangian to a sum of squares:

$$L = \tfrac{1}{2}m(\dot{q}_1^2 - \omega_1^2 q_1^2 + \dot{q}_2^2 - \omega_2^2 q_2^2 + \dot{q}_3^2 - \omega_3^2 q_3^2),$$

while the equations of motion become one-dimensional:

$$\ddot{q}_i + \omega_i^2 q_i = 0, \quad i = 1, 2, 3.$$

This is similar to the way the problem of the motion of two interacting bodies is reduced to the problem of the centre-of-mass motion and the motion of a particle with the reduced mass in the given field of force.

6.3. The motion is described by the equations

$$x = a\cos(\omega_1 t+\varphi_1), \quad y = b\cos(\omega_2 t+\varphi_2).$$

The constants a, b, φ_1, and φ_2 are determined by the initial conditions. The orbit lies inside the rectangle $-a \leqq x \leqq a$, $-b \leqq y \leqq b$ (see Fig. 95).

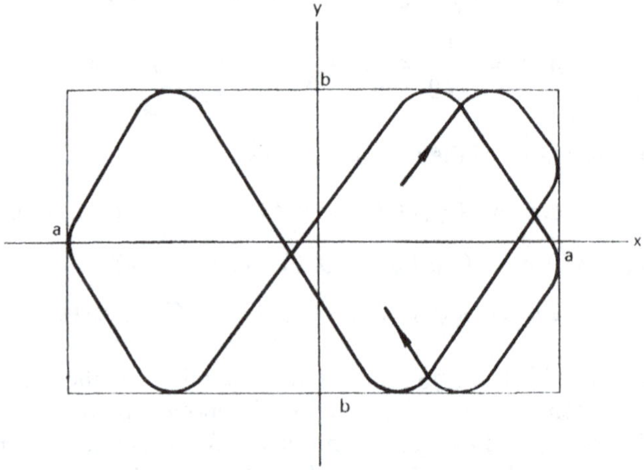

FIG. 95

Generally speaking, the orbit "fills" the whole rectangle. More precisely, if the ratio ω_1/ω_2 is irrational, the orbit comes arbitrarily close to any point inside this rectangle. The motion of the point is in that case not periodic, although the motion of its components along the two coordinate axes is period. However, if the ratio is rational ($l\omega_1 = n\omega_2$ with l and n integers) the orbit is a closed curve, a so-called Lissajous figure. The motion is periodic in this case—with period $2\pi l/\omega_2$.

6.4. (a) The transformation to normal coordinates is for this system simply a rotation in the xy-plane (Fig. 96):

$$x = Q_1\cos\varphi - Q_2\sin\varphi, \quad y = Q_1\sin\varphi + Q_2\cos\varphi. \tag{1}$$

Indeed, the kinetic energy does not change its form under the rotation while the coefficient of Q_1Q_2 in the potential energy, which is equal to $-\frac{1}{2}(\omega_1^2-\omega_2^2)\sin 2\varphi - \alpha\cos 2\varphi$, can be made to vanish, if we determine the parameter φ from the condition $\cot 2\varphi = (\omega_2^2-\omega_1^2)/2\alpha$. The way φ depends on ω_1 is shown in Fig. 97; the region where φ changes from 0 to 2π has a

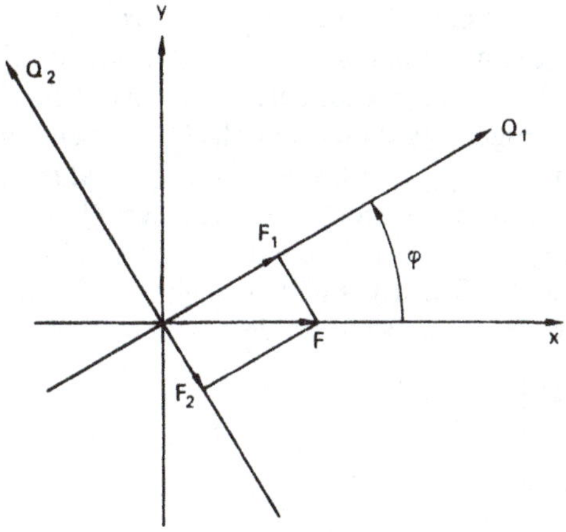

FIG. 96

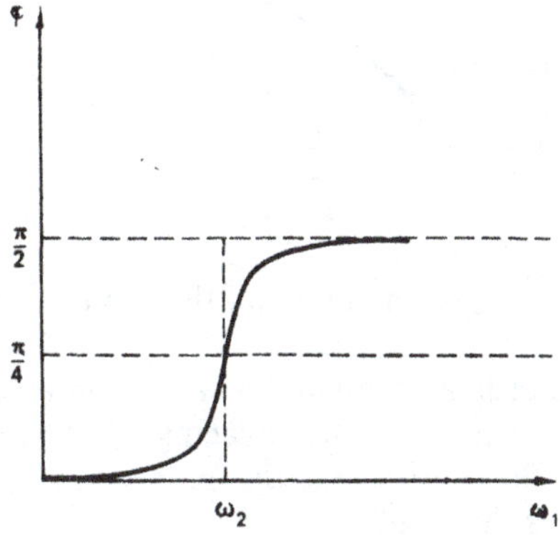

FIG. 97

width of the order of α/ω. When the coupling is weak, $\alpha \ll |\omega_1^2-\omega_2^2|$, the normal oscillations are localised, that is, when $\omega_1 < \omega_2$, we have $\varphi \approx 0$ and $x \approx Q_1, y \approx Q_2$, while for $\omega_1 > \omega_2, \varphi \approx \pi/2$ and $x \approx -Q_2, y \approx Q_1$. When $\omega_1 = \omega_2$ the normal vibrations are no longer normalised, whatever the value of $\alpha: \varphi = \pi/4, x = (Q_1-Q_2)/\sqrt{2}, y = (Q_1+Q_2)/\sqrt{2}$ (see Landau and Lifshitz, 1960, § 23, problem 1).

The normal frequencies,

$$\Omega_{1,2}^2 = \tfrac{1}{2}\left(\omega_1^2+\omega_2^2 \mp \sqrt{(\omega_2^2-\omega_1^2)^2+4\alpha^2}\right), \tag{2}$$

lie outside the range of partial frequencies,† that is, $\Omega_1 < \omega_1$ and $\Omega_2 > \omega_2$ (to fix the ideas we assume that $\omega_1 < \omega_2$). Relations of this kind for systems with many degrees of freedom are known as "Rayleigh's theorem" (Rayleigh, 1890). Figure 98 shows how the $\Omega_{1,2}$ depend on ω_1. It is clear from Fig. 98 that the $\Omega_{1,2}$ differ little from the partial frequencies (just as x and y differ little from the normal coordinates Q_1 and Q_2) when α is small, everywhere, except the degeneracy region, where $|\omega_1^2 - \omega_2^2| \lesssim \alpha$. When ω_1 becomes sufficiently small, one of the frequencies becomes imaginary: the system ceases to be stable.

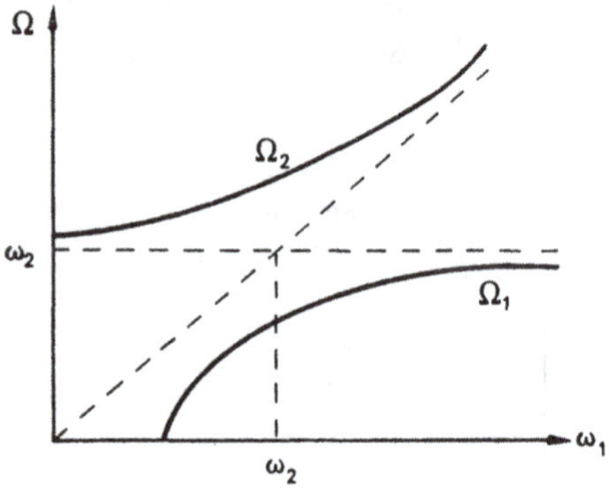

FIG. 98

In terms of Q_1 and Q_2 the motion and the orbits are the same as in the preceding problem.

(b) The normal coordinates can in this case be obtained from the results of the preceding problem, simply by replacing $\omega_{1,2}^2$ by $m_{1,2}$, while the normal frequencies are the reciprocal of the frequencies $\Omega_{1,2}$ of the preceding problem. Why is this the case?

Can one see from the form of the Lagrangian that the normal frequencies are independent of the sign of α (or β) without finding $\Omega_{1,2}$ explicitly?

6.5. (a) The Lagrangian of the system is (see problem 4.21)

$$L = \frac{1}{2}(\mathcal{L}_1\dot{q}_1^2 + \mathcal{L}_2\dot{q}_2^2) - \frac{1}{2}\left[\frac{q_1^2}{C_1} + \frac{q_2^2}{C_2} + \frac{(q_1+q_2)^2}{C}\right],$$

where q_1 and q_2 are the charges on the upper plates of the capacitors C_1 and C_2. Introducing new variables $x = q_1\sqrt{\mathcal{L}_1}$ and $y = q_2\sqrt{\mathcal{L}_2}$ we get

† We follow Mandel'shtam in calling those frequencies which are obtained from the original system when x = constant (or y = constant) partial frequencies.

the Lagrangian of problem 6.4(a), with the parameters

$$\omega_1^2 = \frac{1}{\mathcal{L}_1}\left(\frac{1}{C}+\frac{1}{C_1}\right), \quad \omega_2^2 = \frac{1}{\mathcal{L}_2}\left(\frac{1}{C}+\frac{1}{C_2}\right), \quad \alpha = \frac{1}{C\sqrt{\mathcal{L}_1\mathcal{L}_2}}.$$

(b) By the change of variables $x = q_1/\sqrt{C_1}$ and $y = q_2/\sqrt{C_2}$ we can change the Lagrangian of this system to the Lagrangian of problem 6.4(b) with the parameters

$$m_{1,2} = (\mathcal{L}+\mathcal{L}_{1,2})C_{1,2}, \quad \beta = \mathcal{L}\sqrt{C_1C_2}.$$

Can this system become unstable?

6.6. Let x_1 and x_2 be the displacements of the masses m_1 and m_2 from their equilibrium positions. Writing $x = x_1\sqrt{m_1}$ and $y = x_2\sqrt{m_2}$ we get for the system the same Lagrangian as in problem 6.4(a).

We can obtain the answer to the problem in various limiting cases without solving it. For instance, if all $\varkappa_i = \varkappa$ and $m_1 = m \ll m_2 = M$, we can have a normal vibration with a very low frequency $\Omega_1^2 = 3\varkappa/2M$, $x_1 = \frac{1}{2}x_2$ (the mass m is, so to say, part of the spring, while the mass M vibrates between springs of stiffness $\varkappa/2$ and $\varkappa$) and one with a very high frequency $\Omega_2^2 = 2\varkappa/m$ (when the mass M is almost at rest). One can find the amplitude of the oscillations of the second mass by considering its motion as being under the influence of an extra force $\varkappa x_1$ with a high frequency (see Landau and Lifshitz, 1960, equation (22.4)): $x_2 = -mx_1/2M$.

It is of interest to consider in a similar way the cases

(a) $m_1 = m_2, \quad \varkappa_1 = \varkappa_2 \equiv \varkappa \ll \varkappa_3 \equiv K$;

(b) all stiffnesses are different, but of the same order of magnitude, and $m_1 \ll m_2$;

(c) $\varkappa_2 \gg \varkappa_1 = \varkappa_3$ and the masses m_1 and m_2 are of the same order of magnitude.

6.7. (a)

$$x_{1,2} = \frac{1}{2}v\left[\frac{1}{\omega_1}\sin\,\omega_1 t \pm \frac{1}{\omega_2}\sin\,\omega_2 t\right];$$

when $\varkappa_1 \ll \varkappa$, the oscillations have the form of beats:

$$x_1 = \frac{v}{\omega_1}\cos\,\varepsilon t\,\sin\,\omega_1 t,$$

$$x_2 = -\frac{v}{\omega_1}\sin\,\varepsilon t\,\cos\,\omega_1 t.$$

(b) $$x_{1,2} = \tfrac{1}{2}a(\cos\,\omega_1 t \pm \cos\,\omega_2 t);$$

when $\varkappa_1 \ll \varkappa$, we have

$$x_1 = a \cos \varepsilon t \cos \omega_1 t,$$
$$x_2 = a \sin \varepsilon t \sin \omega_1 t.$$

Everywhere in this problem $\omega_1 = \sqrt{\varkappa/m}$ and $\omega_2 = \sqrt{(2\varkappa_1+\varkappa)/m}$, $\varepsilon = \varkappa_1\omega_1/2\varkappa$.

6.8. The energy transferred from the first to the second mass during a time dt is equal to the work done by the force $F_{1,2} = \varkappa(x_1-x_2)$: $dE = \varkappa(x_1-x_2)\,dx_2 = \varkappa(x_1-x_2)\,\dot{x}_2\,dt$, and the energy flux is $dE/dt = \varkappa(x_1-x_2)\dot{x}_2$. In the limiting case when $\varkappa_1 \ll \varkappa$ the flux of energy averaged over the fast oscillations is in problem 6.7a equal to $\frac{1}{2}v^2\sqrt{\varkappa m}\sin \varepsilon t$ and changes sign with the frequency of the beats.

6.9. The equations of motion,

$$m\ddot{x}_1+\varkappa x_1+\varkappa_1(x_1-x_2)+\alpha\dot{x}_1 = 0,$$
$$m\ddot{x}_2+\varkappa x_2+\varkappa_1(x_2-x_1)+\alpha\dot{x}_2 = 0,$$

split into two equations for the normal coordinates, when we use the substitution $x_{1,2} = (q_1 \pm q_2)/\sqrt{2}$:

$$\ddot{q}_1+\omega_1^2 q_1+2\lambda\dot{q}_1 = 0, \quad \ddot{q}_2+\omega_2^2 q_2+2\lambda\dot{q}_2 = 0,$$

where $\omega_1^2 = \varkappa/m$, $\quad \omega_2^2 = (\varkappa+2\varkappa_1)/m$, $\quad 2\lambda = \alpha/m$.

We have thus, when $\lambda < \omega_{1,2}$ (see Landau and Lifshitz, 1960, § 25):

$$x_{1,2} = e^{-\lambda t}[a \cos(\gamma_1 t+\varphi_1) \pm b \cos(\gamma_2 t+\varphi_2)],$$

where $\gamma_{1,2} = \sqrt{\omega_{1,2}^2-\lambda^2}$.

The characteristic equation for the system of Fig. 23 is no longer biquadratic when there is friction present, but of fourth degree, and it is therefore considerably more complicated to find the eigen-vibrations.

6.10. Let x_i be the displacement of the ith mass along the circle. The Lagrangian of the system is

$$L = \frac{1}{2}m(\dot{x}_1^2+\dot{x}_2^2+\dot{x}_3^2)-\frac{\varkappa}{2}[(x_1-x_2)^2+(x_2-x_3)^2+(x_3-x_1)^2]. \quad (1)$$

The three masses can rotate with a constant angular velocity:

$$x_1 = x_2 = x_3 = c_1 t+c_2 = \frac{1}{\sqrt{3}}q_1(t), \quad \omega_1 = 0. \quad (2)$$

The oscillations, where the masses A and B move towards one another with equal amplitude,

$$x_1 = -x_2 = \frac{1}{\sqrt{2}} q_2(t) = c_3 \cos(\omega_2 t + c_4), \quad x_3 = 0, \quad \omega_2^2 = 3\varkappa/m, \tag{3}$$

have the same frequency as the oscillations where the masses B and C move towards one another:

$$x_2 = -x_3 = \frac{1}{\sqrt{2}} q_3(t) = c_5 \cos(\omega_3 t + c_6), \quad x_1 = 0, \quad \omega_3 = \omega_2. \tag{4}$$

We introduce the "displacement vector" $\boldsymbol{r} = (x_1, x_2, x_3)$ and we can then write the three oscillations (2), (3), and (4) as three vectors†

$$\boldsymbol{r}_1 = \frac{1}{\sqrt{3}} \begin{pmatrix} 1 \\ 1 \\ 1 \end{pmatrix} q_1, \quad \boldsymbol{r}_2 = \frac{1}{\sqrt{2}} \begin{pmatrix} 1 \\ -1 \\ 0 \end{pmatrix} q_2, \quad \boldsymbol{r}_3 = \frac{1}{\sqrt{2}} \begin{pmatrix} 0 \\ 1 \\ -1 \end{pmatrix} q_3. \tag{5}$$

The normal coordinates must diagonalise simultaneously two quadratic expressions—the kinetic energy and the potential energy. As in (1) the kinetic energy is proportional to the sum of the squares of the velocities, the transformation from the x_i to the normal coordinates which does not change its form must be an orthogonal transformation, and the vectors of the normal oscillations must be mutually orthogonal. The vectors $\boldsymbol{r}_i$ are independent, but not mutually orthogonal: $(\boldsymbol{r}_1 \cdot \boldsymbol{r}_2) = (\boldsymbol{r}_1 \cdot \boldsymbol{r}_3) = 0$, but $(\boldsymbol{r}_2 \cdot \boldsymbol{r}_3) \neq 0$. To obtain the normal coordinates we must orthogonalise the vectors $\boldsymbol{r}_2$ and $\boldsymbol{r}_3$. We note that a superposition of the oscillations $\alpha\boldsymbol{r}_2 + \beta\boldsymbol{r}_3$ s again an oscillation with the frequency $\omega_2 = \omega_3$. The oscillations

$$\boldsymbol{R}_1 = \boldsymbol{r}_1, \quad \boldsymbol{R}_2 = \boldsymbol{r}_2, \quad \text{and} \quad \boldsymbol{R}_3 = \alpha\boldsymbol{r}_2 + \beta\boldsymbol{r}_3 = \frac{1}{\sqrt{6}} \begin{pmatrix} 1 \\ 1 \\ -2 \end{pmatrix} q_3', \tag{6}$$

where $\alpha = 1/\sqrt{3}$ and $\beta = 2/\sqrt{3}$ are found from the condition $(\boldsymbol{R}_3 \cdot \boldsymbol{R}_2) = 0$ and the condition that $\boldsymbol{R}_3$ be normalised, are thus the normal oscillations.

† The factors $1/\sqrt{3}$ and $1/\sqrt{2}$ are introduced in order that the vectors $\boldsymbol{r}_i$ are normalised by the condition $(\boldsymbol{r}_i \cdot \boldsymbol{r}_k) = \delta_{ik} q_k^2$.

The coordinates q_i found from

$$x_1 = \frac{1}{\sqrt{3}} q_1 + \frac{1}{\sqrt{2}} q_2 + \frac{1}{\sqrt{6}} q_3,$$
$$x_2 = \frac{1}{\sqrt{3}} q_1 - \frac{1}{\sqrt{2}} q_2 + \frac{1}{\sqrt{6}} q_3, \qquad (7)$$
$$x_3 = \frac{1}{\sqrt{3}} q_1 - \frac{2}{\sqrt{6}} q_3,$$

reduce (1) to the form

$$L = \tfrac{1}{2} m (\dot{q}_1^2 + \dot{q}_2^2 + \dot{q}_3^2 - \omega_2^2 q_2^2 - \omega_3^2 q_3^2). \qquad (8)$$

Of course, any coordinates q_2' and q_3' obtained from q_2 and q_3 by an orthogonal transformation are normal coordinates—and, correspondingly, any vectors $\boldsymbol{R}_2'$ and $\boldsymbol{R}_3'$ obtained from $\boldsymbol{R}_2$ and $\boldsymbol{R}_3$ simply by a rotation around $\boldsymbol{R}_1$ are vectors of the normal oscillations.

6.11. The initial conditions for the displacements x_i along the circle are $x_1(0) = a$, $x_2(0) = x_3(0) = \dot{x}_i(0) = 0$. We have thus for the normal coordinates q_i (see formula (7) of the preceding problem) the initial conditions $q_1(0) = a/\sqrt{3}$, $q_2(0) = a/\sqrt{2}$, $q_3(0) = a/\sqrt{6}$, $\dot{q}_i(0) = 0$. Therefore, we find $q_1 = a/\sqrt{3}$, $q_2 = (a/\sqrt{2}) \cos \omega_2 t$, $q_3 = (a/\sqrt{6}) \cos \omega_3 t$, and taking into account the fact that $\omega_2 = \omega_3$, we get finally

$$x_1 = \frac{a}{3} - \frac{2}{3} a \cos \omega_2 t, \qquad x_2 = \frac{a}{\sqrt{3}} + \frac{a}{3} \cos \omega_2 t,$$

$$x_3 = \frac{a}{3} + \frac{a}{3} \cos \omega_2 t.$$

6.12. The Lagrangian of the system is

$$L = \tfrac{1}{2} m \sum_i \dot{x}_i^2 - \tfrac{1}{2} \varkappa [(x_1 - x_2)^2 + (x_2 - x_3)^2 + (x_3 - x_4)^2 + (x_4 - x_1)^2].$$

The vectors of the normal oscillations are (see problem 6.10)

$$\boldsymbol{r}_1 = \frac{1}{\sqrt{2}} \begin{pmatrix} 1 \\ 0 \\ -1 \\ 0 \end{pmatrix} q_1(t), \qquad \boldsymbol{r}_2 = \frac{1}{\sqrt{2}} \begin{pmatrix} 0 \\ 1 \\ 0 \\ -1 \end{pmatrix} q_2(t),$$

$$\boldsymbol{r}_{3,4} = \frac{1}{2} \begin{pmatrix} 1 \\ \mp 1 \\ 1 \\ \mp 1 \end{pmatrix} q_{3,4}(t), \qquad (1)$$

where $q_i = A_i \cos(\omega_i t + \varphi_i)$, $i = 1, 2, 3$; $\omega_1 = \omega_2 = \sqrt{2\varkappa/m}$, $\omega_3 = 2\sqrt{\varkappa/m}$; $q_4 = A_4 t + A_5$, $\omega_4 = 0$.

This is, of course, not the only possible choice. Any vectors obtained from the ones given here through a rotation in the plane determined by the vectors $\boldsymbol{r}_1$ and $\boldsymbol{r}_2$ will also be vectors of the normal oscillations. For instance: $\boldsymbol{r}'_{1,2} = 2^{-\frac{1}{2}}(\boldsymbol{r}_1 \pm \boldsymbol{r}_2)$; $\boldsymbol{r}'_{3,4} = \boldsymbol{r}_{3,4}$ (rotation over $\pi/4$). However, the vectors $\boldsymbol{r}_1, \boldsymbol{r}'_2, \boldsymbol{r}_3, \boldsymbol{r}_4$ will not reduce the Lagrangian to a sum of squares, although they also are independent.

6.13. Let x_i and y_i be the displacements of the ith mass from its equilibrium position. The Lagrangian of the system (see problem 5.7) can be reduced to the form

$$L(x, y) = L_1(x) + L_1(y),$$

$$L_1(x) = \frac{1}{2} m \left[\sum_{i=1}^{4} \dot{x}_i^2 - \frac{4\varkappa}{m} \sum_{i=1}^{4} x_i^2 + \frac{2\varkappa}{m}(x_1+x_3)(x_2+x_4) \right]. \tag{1}$$

The orthogonal transformation which reduces the quadratic cross-term $(x_1+x_3)(x_2+x_4)$ to a sum of squares must be the same as the transformation in problem 6.12 in which the Lagrangian has the same form so that we have

$$\begin{aligned} x_1 &= \frac{1}{\sqrt{2}} q_1 + \frac{1}{2} q_3 + \frac{1}{2} q_4, \\ x_2 &= \frac{1}{\sqrt{2}} q_2 - \frac{1}{2} q_3 + \frac{1}{2} q_4, \\ x_3 &= \frac{-1}{\sqrt{2}} q_1 + \frac{1}{2} q_3 + \frac{1}{2} q_4, \\ x_4 &= \frac{-1}{\sqrt{2}} q_2 - \frac{1}{2} q_3 + \frac{1}{2} q_4. \end{aligned} \tag{2}$$

The term $(x_1+x_3)(x_2+x_4)$ is through the transformation (2) reduced to $q_4^2 - q_3^2$ and we have

$$L_1(x) = \frac{1}{2} m \left(\dot{q}_1^2 - \frac{4\varkappa}{m} q_1^2 + \dot{q}_2^2 - \frac{4\varkappa}{m} q_2^2 + \dot{q}_3^2 - \frac{2\varkappa}{m} q_3^2 + \dot{q}_4^2 - \frac{6\varkappa}{m} q_4^2 \right).$$

The term $L_1(y)$ has a similar form in the coordinates q_5, q_6, q_7, and q_8. The normal frequencies are $\omega_1 = \omega_2 = \omega_5 = \omega_6 = \sqrt{4\varkappa/m}$, $\omega_3 = \omega_7 = \sqrt{2\varkappa/m}$, and $\omega_4 = \omega_8 = \sqrt{6\varkappa/m}$. The vectors of the normal oscillations in the x_i have the same form as the vectors $\boldsymbol{r}_i$ of problem 6.12.

6·14. The amplitudes of the normal oscillations satisfy the equations

$$-\omega_l^2 \sum_j m_{ij} A_j^{(l)} + \sum_j \varkappa_{ij} A_i^{(l)} = 0, \tag{1}$$

$$-\omega_s^2 \sum_j m_{ij} A_j^{(s)} + \sum_j \varkappa_{ij} A_j^{(s)} = 0. \tag{2}$$

Multiplying (1) by $A_i^{(s)}$ and (2) by $A_i^{(l)}$ and summing both equations over i we get instead of (1) and (2)

$$-\omega_l^2 \sum_{i,j} m_{ij} A_j^{(l)} A_i^{(s)} + \sum_{i,j} \varkappa_{ij} A_j^{(l)} A_i^{(s)} = 0, \tag{3}$$

$$-\omega_s^2 \sum_{i,j} m_{ij} A_j^{(s)} A_i^{(l)} + \sum_{i,j} \varkappa_{ij} A_j^{(s)} A_i^{(l)} = 0. \tag{4}$$

Subtracting (4) from (3) and using the fact that $m_{ij} = m_{ji}$ and $\varkappa_{ij} = \varkappa_{ji}$, we get

$$(\omega_s^2 - \omega_l^2) \sum_{i,j} m_{ij} A_i^{(s)} A_j^{(l)} = 0,$$

that is, when $\omega_s \neq \omega_l$,

$$\sum_{i,j} m_{ij} A_i^{(s)} A_j^{(l)} = 0, \tag{5}$$

and at the same time from (3)

$$\sum_{i,j} \varkappa_{ij} A_i^{(s)} A_j^{(l)} = 0. \tag{6}$$

It is convenient to use the terminology from linear algebra. We shall call the set of amplitudes of a given oscillation the amplitude vector $A^{(l)} = (A_1^{(l)}, A_2^{(l)}, \ldots, A_n^{(l)})$. The relations (5) and (6) which we have just proved mean that the amplitudes $A^{(s)}$ and $A^{(l)}$ are mutually orthogonal, provided the scalar product is defined by means of the metric tensors m_{ij} or $\varkappa_{ij}$. In the case of degeneracy (if $\omega_s = \omega_l$) the amplitudes $A^{(l)}$ and $A^{(s)}$ do not necessarily satisfy equations (5) and (6). However, one can in that case always choose—indeed, in several ways—such amplitudes that they satisfy (5) and (6) and also reduce the Lagrangian to a sum of squares.

6.15. (a) Let x_i, y_i, and z_i be the displacements of the ith mass from its equilibrium position. The Lagrangian of the system has the form (see problem 5.7)

$$L(x, y, z) = L_1(x) + L_1(y) + L_1(z),$$

$$L_1(x) = \tfrac{1}{2} m \sum_{i=1}^{5} \dot{x}_i^2 - \tfrac{1}{2}\varkappa[x_1^2 + (x_1 - x_5)^2 + (x_5 - x_3)^2 + x_3^2 + x_2^2$$

$$+ (x_2 - x_5)^2 + (x_5 - x_4)^2 + x_4^2],$$

so that the oscillations in the x-, y-, and z-directions proceed independently. We can easily guess three of the normal vibrations in the x-direction:

$$\boldsymbol{r}_1 = q_1(1, 0, -1, 0, 0), \quad \boldsymbol{r}_2 = q_2(0, 1, 0, -1, 0),$$

$$\boldsymbol{r}_3 = q_3(1, \ -1, 1, -1, 0),$$

$$q_i(t) = A_i(\omega_i t + \varphi_i), \quad \omega_1 = \omega_2 = \omega_3 = \sqrt{2\varkappa/m}. \tag{1}$$

The other two normal vibrations must be orthogonal to the vector (1) and $\boldsymbol{r}_{4,5}$ thus has the form†

$$\boldsymbol{r}_{4,5} = (a, a, a, a, d)q_{4,5}. \tag{2}$$

Substituting this vector into the equations of motion for the first and fifth particle,

$$m\ddot{x}_1 + \varkappa(2x_1 - x_5) = 0,$$

$$m\ddot{x}_5 + \varkappa(4x_5 - x_1 - x_2 - x_3 - x_4) = 0,$$

we get two equations to determine the unknown parameter d and the frequencies $\omega_{4,5}$:

$$\left(-\omega^2 + \frac{2\varkappa}{m}\right) a - \frac{\varkappa}{m} d = 0,$$

$$-\frac{4\varkappa}{m} a + \left(-\omega^2 + \frac{4\varkappa}{m}\right) d = 0. \tag{3}$$

Solving (3) we find $\omega_{4,5}^2 = (3 \mp \sqrt{5})(\varkappa/m)$ and $d_{4,5} = (-1 \pm \sqrt{5})a_{4,5}$, and finally

$$\boldsymbol{r}_{4,5} = q_{4,5}(1, 1, 1, 1, -1 \pm \sqrt{5}). \tag{4}$$

The results for the oscillations along the y- and z-axes are the same as for those along the x-axis. There are thus altogether three different frequencies in the system: $\omega_1^2 = 2\varkappa/m$ which is ninefold degenerate and $\omega_{4,5}^2 = (3 \mp \sqrt{5})(\varkappa/m)$ which are threefold degenerate (see problem 6.22 about the lifting of the degeneracy).

† Let $\boldsymbol{r}_{4,5} = (a, b, c, e, d) \equiv \boldsymbol{r}$. The orthogonality conditions $(\boldsymbol{r}\cdot\boldsymbol{r}_1) = 0 = (\boldsymbol{r}\cdot\boldsymbol{r}_2) = (\boldsymbol{r}\cdot\boldsymbol{r}_3) = 0$ leads to the equations $a = b = c = e$.

(b) The oscillations along the z-axis can easily be guessed: $\boldsymbol{r}_1 = (1, 0, -1, 0)q_1$, $\boldsymbol{r}_2 = (0, 1, 0, -1)q_2$, $\boldsymbol{r}_{3,4} = (1, \mp 1, 1, \mp 1)q_{3,4}$, $q_i = A_i \cos(\omega_i t + \varphi_i)$, $\omega_1 = \omega_2 = \omega_3 = \sqrt{(2f/ml)}$, $\omega_4 = \sqrt{(f/ml)}$, where f is the tension in the springs, and l the length of one of the springs at equilibrium.

If $f = \varkappa l$, the oscillations in the x- or y-directions will have the same form as those in the z-direction, if we put $\boldsymbol{r} = (x_1, x_2, x_3, x_4)$ or $\boldsymbol{r} = (y_2, y_1, y_4, y_3)$. If, however, $f \neq \varkappa l$ the degeneracy is lifted. Two of the normal oscillations with frequencies $\omega_1 = \sqrt{(2\varkappa/m)}$ and $\omega_2 = \sqrt{(2f/ml)}$ are the same as $\boldsymbol{r}_1$ and $\boldsymbol{r}_2$. The two other ones must have the form $(a, b, a, b) \times \cos(\omega t + \varphi)$ because of the orthogonality condition. To find them it is sufficient to consider the equations of motion of two particles:

$$m\ddot{x}_1 + \varkappa(2x_1 - x_5) = 0, \qquad m\ddot{x}_2 + \frac{f}{l}(2x_2 - x_5) = 0.$$

Here

$$x_5 = \frac{\varkappa(x_1 + x_3) + \frac{f}{l}(x_2 + x_4)}{\varkappa + \frac{f}{l}}$$

is the coordinate of the point where the springs are joined together which is determined from the condition that the potential energy be a minimum for given values of $x_{1,\,2,\,3,\,4}$.

Solving these equations we get

$$\omega_3^2 = \frac{f + \varkappa l}{ml}, \quad b_3 = -\frac{f}{\varkappa l} a_3, \quad \text{and} \quad \omega_4^2 = \frac{2\varkappa f}{m(f + \varkappa l)}, \quad b_4 = \frac{\varkappa l}{f} a_4.$$

6.16. Let x_i be the displacement of the ith mass along the circle. We can easily guess two normal vibrations:

$$\boldsymbol{r}_1 = (1, 1, 1, 1)q_1(t), \qquad q_1(t) = c_1(t) + c_2, \qquad \omega_1 = 0;$$

$$\boldsymbol{r}_2 = (1, 0, -1, 0)q_2(t), \quad q_2(t) = A_2 \cos(\omega_2 t + \varphi_2), \quad \omega_2^2 = 2\varkappa/m. \qquad (1)$$

The two other vectors must be orthogonal to the vectors (1) in the metric determined by the coefficients of the quadratic form of the kinetic energy (see problem 6.14), that is, they must have the form

$$\boldsymbol{r} = (a, b, a, -a - \tfrac{1}{2}b)\, q(t). \qquad (2)$$

Substituting (2) into the equations of motion for the first and the second mass,

$$m\ddot{x}_1+\varkappa(2x_1-x_4-x_2) = 0, \quad m\ddot{x}_2+\varkappa(2x_2-x_1-x_3) = 0,$$

we get two equations to determine the quantities a and b and the frequencies:

$$\left(-\omega^2+\frac{3\varkappa}{m}\right) a-\frac{\varkappa}{2m} b = 0,$$

$$-\frac{2\varkappa}{m} a+\left(-\omega^2+\frac{2\varkappa}{m}\right) b = 0. \qquad (3)$$

Solving (3), we find $\omega_{3,4}^2 = \frac{1}{2}(5\mp\sqrt{5})(\varkappa/m)$, $b_{3,4} = (1\pm\sqrt{5})a_{3,4}$, or $\boldsymbol{r}_{3,4} = (1, 1\pm\sqrt{5}, 1, -\frac{3}{2}\mp\frac{1}{2}\sqrt{5})\, q_3(t)$, $\quad q_{3,4} = A_{3,4}\cos(\omega_{3,4}t+\varphi_{3,4})$.

6.17. The normal oscillations are $(1, 1, 1, 1)q_1, (1, 0, -1, 0)q_2$, $(0, 1, 0, -1)q_3$, and $(1, -m/M, -m/M, 1)q_4$, where $q_1 = At+B$, $q_i = A_i \cos(\omega_i t+\varphi_i)$ $(i = 2, 3, 4)$, $\omega_2^2 = 2\varkappa/m$, $\omega_3^2 = 2\varkappa/M$, $\omega_4^2 = 2\varkappa(M+m)/mM$. The first three oscillations can easily be guessed, while the last one is found from the condition that it be orthogonal to the first three. As the masses of the particles are different the orthogonality condition for two oscillations $\boldsymbol{a}$ and $\boldsymbol{b}$ has the form: $ma_1b_1+Ma_2b_2+ma_3b_3+Ma_4b_4 = 0$ (see problem 6.14).

6.18. It is convenient to use for the solution the method explained in problem 6.16.

(a) The normal vibrations are

$$\boldsymbol{r}_1 = (1, 1, 1)(C_1t+C_2), \quad \boldsymbol{r}_2(1, -1, 0)A_2\cos(\omega_2t+\varphi_2),$$
$$\boldsymbol{r}_3 = (1, 1, -2)A_3\cos(\omega_3t+\varphi_3), \qquad (1)$$
$$\omega_2^2 = (3+2\varepsilon)\varkappa/m, \quad \omega_3^2 = 3\varkappa/m, \quad \varepsilon = \delta\varkappa/\varkappa;$$

for small ε they are close to the oscillations (6) of problem 6.10: the amplitudes of the oscillations are the same, but all frequencies are different. Therefore, although in problem 6.10 any superposition of the vectors $\boldsymbol{R}_2$ and $\boldsymbol{R}_3$ again gave normal vibrations, now the choice of the vectors $\boldsymbol{r}_1$, $\boldsymbol{r}_2$, and $\boldsymbol{r}_3$ is completely unambiguous.

(b) The normal vibrations

$$\boldsymbol{r}_1 = (1, 1, 1)(C_1t+C_2), \quad \boldsymbol{r}_2 = (1, -1, 0)A_2\cos\left(\sqrt{3\varkappa/m}\, t+\varphi_2\right),$$
$$\boldsymbol{r}_3 = \left(1, 1, \frac{-2}{1+\varepsilon}\right) A_3\cos(\omega_3t+\varphi_3), \quad \omega_3^2 = (3+\varepsilon)\varkappa/(1+\varepsilon)m, \qquad (2)$$
$$\varepsilon = \delta m/m,$$

are for small ε close to the oscillations (6) of problem 6.10. If the extra mass had been added to the particle B, the normal oscillations,

$$\boldsymbol{r}_1 = (1, 1, 1)(C_1 t + C_2), \quad \boldsymbol{r}_2 = (1, 0, -1)A_2 \cos\left(\sqrt{3\varkappa/m}\, t + \varphi_2\right),$$

$$\boldsymbol{r}_3 = \left(1, \frac{-2}{1+\varepsilon}, 1\right) A_3 \cos(\omega_3 t + \varphi_3),$$

would be close to the following superposition of the normal oscillations (6) of problem 6.10:

$$\boldsymbol{R}_1' = \boldsymbol{R}_1, \quad \boldsymbol{R}_2' = (\boldsymbol{R}_2 + \boldsymbol{R}_3\sqrt{3})/\sqrt{2}, \quad \boldsymbol{R}_3' = (3\boldsymbol{R}_2 - \boldsymbol{R}_3\sqrt{3})/\sqrt{2}.$$

(c) $\boldsymbol{r}_1 = (1, 1, 1)(C_1 t + C_2)$,

$$\boldsymbol{r}_{2,3} = \{a_{2,3}(1, -1, 0) + b_{2,3}(1, 1, -2)\} \cos(\omega_{2,3} t + \varphi_{2,3}),$$

where ($\varepsilon_i = \delta m_i / m_i$)

$$\frac{b_{2,3}}{a_{2,3}} \approx \frac{\varepsilon_1 - \varepsilon_2 \pm \sqrt{\varepsilon_1^2 + \varepsilon_2^2 - \varepsilon_1\varepsilon_2}}{\varepsilon_2 + \varepsilon_1 \mp \sqrt{\varepsilon_1^2 + \varepsilon_2^2 - \varepsilon_1\varepsilon_2}},$$

$$\omega_{2,3}^2 \approx \frac{\varkappa}{m}\left(3 - \varepsilon_1 - \varepsilon_2 \mp \sqrt{\varepsilon_1^2 + \varepsilon_2^2 - \varepsilon_1\varepsilon_2}\right).$$

6.19. (a) We expand the initial displacement $\boldsymbol{r}(0) = (a, 0, -a)$ in terms of the vectors $\boldsymbol{r}_i$ (see equation (1) of the preceding problem), taken at $t = 0$:

$$\boldsymbol{r}(0) = \boldsymbol{r}_1(0) + \boldsymbol{r}_2(0) + \boldsymbol{r}_3(0). \tag{1}$$

We do the same for the vector of the initial velocities:

$$\dot{\boldsymbol{r}}(0) = \dot{\boldsymbol{r}}_1(0) + \dot{\boldsymbol{r}}_2(0) + \dot{\boldsymbol{r}}_3(0). \tag{2}$$

From the set of equations (1) and (2) we find for the constants the following values: $A_2 = A_3 = \frac{1}{2}a$, $C_1 = C_2 = \varphi_2 = \varphi_3 = 0$, or

$$\boldsymbol{r} = \tfrac{1}{2}a(\cos\omega_2 t + \cos\omega_3 t, \quad -\cos\omega_2 t + \cos\omega_3 t, \quad -2\cos\omega_3 t)$$

$$\approx a\left(\cos(\tfrac{1}{6}\varepsilon\omega_3 t)\cos\omega_3 t, \quad \sin(\tfrac{1}{6}\varepsilon\omega_3 t)\sin\omega_3 t, \quad -\cos\omega_3 t\right).$$

The motion of the particles A and B thus shows beats with a frequency which is determined by the perturbation $\delta\varkappa$, while the particle C performs a simple oscillation with frequency ω_3. We emphasise that even a very small perturbation $\delta\varkappa$ leads to secular changes which become appreciable after sufficiently long times (compare problem 2.32).

6.20. (a, b)

$$\boldsymbol{r}_1 = (1,\ -1,\ -1,\ 1)q_1(t), \quad \boldsymbol{r}_2 = (1,\ 1,\ -1,\ -1)q_2(t),$$

$$\boldsymbol{r}_{3,4} = (1,\ \pm 1,\ 1,\ \pm 1)q_{3,4}(t);$$

(c) the same as in problem 6.12, equation (1).

6.21. $x_{1,2} = -x_{3,4} = \pm\frac{1}{2}a\cos\left[\sqrt{(2\varkappa+2\delta\varkappa)/m}\,t\right]+\frac{1}{2}a\cos\left[\sqrt{2\varkappa/m}\,t\right]$: the oscillations of the particles show beats (compare problem 6.19).

6.22. When the tension is changed but little, $(l-l_1)/l = \varepsilon \ll 1$, the non-degenerate oscillations $\boldsymbol{r}_{4,5}$ (see (4) in problem 6.15) change little. We can easily guess two more oscillations:

$$\boldsymbol{r}_1 = (1, 0, -1, 0, 0)A_1\cos(\omega_1 t+\varphi_1), \quad \omega_1^2 = 2\varkappa/m,$$

$$\boldsymbol{r}_2 = (0, 1, 0, -1, 0)A_2\cos(\omega_2 t+\varphi_2), \quad \omega_2^2 = 2\varkappa l_1/ml = (2\varkappa/m)(1-\varepsilon).$$

They are close to two of the vectors (1) of problem 6.15. The last normal oscillation which is orthogonal to all the others must thus necessarily be close to the third of the vectors (1). We find the secular changes by taking for the amplitudes the zeroth and for the frequencies the first order approximation in ε, that is, by taking†

$$\boldsymbol{r}_3 = (1, -1, 1, -1, 0)A_3\cos(\omega_3 t+\varphi_3), \quad \omega_3^2 = (2\varkappa/m)\left(1-\tfrac{1}{2}\varepsilon\right).$$

Expanding the vector of the initial displacement, $\boldsymbol{r}_0 = (a, 0, 0, -a, 0)$ in terms of the vectors $\boldsymbol{r}_1$, $\boldsymbol{r}_2$, and $\boldsymbol{r}_3$, taken at $t = 0$, and the vector of the initial velocity $\dot{\boldsymbol{r}}_0 = 0$ in terms of the vectors $\dot{\boldsymbol{r}}_i$ at $t = 0$, we find $A_1 = A_2 = A_3 = \frac{1}{2}a$, $A_4 = A_5 = \varphi_i = 0$, or

$$x_{1,3} = \tfrac{1}{2}a(\pm\cos\omega_1 t+\cos\omega_3 t), \quad x_{2,4} = \tfrac{1}{2}a(\pm\cos\omega_2 t-\cos\omega_3 t), \quad x_5 = 0;$$

the oscillations show beats (compare problem 6.19).

† The vector $\boldsymbol{r}_3$ must be orthogonal to $\boldsymbol{r}_1$ and $\boldsymbol{r}_2$ and thus be of the form $\boldsymbol{r}_3 = (a, b, a, b, c)\cos(\omega_3 t+\varphi_3)$. Substituting this expression into the equations of motion, we get only three independent equations. The cubic equation to determine the frequencies,

$$(-x+2)\,[(-x+2-2\varepsilon)(-x+4-2\varepsilon)-2(1-\varepsilon)^2]-2(-x+2-2\varepsilon) = 0, \quad x = m\omega^2/\varkappa,$$

can easily be solved approximately, by putting $x = 2+\delta x$ and retaining only terms which are linear in δx and ε.

6.23. We choose the vector potential to be $A = \frac{1}{2}H(-y, x, 0)$; the Lagrangian is then

$$L = \tfrac{1}{2}m(\dot{x}^2+\dot{y}^2+\dot{z}^2)-\tfrac{1}{2}m(\omega_1^2x^2+\omega_2^2y^2+\omega_3^2z^2)+\tfrac{1}{2}m\omega_H(x\dot{y}-y\dot{x}),$$

where $\omega_H = eH/mc$. For x and y we get the equations

$$\ddot{x}+\omega_1^2x-\omega_H\dot{y} = 0,$$
$$\ddot{y}+\omega_2^2y+\omega_H\dot{x} = 0.$$

It is convenient to look for oscillations in the form

$$x = \mathrm{Re}\,(Ae^{i\Omega t}), \quad y = \mathrm{Re}\,(Be^{i\Omega t}).$$

The set of equations

$$(\omega_1^2-\Omega^2)A-i\omega_H\Omega B = 0,$$
$$i\omega_H\Omega A+(\omega_2^2-\Omega^2)B = 0,$$

leads to the oscillations

$$x = \mathrm{Re}\,(A_ke^{i\Omega_k t}) = a_k\cos(\Omega_k t+\varphi_k),$$

$$y = \mathrm{Re}\left[A_k\frac{i\omega_H\Omega_k}{\Omega_k^2-\omega_2^2}e^{i\Omega_k t}\right] = \frac{a_k\omega_H\Omega_k}{\omega_2^2-\Omega_k^2}\sin(\Omega_k t+\varphi_k),$$

$$A_k = a_ke^{i\varphi_k}, \quad k = 1, 2,$$

with frequencies

$$\Omega_{1,2}^2 = \tfrac{1}{2}(\omega_1^2+\omega_2^2+\omega_H^2)\pm\tfrac{1}{2}[(\omega_1^2+\omega_2^2+\omega_H^2)^2-4\omega_1^2\omega_2^2]^{\frac{1}{2}}.$$

To fix our ideas let $\omega_1 > \omega_2$, $\omega_H > 0$. The first of the oscillations which we have found is then a clockwise motion along an ellipse with its major axis along the x-axis, while the second oscillation is a counterclockwise motion along an ellipse with its major axis along the y-axis.

The motion along the z-axis turns out to be a harmonic motion which is independent of the magnetic field,

$$z = a_3\cos(\omega_3 t+\varphi_3).$$

The free motion of the oscillator is a superposition of the oscillations obtained. We can call these oscillations normal oscillations, thus generalising the concept of normal oscillations: the motion in the x- and y-directions occurs with the same frequency, but with a shift in phase. It is impossible to reduce the Lagrangian to diagonal form using only a linear transformation of the coordinates as the transition to normal coordinates is in the present case connected with a canonical transformation (see problem 11.21).

If the magnetic field is weak, $\omega_H \ll \omega_1 - \omega_2$, the ellipses of the normal vibrations are strongly elongated, and the frequencies $\Omega_{1,2} \approx \omega_{1,2} \pm \omega_H^2 \omega_{1,2}/2(\omega_1^2 - \omega_2^2)$ are close to $\omega_{1,2}$. The orbit of the oscillator without a magnetic field fills a rectangle with sides parallel to the coordinate axes (see problem 6.3); the influence of a weak magnetic field is merely to deform slightly the region filled by the orbit. (The Larmor theorem is here not applicable as the field U is not symmetric with respect to the z-axis.)

In a strong magnetic field, $\omega_H > \omega_{1,2}$, the normal oscillation with frequency $\Omega_1 \approx \omega_H$ takes place along a circle, and the normal oscillation with frequency $\Omega_2 \approx \omega_1 \omega_2/\omega_H$ along an ellipse with axes which are in the x- and y-directions and which stand in the ratio ω_2/ω_1. The motion is thus along a circle with a centre which moves slowly along an ellipse. It is well known that if a charged particle moves in a strong uniform magnetic field in a plane at right angles to the field, the occurrence of a weak, quasi-uniform potential $U(\boldsymbol{r})$ (that is, a potential such that the force $\boldsymbol{F} = -\nabla U$ changes little within the circular orbit) leads to a slow displacement (drift) of the centre of the orbit in a direction at right angles to $\boldsymbol{F}$ (that is, along the equipotential lines of $U(\boldsymbol{r})$; see Landau and Lifshitz, 1962, § 22). We note that in our case a similar drift occurs also in a strongly inhomogeneous oscillator field.

If $\omega_1 = \omega_2$, the normal oscillations in the xy-plane correspond to motions along a circle in opposite senses with frequencies $\Omega_{1,2} = \tilde{\omega} \pm \frac{1}{2}\omega_H$, where $\tilde{\omega} = \sqrt{\omega_1^2 + \frac{1}{4}\omega_H^2}$. In a system rotating with frequency $-\frac{1}{2}\omega_H$ the frequencies of both motions thus turn out to be equal to $\tilde{\omega}$. Such motions are the normal oscillations of an isotropic oscillator with frequency $\tilde{\omega}$. Indeed, the sum and difference of such oscillations with equal amplitudes,

$$\begin{pmatrix} \cos \tilde{\omega} t \\ -\sin \tilde{\omega} t \end{pmatrix} \pm \begin{pmatrix} \cos \tilde{\omega} t \\ \sin \tilde{\omega} t \end{pmatrix},$$

are linear oscillations in the x- and y-directions (if we neglect the motion in the direction of the magnetic field). If the magnetic field is weak, $\omega_H \ll \omega_1$, we have $\tilde{\omega} \approx \omega_1$, and the whole effect of the field on the motion of the oscillator reduces to a rotation ("precession") around the z-axis with a frequency $-\frac{1}{2}\omega_H$ (Larmor theorem; compare Landau and Lifshitz, 1962, § 45). If, however, $\omega_H \gtrsim \omega_1$, there is no longer any obvious use for the rotating system which we have employed.

Note that the time-dependence of x and y in this problem is similar to the way the x- and y-components of the electrical induction $\boldsymbol{D}$ of a wave propagating through an anisotropic, optically active medium depend on the distance along the direction of propagation (see Landau and Lifshitz, 1960a, § 82).

6.24. We can solve the equations of motion,

$$\ddot{x}+\omega_1^2 x = \omega_z \dot{y},$$
$$\ddot{y}+\omega_2^2 y = -\omega_z \dot{x}+\omega_x \dot{z},$$
$$\ddot{z}+\omega_3^2 z = -\omega_x \dot{y},$$

with

$$\omega_x = eH_x/mc, \quad \omega_z = eH_z/mc,$$

by the method of successive approximations. We look for the coordinates in the form $x = x^{(1)}+x^{(2)}$, $y = y^{(1)}+y^{(2)}$, $z = z^{(1)}+z^{(2)}$, where $x^{(2)}$, $y^{(2)}$, and $z^{(2)}$ are small compared to $x^{(1)}$, $y^{(1)}$, and $z^{(1)}$. In first approximation we neglect small terms in the right-hand sides of the equations:

$$x^{(1)} = A\cos(\omega_1 t+\alpha), \quad y^{(1)} = B\cos(\omega_2 t+\beta), \quad z^{(1)} = C\cos(\omega_3 t+\gamma).$$

The corrections $x^{(2)}$, $y^{(2)}$, and $z^{(2)}$ are determined by the equations

$$\begin{aligned} \ddot{x}^{(2)}+\omega_1^2 x^{(2)} &= \omega_z \dot{y}^{(1)}, \\ \ddot{y}^{(2)}+\omega_2^2 y^{(2)} &= -\omega_z \dot{x}^{(1)}+\omega_x \dot{z}^{(1)}, \\ \ddot{z}^{(2)}+\omega_3^2 z^{(2)} &= -\omega_x \dot{y}^{(1)}. \end{aligned} \tag{1}$$

We get

$$\begin{aligned} x^{(2)} &= \frac{-\omega_z\omega_2 B\sin(\omega_2 t+\beta)}{\omega_1^2-\omega_2^2}, \\ y^{(2)} &= \frac{\omega_1\omega_z A\sin(\omega_1 t+\alpha)}{\omega_2^2-\omega_1^2}-\frac{\omega_x\omega_3 C\sin(\omega_3 t+\gamma)}{\omega_2^2-\omega_3^2}, \\ z^{(2)} &= \frac{\omega_x\omega_2 B\sin(\omega_2 t+\beta)}{\omega_3^2-\omega_2^2}. \end{aligned} \tag{2}$$

The corrections turn out to be small, provided $|\omega_z| \ll |\omega_1-\omega_2|$ and $|\omega_x| \ll |\omega_2-\omega_3|$. The normal oscillations are oscillations along ellipses which are strongly elongated along the coordinate axes.

If, however, for example, $|\omega_z| \gtrsim |\omega_1-\omega_2|$, $|\omega_x| \ll |\omega_2-\omega_3|$, according to (2) $x^{(2)}$ and $y^{(2)}$ are no longer small. This is connected with the fact that the frequencies of the "forces" $\omega_z\dot{y}^{(1)}$ and $-\omega_z\dot{x}^{(1)}$ in (1) turn out to lie close to the eigen-frequencies of the oscillator. In that case we must retain the resonance terms in the first approximation equations:

$$\begin{aligned} \ddot{x}^{(1)} + \omega_1^2 x^{(1)} - \omega_z \dot{y}^{(1)} &= 0, \\ \ddot{y}^{(1)} + \omega_2^2 y^{(1)} + \omega_z \dot{x}^{(1)} &= 0, \\ \ddot{z}^{(1)} + \omega_3^2 z^{(1)} \qquad\qquad &= 0, \end{aligned} \tag{3}$$

that is, it is necessary to take the effect of H_z on the motion exactly into account. We considered the set (3) in problem 6.23. For the second order corrections we have the equations

$$\begin{aligned} x^{(2)} &= 0, \\ \ddot{y}^{(2)} + \omega_2^2 y^{(2)} &= \omega_x \dot{z}^{(1)}, \\ \ddot{z}^{(2)} + \omega_3^2 z^{(2)} &= -\omega_x \dot{y}^{(1)}. \end{aligned}$$

For the sake of simplicity we restrict ourselves to the case $\omega_1 = \omega_2$ and we have then the following normal oscillations:

$$\begin{pmatrix} x \\ y \\ z \end{pmatrix} = \mathrm{Re}\left\{ A_1 \begin{pmatrix} 1 \\ i \\ \dfrac{\omega_1\omega_x}{\omega_3^2-\omega_1^2} \end{pmatrix} e^{i(\omega_1+\frac{1}{2}\omega_x)t} + A_2 \begin{pmatrix} 1 \\ -i \\ \dfrac{\omega_1\omega_x}{\omega_3^2-\omega_1^2} \end{pmatrix} e^{i(\omega_1-\frac{1}{2}\omega_x)t} + A_3 \begin{pmatrix} 0 \\ \dfrac{i\omega_x\omega_3}{\omega_3^2-\omega_1^2} \\ 1 \end{pmatrix} e^{i\omega_3 t} \right\}. \tag{4}$$

In the approximation used, the normal oscillations (4), with frequencies $\omega_1 \pm \frac{1}{2}\omega_x$, take place along a circle in planes which make angles $\mp\omega_x\omega_1/(\omega_3^2-\omega_1^2)$ with the xy-plane, while the oscillation with frequency ω_3 is along an ellipse in the yz-plane which is strongly elongated in the z-direction.

6.25. We assume that the oscillations of the pendulum are small oscillations: we reckon the angle φ counterclockwise from the vertical, and as the second coordinate we choose the charge q on the left-hand plate. When the pendulum is deflected over an angle φ, the magnetic flux through the circuit is equal to $\Phi = \text{constant} - \frac{1}{2}l^2\varphi H$. This leads to an emf in the circuit which is equal to $E = -d\Phi/dt = \frac{1}{2}Hl^2\dot{\varphi}$, corresponding to an external force, so that the Lagrangian of the system is equal to (see Landau and Lifshitz, 1960a, § 48; see also problem 4.20)

$$L = \frac{1}{2}\left(ml^2\dot{\varphi}^2 - mgl\varphi^2 + \mathcal{L}\dot{q}^2 - \frac{q^2}{C} + Hl^2\dot{\varphi}q\right).$$

If we introduce the coordinates $x = l\varphi$ and $y = \sqrt{\mathcal{L}/m}q$, the Lagrangian of our system differs from the one considered in problem 6.23 (with parameters $\omega_1^2 = g/l$, $\omega_2^2 = 1/\mathcal{L}C$, $\omega_H = Hl/2\sqrt{m\mathcal{L}}$ and $z = 0$) only by a total derivative with respect to the time: $\frac{1}{2}\omega_H\, d(xy)/dt$. The equations of motion of problem 6.23 and their solutions are thus also valid in the present case.

6.26. (a) The Lagrangian of the system is (compare problem 6.1)†

$$L = \tfrac{1}{2}m(\dot{x}_1^2 + \dot{x}_2^2) - \tfrac{1}{2}\varkappa[(x_1 - a\cos\omega t)^2 + (x_1 - x_2)^2],$$

while the equations of motion,

$$m\ddot{x}_1 + \varkappa(2x_1 - x_2) = \varkappa\, a\cos\omega t, \qquad (1)$$
$$m\ddot{x}_2 + \varkappa(x_2 - x_1) = 0,$$

can be reduced to a homogeneous linear set of two equations to determine A and B through the substitution‡

$$x_1 = A\cos\omega t, \qquad x_2 = B\cos\omega t. \qquad (2)$$

We get thus

$$A = \frac{a\varkappa(-m\omega^2 + \varkappa)}{m^2(\omega^2 - \omega_1^2)(\omega^2 - \omega_2^2)}, \qquad B = \frac{a\varkappa^2}{m^2(\omega^2 - \omega_1^2)(\omega^2 - \omega_2^2)},$$

where $\omega_{1,2}^2 = \frac{1}{2}(3 \mp \sqrt{5})(\varkappa/m)$ are the eigenfrequencies of the system. The frequency dependence of the amplitudes A and B is shown in Fig. 99a.

When the frequency goes through the resonance values $\omega = \omega_{1,2}$, the amplitudes A and B change sign; this corresponds to a change of π in the

† It can also be written in the form $L = \frac{1}{2}m(\dot{x}_1^2 + \dot{x}_2^2) - \frac{1}{2}\varkappa[x_1^2 + (x_1 - x_2)^2] + x_1\varkappa a \times \cos\omega t$, the difference, $-\frac{1}{2}\varkappa a^2\cos^2\omega t$ being a total derivative with respect to the time. This way of writing the Lagrangian is more convenient as it enables us to write down at once the external force vector: $\boldsymbol{F} = (\varkappa a\cos\omega t, 0)$

‡ The general solution of the set of equations (1) is a superposition of free and forced oscillations. As soon as there is even the smallest amount of friction present, the free oscillations are damped so that after a long time interval the solution of equations (1) is independent of the initial conditions and consists of the forced oscillations (2).

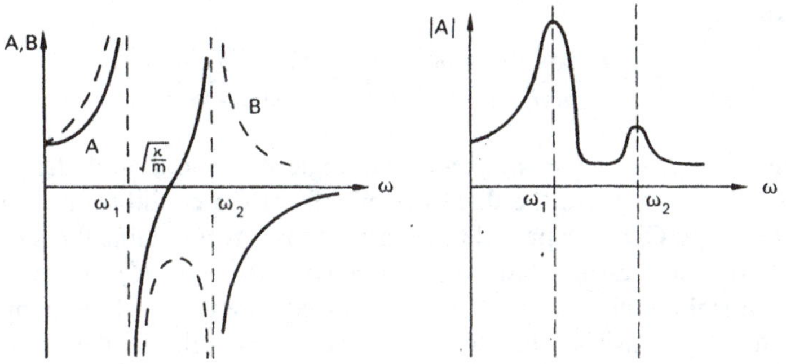

(a) (b)

FIG. 99

phase of the oscillations. At the frequency $\omega = \sqrt{\varkappa/m}$ the oscillations of the upper mass are completely damped: $A = 0$. In Fig. 99b we have shown qualitatively how $|A|$ depends on the frequency of the applied force when there is friction present.

At what frequency ω will the oscillations of the upper mass be damped, if we suspend from the lower mass another mass on the same spring?

(b) Introducing the normal coordinates (see problem 6.1)

$$x_1 = q_1 + q_2, \qquad x_2 = \frac{2}{\sqrt{5}-1}\, q_1 - \frac{2}{\sqrt{5}+1}\, q_2,$$

we can write the Lagrangian of the system in the form

$$L = L_1(q_1, \dot{q}_1) + L_2(q_2, \dot{q}_2),$$

$$L_{1,2} = \frac{1}{2}\, m(5 \pm \sqrt{5}) \left[\dot{q}_{1,2}^2 - \omega_{1,2}^2 q_{1,2}^2 + \frac{4\varkappa a(t)}{(5 \pm \sqrt{5} m)}\, q_{1,2} \right].$$

The problem is thus reduced to finding the stable oscillations of two independent harmonic oscillators on each of which a sawtoothed force acts (see problem 5.19(a)).

6.27.

$$x_1 = \frac{a\varkappa(\varkappa_1 + \varkappa - m\omega^2)}{m^2(\omega^2 - \omega_1^2)(\omega^2 - \omega_2^2)} \cos \omega t, \qquad x_2 = \frac{a\varkappa\varkappa_1 \cos \omega t}{m^2(\omega^2 - \omega_1^2)(\omega^2 - \omega_2^2)},$$

where $\omega_1^2 = \varkappa/m$, $\omega_2^2 = (\varkappa + 2\varkappa_1)/m$.

6.28. (a)

$$x = \frac{F_0 \cos\varphi \cos\omega t}{m(\omega_1^2 - \omega^2)}, \quad y = \frac{F_0 \sin\varphi \cos\omega t}{m(\omega_2^2 - \omega^2)},$$

where $\omega_1^2 = \varkappa_1/m$, $\omega_2^2 = \varkappa/m$, φ is the angle between $\boldsymbol{F}$ and the x-axis (AB), and x and y are the displacements from the equilibrium position along AB and CD. The particle oscillates along a straight line through the centre. It is interesting that when $\omega^2 = \omega_1^2 \sin^2\varphi + \omega_2^2 \cos^2\varphi$ this straight line is at right angles to the vector $\boldsymbol{F}_0$. In that case the work done by the applied force vanishes. Therefore, it seems that even the smallest amount of friction must lead to a damping of the oscillations. Explain this situation.

(b)

$$x = \frac{F \cos\omega t}{m(\omega_1^2 - \omega^2)}, \quad y = \frac{F \sin\omega t}{m(\omega_2^2 - \omega^2)}.$$

The trajectory is an ellipse with semi-axes $a = F/m(\omega_1^2 - \omega^2)$ and $b = F/m|\omega_2^2 - \omega^2|$. If the quantities $\omega_1^2 - \omega^2$ and $\omega_2^2 - \omega^2$ have opposite signs, the particle moves clockwise along the ellipse, while the force vector rotates counterclockwise.

How does the picture given here of the motion of the particle change when the tension in the springs in the equilibrium position differs from zero?

6.29. $x_1 = x_2 = a\varkappa \cos\omega t/(\varkappa - m\omega^2)$, where the x_i are the displacement along the circle from the equilibrium position of the two particles. Resonance is possible only at one of the normal frequencies when $\omega^2 = \varkappa/m$ (see problem 6.31).

6.30. Using the notation of problem 6.2 we have

$$x_1 = x_3 = \frac{a\varkappa(\omega_2^2 - \omega^2)\cos\omega t}{m(\omega^2 - \omega_1^2)(\omega^2 - \omega_3^2)}, \quad x_2 = \frac{2a\varkappa^2 \cos\omega t}{m^2(\omega^2 - \omega_1^2)(\omega^2 - \omega_3^2)}.$$

We draw attention to the fact that if $\omega = \omega_2$, $x_1 = x_3 = 0$, and $x_2 = -a\cos\omega t$. Why is the number of resonance frequencies less than that of eigen-frequencies?

6.31. Substituting $x_j = \sum_l \lambda^{(l)} A_j^{(l)} \cos\omega t$ into the equations of motion,

$$\sum_j m_{ij}\ddot{x}_j + \sum_j \varkappa_{ij} x_j = f_i \cos\omega t, \tag{1}$$

we get the following equations to determine the coefficients $\lambda^{(l)}$:

$$-\omega^2 \sum_{j,l} m_{ij}\lambda^{(l)}A_j^{(l)} + \sum_{j,l} \varkappa_{ij}\lambda^{(l)}A_j^{(l)} = f_i. \tag{2}$$

The simplest way to solve these equations is by using the orthogonality relations (5) and (6) of problem 6.14. To do this we multiply equations (2) by $A_i^{(s)}$ and sum over i; we get then

$$\lambda^{(s)} = \frac{F_s}{m_s(\omega_s^2-\omega^2)}, \quad \text{where} \quad F_s = \sum_i A_i^{(s)}f_i,$$

$$m_s = \sum_{i,j} m_{ij}A_i^{(s)}A_j^{(s)}, \quad \omega_s^2 = \varkappa_s/m_s, \quad \varkappa_s = \sum_{i,j} \varkappa_{ij}A_i^{(s)}A_j^{(s)}.$$

The quantity ω_s is the sth eigen-frequency of the system, in accordance with equation (4) of problem 6.14.† The ω-dependence of the $\lambda^{(s)}$ shows resonances.

For the normal coordinates q_s, introduced by the equations

$$x_i = \sum A_i^{(s)} q_s(t), \tag{3}$$

we have instead of equations (1) the following equations of motion:

$$m_s\ddot{q}_s + \varkappa_s q_s = F_s \cos \omega t. \tag{4}$$

It is clear from (4) that if the force vector f_i is orthogonal to the amplitude vector of the sth normal vibration,

$$\sum A_i^{(s)} f_i = 0,$$

the corresponding normal coordinate satisfies the equation for free oscillations and there is no resonance for $\omega = \omega_s$. We note that the work done by the applied force is in this case equal to zero:

$$\sum_i f_i\, dx_i = \sum_i f_i A_i^{(s)}\, dq_s = 0.$$

Consider the case where the force vector is parallel to the amplitude vector of one of the normal oscillations, $f_i/A_i^{(s)} =$ constant ($i = 1, 2, \ldots, N$). Can such a force excite other normal vibrations?

6.32. Let us to simplify matters consider only the motion of the particles along AB. Let N be the number of particles in the system, and x_i the dis-

† If some of the eigen-frequencies are degenerate we shall assume that the amplitudes of the eigen-vibrations corresponding to them are chosen in such a way that they satisfy the orthogonality relations (5) and (6) of problem 6.14.

placement of the ith particle from its equilibrium position. Let us consider one of the normal vibrations

$$\boldsymbol{r} = (A_1, A_2, \ldots, A_N) \cos(\omega t+\varphi). \qquad (1)$$

As the substitution $x_i \to x_{N-i+1}$ leaves the Lagrangian invariant, there must be together with (1) a normal vibration of the form

$$\boldsymbol{r}_1 = (A_N A_{N-1}, \ldots, A_1) \cos(\omega t+\varphi). \qquad (2)$$

(a) If the frequency ω is non-degenerate, the solution (2) can differ from (1) only by its sign, so that either $A_i = A_{N-i+1}$, that is, masses at the same distance from the centre of the system move in phase, or $A_i = -A_{N-i+1}$, that is, corresponding masses move in antiphase,

(b) If the frequency ω is degenerate, the vibrations (1) and (2) need not be the same. However, their sum and difference

$$(x_1, x_2, \ldots, x_N) = \boldsymbol{r} \pm \boldsymbol{r}_1$$
$$= (A_1 \pm A_N, A_2 \pm A_{N-1}, \ldots, A_N \pm A_1) \cos(\omega t+\varphi)$$

are also normal vibrations with the same frequency and they have the required symmetry properties.

What are the symmetry properties of the normal vibrations of systems with a centre of symmetry (see, for example, Fig. 28)?

6.33. Let the points A and B oscillate in phase with an amplitude $a(t)$; the force vector, acting on the system, then is of the form $\boldsymbol{f}(t) = (1, 0, 0, \ldots, 0, 1)\varkappa a(t)$. It is clear that it is orthogonal to those normal vibrations for which masses which are equidistant from the centre move in antiphase, that is, $x_i = -x_{N-i+1}$. According to the results of problem 6.31 these normal vibrations will not be excited. One can show similarly that if $\boldsymbol{f}(t) = (1, 0, 0, \ldots, 0, -1)\varkappa a(t)$, the normal vibrations with $x_i = x_{N-i+1}$ will not be excited.

6.34. It is clear that the motions of the particles in the horizontal and the vertical directions are independent. We shall consider the motion in the horizontal direction. Displacements to the left for the first and fourth, and to the right for the second and third particle shall be taken to be positive. According to the result of the preceding problem we can choose the normal oscillations to be symmetric or antisymmetric with respect to the lines AA and BB. For an oscillation which is symmetric with respect to AA, we have $x_1 = x_4$, $x_2 = x_3$. If this oscillation is also symmetric with respect to BB we have $x_1 = x_2$, $x_3 = x_4$ so that for this doubly symmetric oscillation we have $\boldsymbol{r}_{ss} = (1, 1, 1, 1)\, q_{ss}$.

For the oscillation which is symmetric with respect to AA and anti-symmetric with respect to BB we have $x_1 = x_4$, $x_2 = x_3$ and $x_1 = -x_2$, $x_4 = -x_3$ so that $\boldsymbol{r}_{sa} = (1, -1, -1, 1)\, q_{sa}$. Similarly we find $\boldsymbol{r}_{as} = (1, 1, -1, -1)\, q_{as}$, $\boldsymbol{r}_{aa} = (1, -1, 1, -1)\, q_{aa}$. In the same way we can find the normal oscillations in the vertical direction. The frequencies of the oscillations can be found by substituting the eigen-vectors into the equations of motion.

If the normal oscillations are degenerate, they cannot have these symmetry properties (see problem 6.13).

6.35. We shall look for solution of the equations of motion (see problem 6.27)

$$m\ddot{x}_1+\alpha\dot{x}_1+\varkappa x_1+\varkappa_1(x_1-x_2) = \varkappa a \operatorname{Re} e^{i\omega t},$$
$$m\ddot{x}_2+\alpha\dot{x}_2+\varkappa x_2+\varkappa_1(x_2-x_1) = 0,$$

in the form

$$x_1 = \operatorname{Re} Ae^{i\omega t}, \quad x_2 = \operatorname{Re} Be^{i\omega t}.$$

For A and B we get the equations

$$(-m\omega^2+2m\lambda i\omega+\varkappa+\varkappa_1)A-\varkappa_1 B = \varkappa\alpha, \quad 2\lambda m = \alpha,$$
$$-\varkappa_1 A+(-m\omega^2+2m\lambda i\omega+\varkappa+\varkappa_1)B = 0,$$

whence

$$A = \frac{a\varkappa(\varkappa+\varkappa_1-m\omega^2+2i\lambda m\omega)}{m^2(\omega^2-2i\lambda\omega-\omega_1^2)(\omega^2-2i\lambda\omega-\omega_2^2)},$$

$$B = \frac{a\varkappa\varkappa_1}{m^2(\omega^2-2i\lambda\omega-\omega_1^2)(\omega^2-2i\lambda\omega-\omega_2^2)},$$

$$x_1 = \frac{a\varkappa\sqrt{(\omega^2-\frac{1}{2}\omega_1^2-\frac{1}{2}\omega_2^2)^2+4\lambda^2\omega^2}\cos(\omega t+\varphi_1+\varphi_2+\psi)}{m\sqrt{[(\omega^2-\omega_1^2)^2+4\lambda^2\omega^2][(\omega_2^2-\omega^2)^2+4\lambda^2\omega^2]}},$$

$$x_2 = \frac{a\varkappa\varkappa_1\cos(\omega t+\varphi_1+\varphi_2)}{m^2\sqrt{[(\omega^2-\omega_1^2)^2+4\lambda^2\omega^2][(\omega_2^2-\omega^2)^2+4\lambda^2\omega^2]}},$$

$$\omega_1^2 = \frac{\varkappa}{m}, \quad \omega_2^2 = \frac{\varkappa+2\varkappa_1}{m}, \quad \tan\varphi_{1,2} = \frac{2\lambda\omega}{\omega^2-\omega_{1,2}^2},$$

$$\tan\psi = \frac{4\lambda\omega}{\omega_1^2+\omega_2^2-2\omega^2}.$$

There is a phase difference φ between the oscillations of the two masses; the oscillations of the first mass are never completely damped. As functions of the frequency of the applied force, ω, the amplitudes of the oscillations have either one or two maxima, depending on the ratios of the quantities ω_1, ω_2, and λ.

6.36. If x and y are the displacements from the equilibrium position of the first and the second mass, respectively, we have for the Lagrangian of the system

$$L = \frac{1}{2} m \left(\dot{x}^2+\dot{y}^2 - \frac{\varkappa_1+\varkappa_2}{m} x^2 - \frac{\varkappa_2+\varkappa_3}{m} y^2 + \frac{\varkappa_2}{m} xy\right) + \varkappa_1 a x \cos \omega t;$$

it differs from the Lagrangian considered in problem 6.4a only in the term $\varkappa_1 x a \cos\omega t$, corresponding to a force $\varkappa_1 a \cos\omega t$ acting upon the first mass. We shall use here the notation of problem 6.4a. The partial frequency $\omega_{1,2}^2 = (\varkappa_{1,3}+\varkappa_2)/m$ corresponds to the eigen-frequency of a system which we obtain by fixing the second (first) mass, that is, by putting $y = 0$ (respectively, $x = 0$). When we change to the normal coordinates Q_1 and Q_2, the Lagrangian becomes

$$L = \tfrac{1}{2} m(\dot{Q}_1^2 - \Omega_1^2 Q_1^2 + \dot{Q}_2^2 - \Omega_2^2 Q_2^2) + Q_1 \varkappa_1 a \cos\varphi \cos\omega t - Q_2 \varkappa_1 a \sin\varphi \cos\omega t.$$

For the coordinate Q_1 (Q_2) we get the equation of motion of a harmonic oscillator with frequency Ω_1 (Ω_2) under the action of an applied force $\varkappa_1 a \cos\varphi \cos\omega t$ (respectively, $-\varkappa_1 a \sin\varphi \cos\omega t$). The initial conditions are $Q_i(0) = \dot{Q}_i(0) = 0$. We get

$$Q_{1,2} = \frac{F_{1,2}(\cos\omega t - \cos\Omega_{1,2} t)}{m(\Omega_{1,2}^2 - \omega^2)},$$

where $F_1 = \varkappa_1 a \cos\varphi$ and $F_2 = -\varkappa_1 a \sin\varphi$ are the components of the amplitude of the force $F = \varkappa_1 a$ along the normal coordinates Q_1 and Q_2 (see Fig. 96). It is interesting to consider resonance at the second eigen-frequency for the system in the weak coupling approximation, $\varepsilon = \varkappa_2/(\varkappa_1-\varkappa_3) \ll 1$ (to fix the ideas we have assumed that $\varkappa_1 > \varkappa_3$). If we put $\omega = \Omega_2(1+\varepsilon_1)$ and $|\varepsilon_1| \ll 1$, we have

$$Q_1 = \frac{\varkappa_1 a}{\varkappa_1 - \varkappa_3}(\cos\omega_2 t - \cos\omega_1 t);$$

$$Q_2 = -\frac{\varkappa_1 a \varepsilon}{m\omega_2^2 \varepsilon_1} \sin\left(\tfrac{1}{2}\varepsilon_1 \omega_2 t\right) \sin\omega_2 t, \quad \text{when} \quad |\varepsilon_1| \ll 1,$$

$$Q_2 = \frac{-\varkappa_1 a}{2m\omega_2} \varepsilon t \sin\omega_2 t \quad \text{when} \quad \varepsilon_1 = 0.$$

We see thus that for even the smallest coupling the amplitude Q_2 can become large or even steadily increase with time, although the rate of change will then be small. Since the angle of rotation is small ($\sin \varphi = \varepsilon$), we have for the displacements $x = Q_1 - \varepsilon Q_2$, and $y = Q_2$.

What is the rate of change of the amplitude of the vibrations for resonance near the first frequency $\omega = \Omega_1$?

How will the character of the vibrations change if on both particles we have acting a small frictional force, proportional to the velocity (compare problem 5.11)?

6.37. The Lagrangian is

$$L = \tfrac{1}{2}m(\dot{u}_1^2+\dot{u}_2^2+\dot{u}_3^2) - \tfrac{1}{2}\varkappa\{(|\boldsymbol{r}_{10}-\boldsymbol{r}_{20}+\boldsymbol{u}_1-\boldsymbol{u}_2|-l)^2 + (|\boldsymbol{r}_{20}-\boldsymbol{r}_{30}+\boldsymbol{u}_2-\boldsymbol{u}_3|-l)^2 + (|\boldsymbol{r}_{30}-\boldsymbol{r}_{10}+\boldsymbol{u}_3-\boldsymbol{u}_1|-l)^2\}, \quad (1)$$

where $l = |\boldsymbol{r}_{10}-\boldsymbol{r}_{20}| = |\boldsymbol{r}_{20}-\boldsymbol{r}_{30}| = |\boldsymbol{r}_{30}-\boldsymbol{r}_{10}|$; $\boldsymbol{u}_a$ is the displacement of the ath atom from its equilibrium position, which is determined by the radius vector $\boldsymbol{r}_{a0}$. Since $|\boldsymbol{u}_a| \ll l$, we have

$$L = \tfrac{1}{2}m(\dot{u}_1^2+\dot{u}_2^2+\dot{u}_3^2) - \tfrac{1}{2}\varkappa\{(\boldsymbol{e}_{12}\cdot[\boldsymbol{u}_1-\boldsymbol{u}_2])^2 + (\boldsymbol{e}_{23}\cdot[\boldsymbol{u}_2-\boldsymbol{u}_3])^2 + (\boldsymbol{e}_{31}\cdot[\boldsymbol{u}_3-\boldsymbol{u}_1])^2\},$$

where

$$\boldsymbol{e}_{ij} = \frac{\boldsymbol{r}_{i0}-\boldsymbol{r}_{j0}}{l}.$$

In the system of reference where the total momentum $m(\dot{\boldsymbol{u}}_1+\dot{\boldsymbol{u}}_2+\boldsymbol{u}_3)=0$, the condition

$$\boldsymbol{u}_1+\boldsymbol{u}_2+\boldsymbol{u}_3 = 0 \quad (2)$$

is satisfied. Moreover, we impose upon the $\boldsymbol{u}_a$ the condition

$$[\boldsymbol{r}_{10} \wedge \boldsymbol{u}_1]+[\boldsymbol{r}_{20} \wedge \boldsymbol{u}_2]+[\boldsymbol{r}_{30} \wedge \boldsymbol{u}_3] = 0, \quad (3)$$

which is equivalent to requiring that the angular momentum of the molecule,

$$\boldsymbol{M} = m\sum_{\alpha} [\{\boldsymbol{r}_{a0}+\boldsymbol{u}_a\} \wedge \dot{\boldsymbol{u}}_a], \quad (4)$$

vanishes up to and including terms of first order in the $\boldsymbol{u}_a$.

It turns out to be convenient for the description of the motion to introduce for each atom its own Cartesian system of coordinates

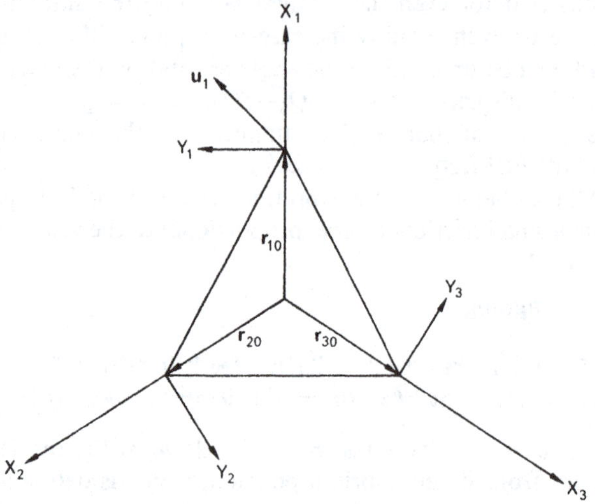

FIG. 100

(Fig. 100), thus retaining symmetry in the description of the system. Equations (2) and (3) give in terms of those coordinates†

$$y_1+(-\tfrac{1}{2}y_2-\tfrac{1}{2}x_2\sqrt{3})+(-\tfrac{1}{2}y_3+\tfrac{1}{2}x_3\sqrt{3}) = 0, \tag{5}$$

$$y_2+(-\tfrac{1}{2}y_3+\tfrac{1}{2}x_3\sqrt{3})+(-\tfrac{1}{2}y_1-\tfrac{1}{2}x_1\sqrt{3}) = 0, \tag{6}$$

$$y_1+y_2+y_3 = 0,$$

and hence

$$y_1 = \frac{x_2-x_3}{\sqrt{3}}, \quad y_2 = \frac{x_3-x_1}{\sqrt{3}}, \quad y_3 = \frac{x_1-x_2}{\sqrt{3}},$$

nd

$$L = \frac{5m}{6}(\dot{x}_1^2+\dot{x}_2^2+\dot{x}_3^2)-\frac{3m}{2}(\dot{x}_1\dot{x}_2+\dot{x}_2\dot{x}_3+\dot{x}_3\dot{x}_1)-\frac{3}{2}\varkappa(x_1^2+x_2^2+x_3^2).$$

† For instance, multiplying equation (2) by $\boldsymbol{e}_{23}$, we get (5). One must bear in mind that the vector $\boldsymbol{e}_{23}$ in the different coordinate systems has the coordinates $\boldsymbol{e}_{23} = (0, 1)_1 = (\frac{1}{2}\sqrt{3}, -\frac{1}{2})_2 = (-\frac{1}{2}\sqrt{3}, -\frac{1}{2})_3$ while $\boldsymbol{u}_a = (x_a, y_a)_a$. Equation (6) follows from (5) through a cyclic permutation.

The equations of motion are

$$\begin{aligned} \tfrac{1}{3}m(5\ddot{x}_1-\ddot{x}_2-\ddot{x}_3)+3\varkappa x_1 &= 0, \\ \tfrac{1}{3}m(5\ddot{x}_2-\ddot{x}_3-\ddot{x}_1)+3\varkappa x_2 &= 0, \\ \tfrac{1}{3}m(5\ddot{x}_3-\ddot{x}_1-\ddot{x}_2)+3\varkappa x_3 &= 0. \end{aligned} \tag{7}$$

One normal oscillation is obvious:

$$x_1^{(1)} = x_2^{(1)} = x_3^{(1)} = q_1. \tag{8}$$

Substituting (8) into (7) we find the frequency of this oscillation, $\omega_1 = \sqrt{3\varkappa/m}$. The two other normal oscillations are orthogonal to the first one which, using the metric $\varkappa_{ij}$, leads to the condition

$$x_1^{(s)}+x_2^{(s)}+x_3^{(s)} = 0, \quad s = 2, 3. \tag{9}$$

Substituting (9) into (7) we find $\omega_s = \sqrt{3\varkappa/2m}$; this frequency turns out to be twofold degenerate.

The substitution (compare eq. (7) in problem 6.10)

$$x_1 = q_1+\tfrac{1}{2}q_2\sqrt{3}+\tfrac{1}{2}q_3, \quad x_2 = q_1-\tfrac{1}{2}q_2\sqrt{3}+\tfrac{1}{2}q_3, \quad x_3 = q_1-q_3$$

leads to a Lagrangian of the form

$$L = \tfrac{3}{2}m(\dot{q}_1^2+\dot{q}_2^2+\dot{q}_3^2)-\tfrac{9}{4}\varkappa(2q_1^2+q_2^2+q_3^2). \tag{10}$$

The normal coordinates corresponding to these coordinates are shown in Fig. 101.

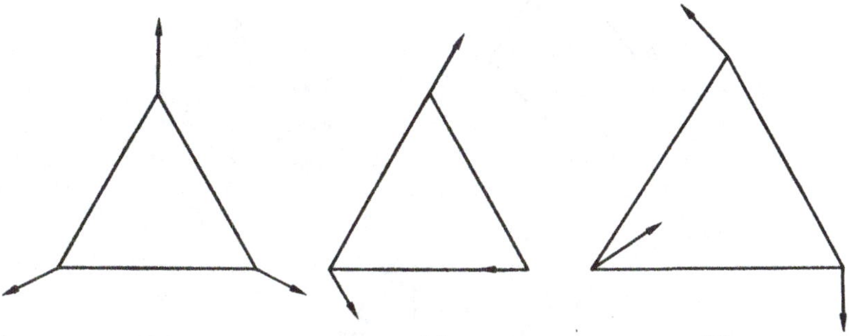

(a) (b) (c)

FIG. 101

The form of the Lagrangian (10) is retained under a rotation in the q_2, q_3-plane.

If we include terms which are quadratic in the u_α, the angular momentum

$$|M| = m\sum_\alpha [u_\alpha \wedge \dot{u}_\alpha] = m|q_2\dot{q}_3 - q_3\dot{q}_2| \tag{12}$$

can be non-zero, if there is a phase difference between the oscillations q_2 and q_3.

It is interesting to analyse what changes are introduced if we consider now the possibility that the potential energy may depend on the angles between the bonds. It is clear that such a dependence will not affect the frequency of the q_1 oscillation. The frequencies of the q_2 and q_3 oscillation will be changed, but a twofold degeneracy will remain. Indeed, together with a q-oscillation we can also have another oscillation obtained from the original q-oscillation by a rotation over 120°. Its frequency must be the same as that of the original oscillation. On the other hand, the q-coordinate will differ (only the q_1 oscillation remains the same under a rotation over 120°). We find thus two independent oscillations with the same frequency. The normal coordinates must in this case satisfy only one condition: they must be orthogonal to q_1; in particular, q_2 and q_3 remain normal coordinates.

6.38. Let the oscillation for which the molecule retains its shape (Fig. 102a) have a frequency ω_1.

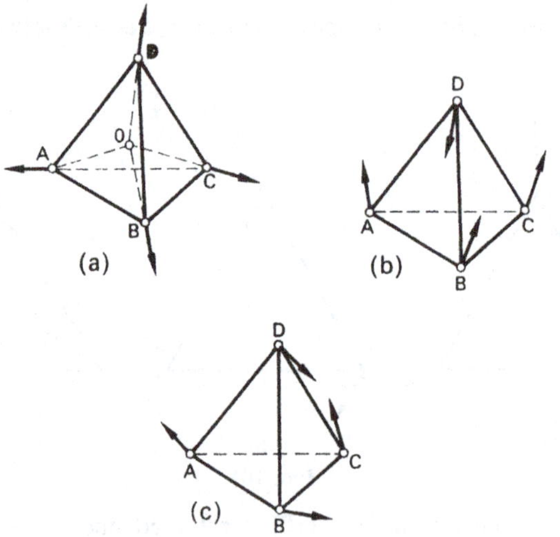

FIG. 102

The frequency ω_2 of the oscillation which retains its form under rotations around OD over $2\pi/3$ (Fig. 102b) is, in general, different from ω_1. One can obtain another displacement of the atoms by taking a reflection in the plane BCO; we obtain oscillations which differ from the second one only in that atoms A and D change roles. The frequency of that oscillation $\omega_3 = \omega_2$. Similarly, in the reflection in the plane AOC the roles of atoms B and D are changed, while the frequency remains the same, $\omega_4 = \omega_2$. This fourth oscillation cannot be reduced to a superposition of the previous ones as, in contrast to those, it is not symmetric with respect to the plane AOD.

The oscillation which is symmetric with respect to the planes AOB and DOC (Fig. 102c) has a frequency ω_5 which is different from ω_1 and ω_2. A rotation over an angle $2\pi/3$ around OD which results in a cyclic permutation of A, B, and C, leads to an oscillation which is symmetric with respect to the planes COA and DOB, and its frequency $\omega_3 = \omega_5$.

The molecule has thus three eigen-frequencies which are, respectively, non-degenerate and twofold and threefold degenerate.

In conclusion we note that the molecules considered in problems 6.37 and 6.38 are, clearly, not to be found in nature. However, a similar approach can be used also for real molecules.

7. Oscillations of Linear Chains

7.1. The Lagrangian of the system is

$$L(x, \dot{x}) = \tfrac{1}{2}m \sum_{n=1}^{N} \dot{x}_n^2 - \tfrac{1}{2}\varkappa\left[x_1^2 + \sum_{n=2}^{N} (x_n - x_{n-1})^2 + x_N^2\right], \tag{1}$$

where the x_n are the displacements of the nth mass from its equilibrium position. We also introduce the coordinate of the equilibrium position of the nth mass, $y_n = na$, where a is the equilibrium length of one spring. The Lagrangian equations of motion

$$\left.\begin{aligned} &m\dot{x}_1 + \varkappa(2x_1 - x_2) = 0, \\ &m\dot{x}_n + \varkappa(2x_n - x_{n-1} - x_{n+1}) = 0, \quad n = 2, 3, \ldots, N-1, \\ &m\dot{x}_N + \varkappa(2x_N - x_{N-1}) = 0, \end{aligned}\right\} \tag{2}$$

are equivalent to the set

$$m\ddot{x}_n + \varkappa(2x_n - x_{n-1} - x_{n+1}) = 0, \quad n = 1, 2, \ldots, N, \tag{3}$$

with the additional condition

$$x_0 = x_{N+1} \equiv 0. \tag{4}$$

We expect from physical considerations that the normal oscillations of the system will be standing waves. It is, however, convenient to consider

$$x_n = Ae^{i(\omega t \pm n\varphi)}. \tag{5}$$

The set of N equations (3) then reduces to the one equation

$$\omega^2 = 4\frac{\varkappa}{m}\sin^2\frac{1}{2}\varphi, \tag{6}$$

which determines the relation between the frequency ω and the difference in the phase of neighbouring particles φ. The meaning of the substitution (5) consists in the choice for the x_n of a solution in the form of a travelling wave with a wave vector $p = \varphi/a$ such that $n\varphi = nap = py_n$. Equation (6) thus establishes the relation between the frequency and the wave vector.

Conditions (4) can be satisfied by taking a superposition of waves travelling in two directions,

$$x_n = Ae^{i(\omega t - n\varphi)} + Be^{i(\omega t + n\varphi)}.$$

The condition $x_0 = 0$ gives $A = -B$, or $x = 2iB \sin n\varphi\, e^{i\omega t}$, that is, a standing wave. From the condition at the other end, $x_{N+1} = 0$ we determine the spectrum of possible frequencies. The equation $\sin(N+1)\varphi = 0$ has N independent solutions

$$\varphi_s = \frac{\pi s}{N+1}, \quad s = 1, 2, \ldots, N. \tag{7}$$

In fact, $s = 0$ and $s = N+1$ give vanishing solutions; for $s = N+l$ the phase $\varphi_{N+l} = -\varphi_{N-l+2} + 2\pi$, that is, the solution corresponding to $s = N+l$ can be expressed in terms of the solution for $s = N-l+2$. From (6) and (7) we find N different frequencies:

$$\omega_s = 2\sqrt{\frac{\varkappa}{m}}\sin\frac{1}{2}\varphi_s = 2\sqrt{\frac{\varkappa}{m}}\sin\frac{\pi s}{2(N+1)}, \quad s = 1, 2, \ldots, N. \tag{8}$$

The different frequencies are shown in Fig. 103 by the discrete points on the sine curve. The vector of the normal oscillation corresponding to the sth frequency is

$$\boldsymbol{r}_s = (x_1, x_2, \ldots, x_N) = \sqrt{\frac{2}{N+1}}(\sin\varphi_s, \sin 2\varphi_s, \ldots, \sin N\varphi_s)\, q_s(t), \tag{9}$$

where

$$q_s(t) = \operatorname{Re}(2iB_s e^{i\omega_s t}) = c_s \cos(\omega_s t + \alpha_s)$$

is the sth normal coordinate while the factor

$$\sqrt{\frac{2}{N+1}} = \left[\sum_{n=1}^{N} \sin^2 n\varphi_s\right]^{-\frac{1}{2}}$$

is introduced to get the normalisation $(\boldsymbol{r}_s \cdot \boldsymbol{r}_{s'}) = \delta_{ss'} q_s^2$.

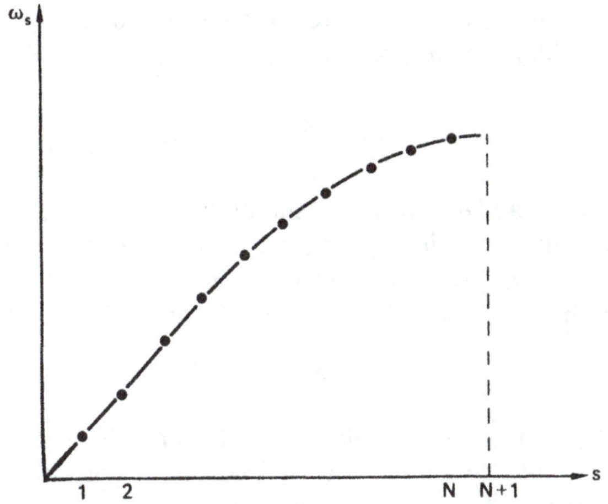

FIG. 103

The general solution is a superposition of all normal oscillations:

$$x_n = \sum_{s=1}^{N} \sqrt{\frac{2}{N+1}} \sin n\varphi_s \, q_s(t). \tag{10}$$

The matrix giving the transition from the x_n to the q_s,

$$U_{ns} = \sqrt{\frac{2}{N+1}} \sin \frac{\pi n s}{N+1},$$

is an orthogonal matrix which reduces the Lagrangian to a sum of squares corresponding to a set of N different oscillators:

$$L(x, \dot{x}) = \sum_{s=1}^{N} L_s(q_s, \dot{q}_s); \qquad L_s(q_s, \dot{q}_s) = \tfrac{1}{2} m \left[\dot{q}_s^2 - \omega_s^2 q_s^2\right].$$

7.2. The equations of motion for the given system are the same as equations (3) of the previous problem but now with the additional conditions

$x_0 = 0$, $x_N = x_{N+1}$. We get thus

$$\varphi_s = \frac{(2s-1)\pi}{2N+1}, \quad s = 1, 2, \ldots, N; \qquad \omega_s = 2\sqrt{\frac{\varkappa}{m}} \sin \frac{(2s-1)\pi}{2(2N+1)};$$

$$x_n = \sum_s A_s \sin n\varphi_s \cos (\omega_s t + \alpha_s).$$

For the particular case when $N = 2$, see problem 6.1.

7.3. The equations of motion are the same as equations (3) of problem 7.1 but now with the conditions $x_0 = x_N$ and $x_{N+1} = x_1$. We get thus

$$\varphi_s = \frac{2\pi s}{N}, \quad s = 0, 1, \ldots, N-1; \qquad \omega_s = 2\sqrt{\frac{\varkappa}{m}} \sin \frac{\pi s}{N};$$

the frequencies ω_s and ω_{N-s} are the same and the wave vectors corresponding to them differ only in sign: $\varphi_s = 2\pi - \varphi_{N-s}$. The frequency $\omega_0 = 0$ corresponds to the motion of all masses along the ring with a constant velocity. In this system oscillations of the form

$$x_n^{(s)} = \operatorname{Re} A_s e^{i(\omega_s t - n\varphi_s)} \tag{1}$$

are possible, that is, waves which travel along the ring. The above-mentioned twofold degeneracy of the frequencies corresponds to waves moving in opposite directions. The presence of two such waves with equal amplitudes gives a standing wave:

$$x_n^{(s)} \pm x_n^{(N-s)} = 2|A_s| \left\{ \begin{array}{l} \cos n\varphi_s \cos (\omega_s t + \alpha_s) \\ \sin n\varphi_s \sin (\omega_s t + \alpha_s) \end{array} \right\}. \tag{2}$$

This is also a normal oscillations (all points move either in phase or in antiphase).

In terms of the appropriate normal coordinates,

$$x_n = \sum_{s=1}^{R} (q_{s1} \cos n\varphi_s + q_{s2} \sin n\varphi_s) + q_0, \quad R = \tfrac{1}{2}(N-1) \quad (N\text{: odd}), \tag{3}$$

the Lagrangian is reduced to diagonal form:

$$L = \tfrac{1}{2}Nm\{\dot{q}_0^2 + \sum_{s=1}^{R} [\dot{q}_{s1}^2 + \dot{q}_{s2}^2 - \omega_s^2(q_{s1}^2 + q_{s2}^2)]\}. \tag{4}$$

(If the number of particles is even, equations (3) and (4) must be somewhat changed as the frequency $\omega_{N/2}$ is non-degenerate; equation (1) at once defines a standing wave for $s = \frac{1}{2}N$.)

It is interesting to note that rotations in the q_{s1}, q_{s2}-planes,

$$q_{s1} = q'_{s1} \cos \beta_s - q'_{s2} \sin \beta_s, \quad q_{s2} = q'_{s1} \sin \beta_s + q'_{s2} \cos \beta_s,$$

which leave the Lagrangian (4) invariant, correspond to a displacement of the nodes of the standing waves:

$$x_n = q_0 + \sum_{s=1}^{R} [q'_{s1} \cos (n\varphi_s - \beta_s) + q'_{s2} \sin (n\varphi_s - \beta_s)].$$

The average energy flux along the ring is for the travelling waves (1) given by (compare problem 6.8)†

$$S_{\text{av}} = \left(\frac{2\pi}{\omega}\right)^{-1} \int_0^{2\pi/\omega} \varkappa(x_{n+1} - x_n)\, \dot{x}_n\, dt = \frac{1}{2} \varkappa |A|^2 \omega \sin \varphi,$$

while the group velocity is

$$v_{\text{gr}} = \frac{d\omega}{dp} = \sqrt{\frac{\varkappa}{m}}\, a \cos \frac{1}{2}\varphi,$$

where a is the equilibrium length of one spring, while $p = \varphi/a$ is the wave vector. The energy is

$$E = \frac{1}{2} m \sum_n \dot{x}_n^2 + \frac{1}{2} \varkappa \sum_n (x_n - x_{n-1})^2 = 2N |A|^2 \varkappa \sin \frac{1}{2} \varphi,$$

and we have thus $E v_{\text{gr}}/Na = S_{\text{av}}$.

7.4. (a) The equations of motion are ($n = 1, 2, \ldots, N$)

$$m\ddot{x}_{2n-1} + \varkappa(2x_{2n-1} - x_{2n} - x_{2n-2}) = 0,$$
$$M\ddot{x}_{2n} + \varkappa(2x_{2n} - x_{2n-1} - x_{2n+1}) = 0.$$

Here

$$x_0 = x_{2N+1} = 0. \tag{1}$$

We shall look for a solution in the form of travelling waves with different amplitudes

$$\left.\begin{aligned} x_{2n-1} &= A e^{i[\omega t \pm (2n-1)\varphi]}, \\ x_{2n} &= B e^{i[\omega t \pm 2n\varphi]}. \end{aligned}\right\} \tag{2}$$

To determine A and B we get a set of homogeneous equations,

$$\left.\begin{aligned} (-m\omega^2 + 2\varkappa) A - \varkappa(e^{-i\varphi} + e^{i\varphi}) B &= 0, \\ -\varkappa(e^{-i\varphi} + e^{i\varphi}) A + (-M\omega^2 + 2\varkappa) B &= 0, \end{aligned}\right\} \tag{3}$$

† In the following we drop for the sake of simplicity the index s. The calculation of S_{av} and of the energy E is most conveniently carried out using complex variables (compare Landau and Lifshitz, 1962, § 48).

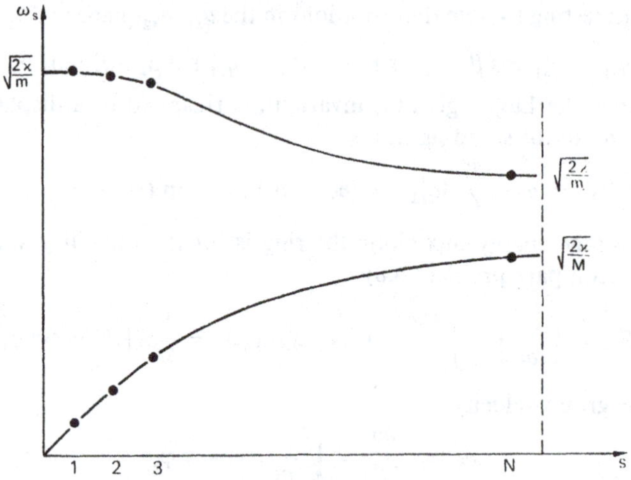

FIG. 104

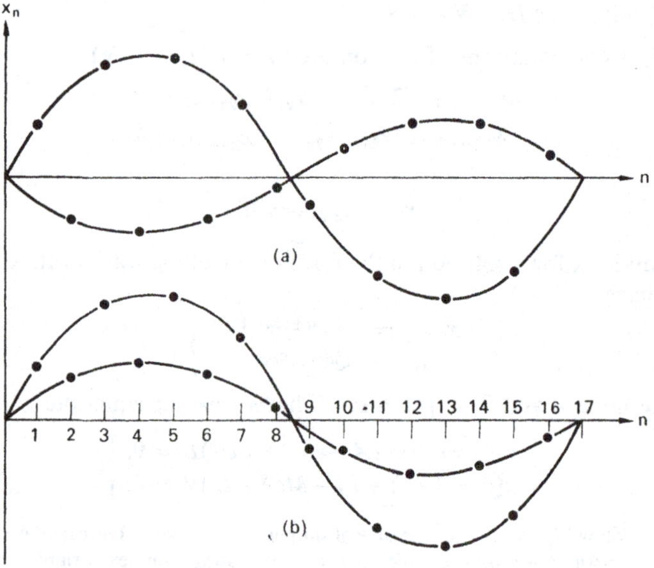

FIG. 105

which have a non-trivial solution only if its determinant vanishes. This condition determines the relations between the frequency and the difference in phase of neighbouring particles:

$$\omega_{\mp}^2 = \frac{\varkappa}{\mu}\left[1 \mp \sqrt{1-\frac{4\mu^2}{mM}\sin^2\varphi}\right], \quad \mu = \frac{mM}{m+M}. \tag{4}$$

The boundary condition (1) is satisfied only by well-defined linear combinations of the travelling waves (2), namely,

$$x_{2n-s} = A_s \sin(2n-1)\varphi_s \cos(\omega_s t+\alpha_s),$$

$$x_{2n} = B_s \sin 2n\varphi_s \cos(\omega_s t+\alpha_s),$$

for which $\varphi_s = s\pi/(2N+1)$. Since $\varphi_{2N+1-s} = \pi - \varphi_s$ we get different frequencies, having chosen one of the two signs in (4), only for $s=1, 2, \ldots, N$. These are indicated (for the case when $M > m$) in Fig. 104 by distinct dots on the two different branches, one of which, the lower one, ω_-, is usually called the acoustic, and the other, the upper one, ω_+, is called the optical branch.

The general solution has the form

$$x_{2n-1} = \sum_{s=1}^{N} \sin(2n-1)\varphi_s[A_{(+)s}\cos(\omega_{(+)s}t+\alpha_s)+A_{(-)s}\cos(\omega_{(-)s}t+\beta_s)],$$

$$x_{2n} = \sum_{s=1}^{N} \sin 2n\varphi_s[B_{(+)s}\cos(\omega_{(+)s}t+\alpha_s)+B_{(-)s}\cos(\omega_{(-)s}t+\beta_s)],$$

where the A and B are according to (3) connected by the relation

$$B_{(\pm)s} = A_{(\pm)s}\frac{-m\omega_{(\pm)s}^2+2\varkappa}{2\varkappa\cos\varphi_s}.$$

It is noteworthy that $B_{(-)}$ and $A_{(-)}$ which correspond to the acoustic frequencies have the same sign while $B_{(+)}$ and $A_{(+)}$ for the optical frequencies have the opposite sign (that is, neighbouring masses m and M move in antiphase). The amplitude of the oscillations for the case $N = 8$, $s = 2$ is shown in Fig. 105 where the ordinate gives the number of the masses and the abscissa gives the amplitude (a gives an optical and b an acoustic mode).

How can one obtain from the results obtained here the limiting case when $m = M$ (see problem 7.1)?

(b) The normal oscillations are

$$x_{2n}^{(s)} = A_s \sin 2n\varphi_s \cos(\omega_s t + \alpha_s),$$

$$x_{2n-1}^{(s)} = A_s \frac{K \sin 2n\varphi_s + \varkappa \sin(2n-2)\varphi_s}{\varkappa + K - m\omega_s^2} \cos(\omega_s t + \alpha_s),$$

where

$$\omega_s^2 = \frac{1}{m}\left[K + \varkappa \mp \sqrt{(K-\varkappa)^2 + 4\varkappa K \cos^2 \varphi_s}\right]$$

is determined from the equations

$$\tan(2N+1)\varphi_s = -\frac{K-\varkappa}{K+\varkappa} \tan\varphi_s, \quad s = 1, 2, \ldots, N, \quad 0 \leqq \varphi_s < \tfrac{1}{2}\pi.$$

Figure 106a shows the optical and acoustic branches of the frequencies for the case $K > \varkappa$.

What happens in the limiting case when $\varkappa = K$?

(c) We have $\varphi_s = \pi s/2(N+1)$; for $s = 1, 2, \ldots, N$ we get $2N$ normal oscillations and normal frequencies which have the same form as under

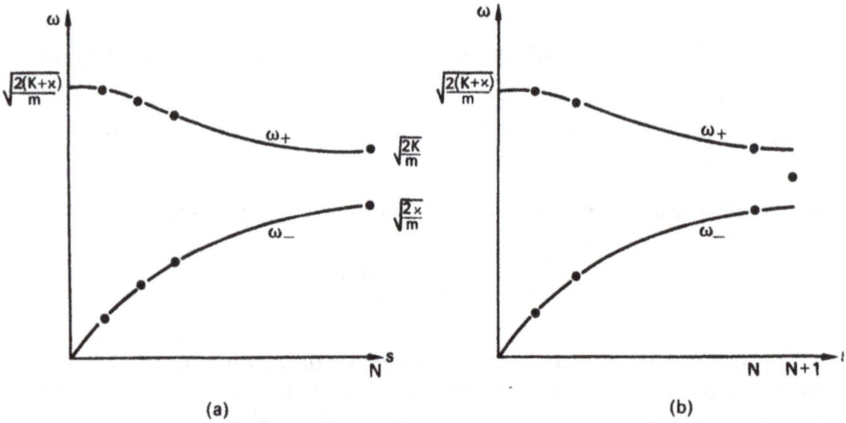

FIG. 106

(b) (see Fig. 106b). How does one find the necessary and very interesting normal oscillation for which $x_{2n} = 0$, $Kx_{2n-1} = \varkappa x_{2n+1}$, the frequency of which, $\omega^2 = (\varkappa + K)/m$, lies in the forbidden band between the optical and acoustic branches? The distribution of the amplitudes of this oscillation is shown in Fig. 107 where the ordinate and abscissa show respectively the number of the masses and their amplitudes. Masses with an even number are not moving while neighbouring masses with odd numbers are moving in antiphase with exponentially damped amplitudes, when we move away from the left-hand end of the chain ("surface phonon").

7.5. We look for a solution of the equations of motion,

$$m\ddot{x}_n + \varkappa(2x_n - x_{n-1} - x_{n+1}) = 0, \quad n = 1, 2, \ldots, N, \tag{1}$$

with the boundary conditions $x_0 = 0$ and $x_{N+1} = a \cos \omega t$ in the form $x_n = A \sin n\varphi \cos \omega t$, so that the first boundary condition is immediately satisfied. From the second boundary condition we find $A = a/\sin(N+1)\varphi$, while from equations (1) we get for the "wave vector" φ of the standing wave

$$\sin^2 \tfrac{1}{2}\varphi = \frac{m\omega^2}{4\varkappa}.$$

When $\omega^2 < 4\varkappa/m$ the stable oscillations

$$x_n = a\frac{\sin n\varphi}{\sin(N+1)\varphi}\cos \omega t \tag{2}$$

have a large amplitude when $\sin(N+1)\varphi$ is close to zero. But this is just

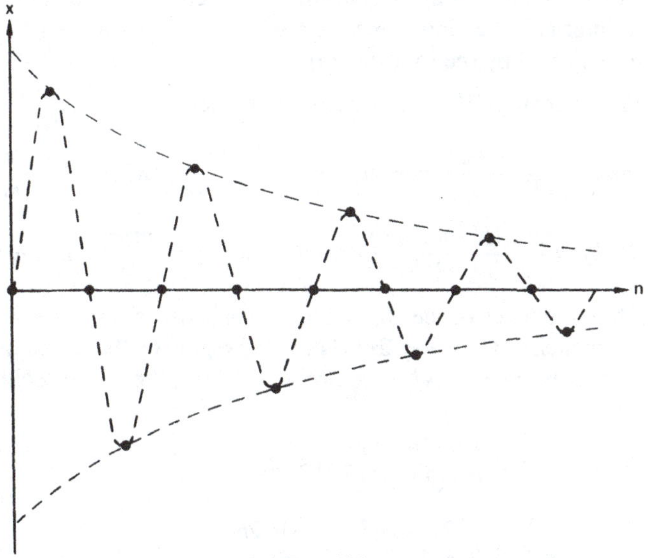

FIG. 107

the condition which determined the spectrum of the eigen-frequencies ω_s of the system (see problem 7.1), that is, we have then a near-resonance situation, $\omega \approx \omega_s$. When $\omega \ll \omega_1 = 2\sqrt{\varkappa/m}\sin[\pi/2(N+1)]$ the oscillations (2) correspond to a slow extension and compression of all springs: $x_n = (an/[N+1])\cos\omega t$.

If $\omega^2 > 4\varkappa/m$, we change φ to $\pi - i\psi$ in (2) and get

$$x_n = (-1)^{N+1+n} a \frac{\sinh n\psi}{\sinh (N+1)\psi} \cos \omega t,$$

where

$$\cos h^2 \tfrac{1}{2}\psi = \frac{m\omega^2}{4\varkappa}.$$

The oscillations are (exponentially when $n\psi \gg 1$) damped towards the left-hand end of the chain. The reasonableness of this result is particularly clear when $\omega^2 \gg 4\varkappa/m$ when the frequency of the applied force lies appreciably above the limit of the spectrum of the norma frequencies. In that case the mass on the extreme right oscillates with a small amplitude in anti-phase with the applied force while the $(N-1)$st mass is in first approximation at rest. Then we can consider the motion of the $(N-1)$st mass as a forced oscillation caused by an applied force of high frequency arising from the Nth mass, and so on.

We note that a similar damping of the wave occurs in the phenomenon of complete internal reflection (for instance, when short wavelength radio-waves are reflected by the ionosphere).

What is the form of the stable oscillation when $\omega^2 = 4\varkappa/m$?

$$x_n = a\frac{\cos (N-n+\frac{1}{2})\varphi}{\cos (N+\frac{1}{2})\varphi}\cos\omega t, \quad \sin^2\tfrac{1}{2}\varphi = \frac{m\omega^2}{4\varkappa}, \quad \text{when } \omega^2 < \frac{4\varkappa}{m};$$

$$x_n = (-1)^n a\frac{\sinh (N-n+\frac{1}{2})\psi}{\sinh (N+\frac{1}{2})\psi}\cos\omega t, \quad \cosh^2\tfrac{1}{2}\psi = \frac{m\omega^2}{4\varkappa}, \quad \text{when } \omega^2 > \frac{4\varkappa}{m}.$$

7.6. If the frequency of the applied force lies in the range of the acoustic normal frequencies, $0 < \omega^2 < 2\varkappa/M$ or in the region of the optical normal frequencies $2\varkappa/m < \omega^2 < 2\varkappa/\mu$ (see problem 7.4 (a)) the stable oscillations are

$$x_{2n-1} = a\frac{\sin (2n-1)\varphi}{\sin (2N+1)\varphi}\cos\omega t,$$

$$x_{2n} = \pm\sqrt{\frac{2\varkappa - m\omega^2}{2\varkappa - M\omega^2}}\, a\frac{\sin 2n\varphi}{\sin (2N+1)\varphi}\cos\omega t,$$

where

$$\cos^2 \varphi = \frac{1}{4\varkappa^2}(2\varkappa - m\omega^2)(2\varkappa - M\omega^2),$$

while the upper (lower) sign corresponds to ω lying in the range of the acoustic (optical) frequencies.

For frequencies lying in the "forbidden band" $2\varkappa/M < \omega^2 < 2\varkappa/m$, we have

$$x_{2n-1} = (-1)^{N+n} a \frac{\cosh (2n-1)\psi}{\cosh (2N+1)\psi} \cos \omega t;$$

$$x_{2n} = (-1)^{N+n} a \sqrt{\frac{2\varkappa - m\omega^2}{M\omega^2 - 2\varkappa}} \frac{\sinh 2n\psi}{\cosh (2N+1)\psi} \cos \omega t;$$

$$\sinh^2 \psi = \frac{-1}{4\varkappa^2}(2\varkappa - M\omega^2)(2\varkappa - m\omega^2),$$

while for frequencies $\omega^2 > \varkappa/\mu$, which lie above the limit of the optical branch,

$$x_{2n-1} = a \frac{\sinh (2n-1)\chi}{\sinh (2N+1)\chi} \cos \omega t;$$

$$x_{2n} = -a \sqrt{\frac{2\varkappa - m\omega^2}{2\varkappa - M\omega^2}} \frac{\sinh 2n\chi}{\sinh (2N+1)\chi} \cos \omega t;$$

$$\cosh^2 \chi = \frac{1}{4\varkappa^2}(M\omega^2 - 2\varkappa)(m\omega^2 - 2\varkappa);$$

the vibrations are damped exponentially towards the left-hand side end of the chain.

7.7. (a) We look for the solution of the equations of motion,

$$m\ddot{x}_n + \varkappa(2x_n - x_{n-1} - x_{n+1}) = 0, \quad n = 1, 2, \ldots, N-1; \tag{1}$$

$$m_N \ddot{x}_N + \varkappa(2x_N - x_{N-1}) = 0 \tag{2}$$

(with the boundary condition $x_0 = 0$), in the form of standing waves:

$$\left.\begin{aligned} x_n &= A \sin n\varphi \cos(\omega t + \alpha), \quad n = 1, 2, \ldots, N-1; \\ x_N &= B \cos(\omega t + \alpha). \end{aligned}\right\} \tag{3}$$

From (1) we get the relation

$$\omega^2 = \frac{4\varkappa}{m} \sin^2 \tfrac{1}{2}\varphi. \tag{4}$$

Using (3) and (4) we get from (1) and (2) the set of equations

$$A \sin N\varphi - B = 0,$$

$$-A \sin (N-1)\varphi + \left(-\frac{4m_N}{m} \sin^2 \tfrac{1}{2}\varphi + 2\right) B = 0.$$

Hence $B = A \sin N\varphi$, while the parameter φ is determined as the solution of the transcendental equation

$$\sin N\varphi \left[\frac{4m_N}{m} \sin^2 \tfrac{1}{2}\varphi - 2 + \cos \varphi\right] = \cos N\varphi \sin \varphi. \quad (5)$$

When $m_N \gg m$, we have apart from the obvious normal oscillations,

$$x_n^{(s)} = A_s \sin n\varphi_s \cos (\omega_s t + \alpha_s), \quad n = 1, 2, \ldots, N-1,$$

$$x_N^{(s)} = A_s \sin N\varphi_s \cos (\omega_s t + \alpha_s),$$

$$\tan N\varphi_s \approx \frac{m}{2m_N} \cos \tfrac{1}{2}\varphi_s, \quad s = 1, 2, \ldots, N-1,$$

when the mass m_N is practically stationary ($\sin N\varphi_s \ll 1$), also a normal vibration with an amplitude which increases linearly to the right-hand side of the chain:

$$x_n^{(N)} = B \frac{n}{N} \cos (\omega_N t + \alpha_N), \quad \omega_N^2 = \frac{\varkappa}{m_N} \left(1 + \frac{1}{N}\right).$$

The mass m_N then oscillates between springs of stiffness $\varkappa$ (to the right) and $\varkappa/N$ (to the left). The fact that equation (5) has such a solution can be seen as follows. Assuming φ to be small and retaining only the main terms we get from (5): $\varphi^2 = (m/m_N)(1+N^{-1})$ completely in accordance with the assumptions made.

When $m_N \ll m$ we have the usual oscillations characteristic for a system of $N-1$ masses with a spring of stiffness $\varkappa/2$ at the right-hand end (the parameters φ_s and the frequencies ω_s, $s = 1, 2, \ldots, N-1$, are determined from the equation $\tan N\varphi = -\sin \varphi/(2 - \cos \varphi)$). Apart from those there is also a normal oscillation with an amplitude which decreases towards the left-hand side of the chain:

$$x_n^{(N)} = (-1)^{N+n} B \frac{\sinh n\psi}{\sinh N\psi} \cos (\omega_N t + \alpha_N);$$

$$\cosh^2 \tfrac{1}{2}\psi = \frac{m}{2m_N} \gg 1, \quad \omega_N^2 = \frac{2\varkappa}{m_N}.$$

Formally, the value of the parameter ψ can be obtained from equation (5) using the substitution $\varphi = \pi - i\psi$, assuming ψ to be large. This normal vibration can in first approximation be considered to be the simple oscillation of the small mass m_N while the other masses are at rest, while we afterwards consider the motion of the other masses as forced oscillations under the action of a high-frequency force,

$$\varkappa x_N = \varkappa B \cos\left(\sqrt{\frac{2\varkappa}{m_N}}\, t + \alpha_N\right),$$

acting upon the right-hand side of the chain of $N-1$ identical masses (compare problem 7.6).

(b) When $\varkappa_{N+1} \ll \varkappa$ the solution is the same as the solution of problem 7.2. When $\varkappa_{N+1} \gg \varkappa$ there are normal oscillations for which the Nth mass is practically at rest:

$$x_n^{(s)} = A_s \sin n\varphi_s \cos(\omega_s t + \alpha_s);$$
$$x_N^{(s)} = A_s \sin N\varphi_s \cos(\omega_s t + \alpha_s);$$
$$\omega^2 = \frac{4\varkappa}{m} \sin^2 \tfrac{1}{2}\varphi_s, \quad \varphi_s \approx \frac{\pi s}{N}, \quad s = 1, 2, \ldots, N-1.$$

The parameter φ_s is determined from the equation

$$\left(2 \sin^2 \tfrac{1}{2}\varphi - \frac{\varkappa_{N+1}}{\varkappa}\right) \sin N\varphi = \cos N\varphi \sin\varphi, \tag{6}$$

which in the approximation considered has the form

$$\tan N\varphi = -\frac{\varkappa}{\varkappa_{N+1}} \sin\varphi.$$

Equation (6) has yet one more solution which we can obtain by putting $\varphi = \pi - i\psi$ and assuming ψ to be large. In that case we have

$$x_n^{(N)} = (-1)^{N+n} B_N \frac{\sinh n\psi}{\sinh N\psi} \cos(\omega_N t + \alpha_N), \quad \cosh^2 \tfrac{1}{2}\psi = \frac{\varkappa_{N+1}}{4\varkappa},$$
$$\omega_N^2 = \frac{\varkappa_{N+1}}{m},$$

that is, the amplitude of this oscillation decreases towards the left-hand side of the chain.

How can we obtain this last oscillation by using the results of problem 7.5)?

7.8. The equations for the oscillations of the discrete system (see equation (3) of problem 7.1) can be written in the form

$$\ddot{x}_n - \varkappa a \frac{a}{m}\left[\frac{x_{n+1}-x_n}{a} - \frac{x_n - x_{n-1}}{a}\right]\frac{1}{a} = 0. \tag{1}$$

The quantity $m/a = Nm/Na$ becomes in the limit the linear density of the rod ϱ. The relative extension of the section a, that is, the quantity $(x_n - x_{n-1})/a$ is proportional to the force acting upon it, $F = \varkappa a(x_n - x_{n-1})/a$, and $\varkappa a$ thus becomes in the limit the elastic modulus Y of the rod. Equation (1) in the limit thus becomes the wave equation

$$\frac{\partial^2 x(\xi, t)}{\partial t^2} - v^2 \frac{\partial^2 x(\xi, t)}{\partial \xi^2} = 0, \tag{2}$$

where $v = \sqrt{(Y/\varrho)}$ is the phase velocity of the wave.

Instead of a set of N coupled differential equations we have obtained one partial differential equation (compare problem 4.26).

We note that in our derivation we had to make the important assumption that the function $x_n(t)$ tends to a well-defined limit $x(\xi, t)$ which is a sufficiently smooth function.

7.9. If a is small we can approximately write the displacement in the form

$$x_n = x(\xi, t),$$

$$x_{n\pm 1} = x(\xi \pm a, t) = x(\xi, t) \pm a \frac{\partial x(\xi, t)}{\partial \xi} + \tfrac{1}{2}a^2 \frac{\partial^2 x(\xi, t)}{\partial \xi^2} \pm \tfrac{1}{6}a^3 \frac{\partial^3 x(\xi, t)}{\partial \xi^3} + \dots$$

Equation (2) of problem 7.8 then changes to the equation

$$\frac{\partial^2 x}{\partial t^2} - \frac{Y}{\varrho}\frac{\partial^2 x}{\partial \xi^2} - \frac{Ya^2}{12\varrho}\frac{\partial^4 x}{\partial \xi^4} = 0. \tag{1}$$

While each of equations (1) of problem 7.8 contains the displacements of three neighbouring points (long-range interaction), equation (1) here contains the displacement x in a given point ξ (short-range interaction). The term $-(Ya^2/12\varrho)(\partial^4 x/\partial \xi^4)$ in equation (1) corresponds to taking approximately into account the small difference between the system considered and a continuous one (see, for instance, Landau and Lifshitz, 1960a, § 83, for a discussion of spatial dispersion in electrodynamics).

8. Non-linear Oscillations

8.1. (a)

$$x(t) = a\cos\omega t - \frac{\beta a^3}{32\omega_0^2}\cos 3\omega t, \qquad \omega = \omega_0 + \frac{3\beta a^2}{8\omega_0}$$

(see Landau and Lifshitz, 1960, § 28). In Fig. 108 we have depicted the function $x(t)$. When $\beta > 0$ there is a "limitation" of the oscillations, when $\beta < 0$, the maxima become sharper. These properties of the oscillations and also the sign of the correction to the energy can easily be considered by looking at the graph of $U(x)$ (Fig. 109).

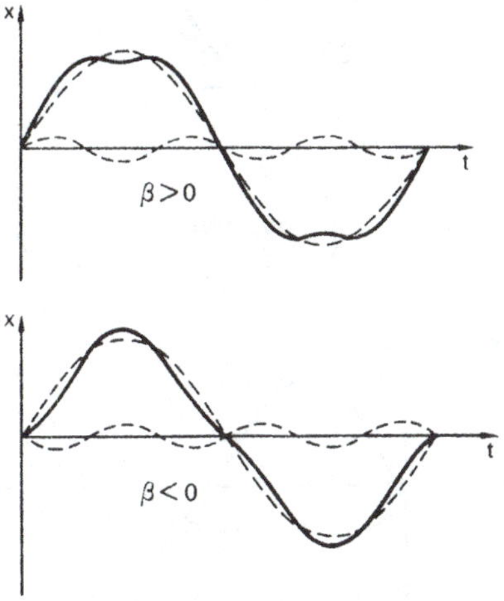

Fig. 108

(b)

$$x = a\cos\omega_0 t - \frac{\alpha a^2}{2\omega_0^2} + \frac{\alpha a^2}{6\omega_0^2}\cos 2\omega_0 t.$$

The distortion of the oscillations is non-symmetric (Fig. 110). The shift in the equilibrium position caused by the influence of the anharmonic corrections plays an important role in the theory of the thermal expansion of crystals (see, for instance, Haug, 1971, or Kittel, 1968).

8.2.

$$x = a\cos\omega t + \tfrac{1}{4}\gamma a^2\cos 2\omega t - \tfrac{3}{32}\gamma^2 a^3\cos 3\omega t, \qquad \omega = \omega_0 + \tfrac{1}{8}\gamma^2 a^2\omega_0.$$

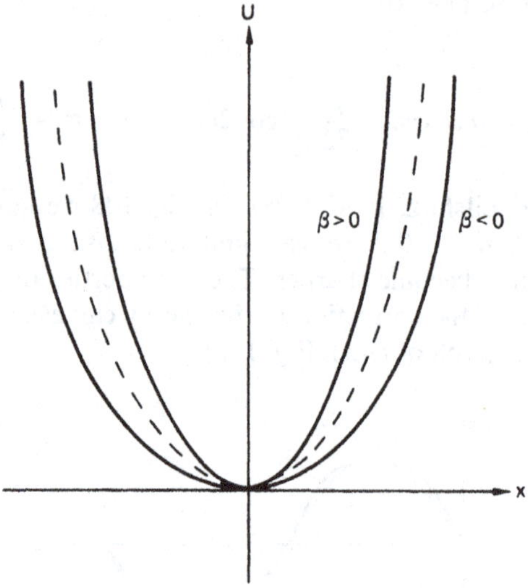

FIG. 109

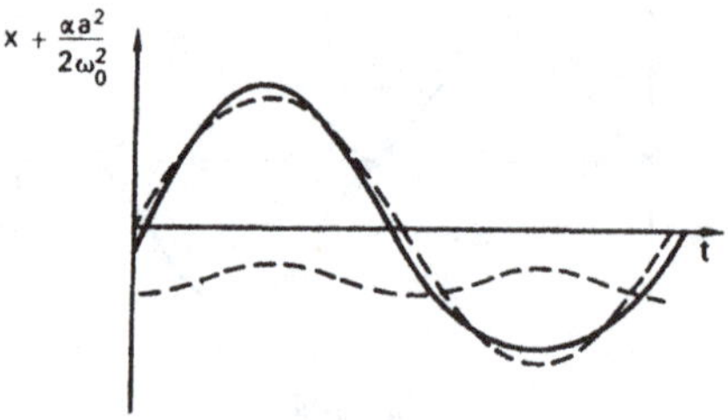

FIG. 110

8.3.

$$\varphi = \frac{a\Omega^2}{g - l\Omega^2} \cos \Omega t + \frac{a^2\Omega^4}{12(g - l\Omega^2)(g - 4l\Omega^2)} \sin 2\Omega t$$

(the notation is that of problem 5.9).

8.4.

$$x = x^{(0)} + x^{(1)} + \ldots;$$

$$x^{(0)} = \frac{f_1 \cos \omega_1 t}{m(\omega_0^2 - \omega_1^2)} + \frac{f_2 \cos \omega_2 t}{m(\omega_0^2 - \omega_2^2)};$$

$$x^{(1)} = \frac{-\alpha f_1^2}{2m\omega_0^2(\omega_0^2-\omega_1^2)^2} - \frac{\alpha f_2^2}{2m\omega_0^2(\omega_0^2-\omega_2^2)^2}$$

$$-\frac{\alpha f_1^2 \cos 2\omega_1 t}{2m(\omega_0^2-4\omega_1^2)(\omega_0^2-\omega_1^2)^2} - \frac{\alpha f_2^2 \cos 2\omega_2 t}{2m(\omega_0^2-4\omega_2^2)(\omega_0^2-\omega_2^2)^2}$$

$$-\frac{\alpha f_1 f_2 \cos(\omega_1-\omega_2)t}{m[\omega_0^2-(\omega_1-\omega_2)^2](\omega_0^2-\omega_1^2)(\omega_0^2-\omega_2^2)}$$

$$-\frac{\alpha f_1 f_2 \cos(\omega_1+\omega_2)t}{m[\omega_0^2-(\omega_1+\omega_2)^2](\omega_0^2-\omega_1^2)(\omega_0^2-\omega_2^2)} \cdot$$

What combinations of frequencies will occur when we take an anharmonic correction of the form $\delta U = \frac{1}{4}m\beta x^4$ into account?

8.5. (a) We look for a solution in the form

$$x = Ae^{i\omega t} + A^* e^{-i\omega t}.$$

Equating the coefficients of $e^{i\omega t}$, we get

$$[\omega_0^2-\omega^2+2i\lambda\omega+3\beta|A|^2]A = \tfrac{1}{2}f,$$

and hence

$$[(\omega_0^2-\omega^2+3\beta|A|^2)^2+4\lambda^2\omega^2]|A|^2 = \tfrac{1}{4}f^2.$$

A study of this equation which is cubic in $|A|^2$ can be done in the same way as the study of the analogous equation (29.4) in Landau and Lifshitz (1960).

8.6. (a) We look for a solution of the oscillations equation

$$\ddot{x}+2\lambda\dot{x}+\omega_0^2(1+h\cos 2\omega t)x+\beta x^3 = 0 \qquad (1)$$

in the form

$$x = Ae^{i\omega t}+A^*e^{-i\omega t}, \qquad (2)$$

and we retain only the terms containing $e^{\pm i\omega t}$.† Putting the coefficients of $e^{\pm i\omega t}$ equal to zero, we find

$$\left.\begin{aligned} \tfrac{1}{2}h\omega_0^2A+(\omega^2-\omega_0^2-2i\omega\lambda-3\beta|A|^2)A^* = 0,\\ \tfrac{1}{2}h\omega_0^2A^*+(\omega^2-\omega_0^2+2i\omega\lambda-3\beta|A|^2)A = 0.\end{aligned}\right\} \qquad (3)$$

† Assuming that the terms in $e^{\pm 3i\omega t}$ are appreciably smaller will be compensated by the contribution to x from the third harmonic, as will become clear in the following.

We can only have a non-vanishing A, if

$$\begin{vmatrix} \frac{1}{2}h\omega_0^2 & \omega^2-\omega_0^2-2i\omega\lambda-3\beta|A|^2 \\ \omega^2-\omega_0^2+2i\omega\lambda-3\beta|A|^2 & \frac{1}{2}h\omega_0^2 \end{vmatrix} = 0. \tag{4}$$

Hence

$$|A|^2 = \frac{1}{3\beta}\left[\omega^2-\omega_0^2 \pm \sqrt{\left(\frac{1}{2}h\omega_0^2\right)^2-(2\omega\lambda)^2}\right]. \tag{5}$$

From (3) we get†

$$\sin 2\varphi = \operatorname{Im}\frac{A}{A^*} = \frac{-4\lambda}{h\omega_0}; \quad \cos 2\varphi = \mp\frac{2}{h\omega_0^2}\sqrt{\left(\frac{1}{2}h\omega_0^2\right)^2-(2\omega\lambda)^2}. \tag{6}$$

Thus,

$$x = a\cos(\omega t+\varphi), \tag{7}$$

where $A = \frac{1}{2}ae^{i\varphi}$.

Figure 111 shows how $|A|^2$ depends on ω^2 (to fix the ideas we have assumed that $\beta > 0$). In some frequency ranges two or three (including zero values) different amplitudes of stable oscillations are possible.

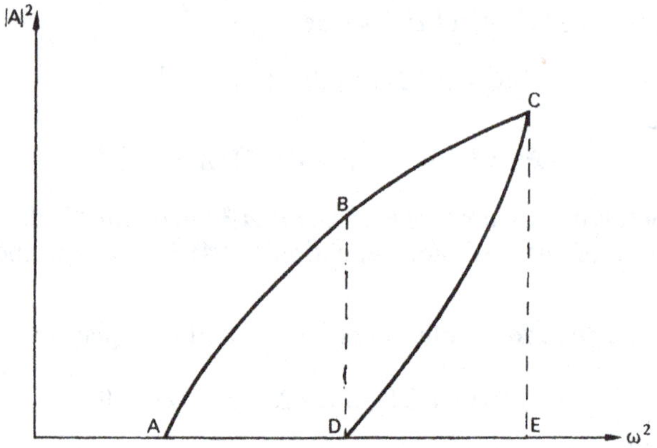

FIG. 111

The amplitudes corresponding to the sections AD and CD are not realised in actual cases since those oscillations are unstable (for a proof of this for the section AD compare the next problem; for a study of the stability of the oscillations along the sections ABC and CD see Bogolyubov and Mitropolskii, 1958).

† Equations (6) determine the phase apart from a term $n\pi$. There is no sense in determining the phase with greater precision as a change in the phase by π corresponds simply to a shift in the time origin.

(b) When we take the third harmonic into account, x has the form

$$x = Ae^{i\omega t}+A^*e^{-i\omega t}+Be^{3i\omega t}+B^*e^{-3i\omega t}. \tag{8}$$

We assume that $|B| \ll |A|$, which will be confirmed by the results. Substituting (8) into (1) we split off the terms containing $e^{3i\omega t}$; we then drop the product of B with small parameters. It turns out that

$$B = \left(\frac{1}{16}h+\frac{1}{8}\frac{\beta A^2}{\omega^2}\right)A, \tag{9}$$

and, indeed, $|B| \ll |A|$.

Therefore

$$x = a\cos(\omega t+\varphi)+b\cos(3\omega t+\psi), \tag{10}$$

where $b = 2|B|$, $\psi = \arg B$.

One notes easily that the fifth harmonic turns out to be small of second order ($\sim h^2A$), the seventh $\sim h^3A$, and so on. The even harmonics do not occur. This is the basis of the method used to evaluate the amplitudes.

8.7. (a) We look for a solution of the equation of motion in the form

$$x(t) = a(t)\cos\omega t+b(t)\sin\omega t, \tag{1}$$

where $a(t)$ and $b(t)$ are slowly changing functions of the time. To determine $a(t)$ and $b(t)$ we get the following set of equations (compare Landau and Lifshitz, 1960, § 27):

$$\left.\begin{aligned} \dot a+[\omega-\omega_0+\tfrac{1}{4}h\omega_0]b &= 0,\\ \dot b-[\omega-\omega_0-\tfrac{1}{4}h\omega_0]a &= 0. \end{aligned}\right\} \tag{2}$$

If $|\omega-\omega_0| < \frac{1}{4}h\omega_0$, its solution is

$$\left.\begin{aligned} a(t) &= \alpha_1(c_1e^{-st}+c_2e^{st}),\\ b(t) &= \alpha_2(c_1e^{-st}-c_2e^{st}), \end{aligned}\right\} \tag{3}$$

where

$$s = \tfrac{1}{4}\sqrt{(h\omega_0)^2-16(\omega-\omega_0)^2}, \quad \alpha_{1,2} = \sqrt{h\omega_0\pm4(\omega-\omega_0)}.$$

Hence

$$x = c'e^{st}\cos(\omega t-\varphi)+C''e^{-st}\cos(\omega t+\varphi), \tag{4}$$

where $\tan\varphi = \alpha_2/\alpha_1$ (see Fig. 112).

The oscillations thus increase, generally speaking, without limit. The rate of their increase which is characterised by the quantity s is, indeed, small. In actual cases the increase in the amplitude of the oscillations is cut off, for instance, if the influence of the anharmonic terms becomes important (see problem 8.6) or the reaction of the oscillations on the device which periodically changes its frequency becomes important.

It is useful to draw attention to the analogy between the result obtained and the particular solution of the problem of the normal oscillations of a chain of masses connected by springs of different stiffness (problem 7.4c). An inhomogeneity with period $2a$ along the chain leads to a build-up along the chain of the amplitude of the stable oscillations, when the "wavelength" is equal to $4a$ (see Fig. 107) in a similar way as a periodic change with time of the frequency of an oscillator will lead to an increase in the amplitude with time. An even more complete analogy can be observed with problem 7.6. The region of instability with respect to parametric resonance corresponds to the forbidden zone in the spectrum of the oscillations of the chain.

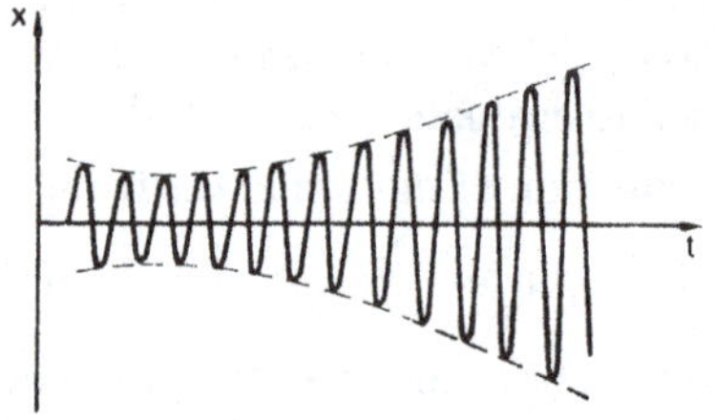

FIG. 112

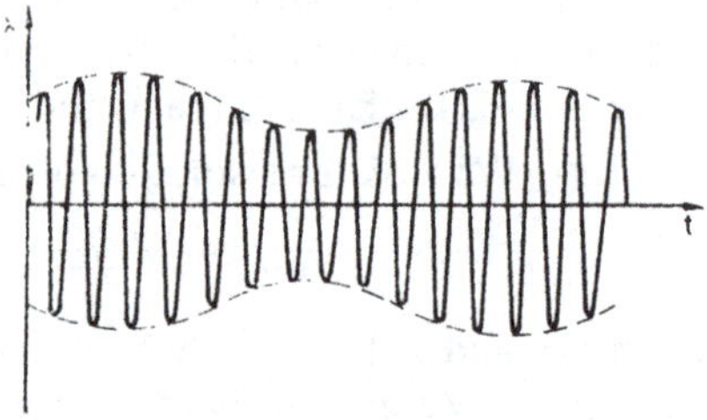

FIG. 113

Similar equations are obtained in quantum mechanics in the problem of the motion of a particle in a periodic field. In that problem we also meet with "forbidden bands" and "surface states".

(b) If $|\omega-\omega_0| > \frac{1}{4}h\omega_0$, we have

$$x = c\beta_1 \sin(\Omega t+\psi)\cos\omega t - c\beta_2\cos(\Omega t+\psi)\sin\omega t,$$

where

$$\Omega = \tfrac{1}{4}\sqrt{16(\omega-\omega_0)^2-(h\omega_0)^2},$$

$$\beta_{1,2} = \sqrt{4(\omega-\omega_0)\pm h\omega_0}, \qquad \text{when} \quad \omega > \omega_0,$$

$$= \pm\sqrt{4(\omega_0-\omega)\pm h\omega_0}, \qquad \text{when} \quad \omega < \omega_0.$$

The oscillations are beats:

$$x = c\sqrt{4(\omega-\omega_0)-h\omega_0\cos(2\Omega t+\psi)}\cos(\omega t+\varphi),$$

where φ is a slowly varying phase (see Fig. 113). If the frequency approaches the limit of the instability region the depth of the modulation of the oscillations approaches the total amplitude and their period increases without limit.

What is the form of the oscillations when $|\omega-\omega_0| = \frac{1}{4}h\omega_0$?

8.8. Let

$$x = e^{i\omega_1 t},$$

when $0 < t < \tau$. We then have in the interval $\tau < t < 2\tau$

$$x = ae^{i\omega_2 t}+be^{-i\omega_2 t},$$

where a and b are determined from the "matching" condition for $t = \tau$:

$$x(\tau-0) = x(\tau+0), \quad \dot{x}(\tau-0) = \dot{x}(\tau+0).$$

Hence we have

$$a = \frac{\omega_1+\omega_2}{2\omega_2} e^{i(\omega_1-\omega_2)\tau},$$

$$b = \frac{\omega_2-\omega_1}{2\omega_2} e^{i(\omega_1+\omega_2)\tau}.$$

Similarly we find that for $2\tau < t < 3\tau$:

$$x = \alpha e^{i\omega_1 t}+\beta e^{-i\omega_1 t},$$

where

$$\alpha = e^{-i\omega_1\tau}\left(\cos\omega_2\tau+i\frac{\omega_1^2+\omega_2^2}{2\omega_1\omega_2}\sin\omega_2\tau\right),$$

$$\beta = i\sin\omega_2\tau\, e^{3i\omega_1\tau}\,\frac{\omega_1^2-\omega_2^2}{2\omega_1\omega_2}.$$

It is clear that oscillations of the form

$$Ae^{i\omega_1 t}+Be^{-i\omega_1 t} \quad \text{for} \quad 0 < t < \tau, \tag{1}$$

after a period 2τ will become

$$A(\alpha e^{i\omega_1 t}+\beta e^{-i\omega_1 t})+B(\alpha^* e^{-i\omega_1 t}+\beta^* e^{i\omega_1 t})$$
$$= (\alpha A+\beta^* B)e^{i\omega_1 t}+(\beta A+\alpha^* B)e^{-i\omega_1 t}.$$

We now look for such a linear combination (1) that it retains its form —apart from a multiplying factor—after a period 2τ:

$$(\alpha A+\beta^* B)e^{i\omega_1 t}+(\beta A+\alpha^* B)e^{-i\omega_1 t} = \mu(Ae^{i\omega_1 t'}+Be^{-i\omega_1 t'}), \tag{2}$$

where

$$t' = t - 2\tau,$$
$$\alpha A + \beta^* B = \mu e^{-2i\omega_1\tau} A,$$
$$\beta A + \alpha^* B = \mu e^{2i\omega_1\tau} B.$$

The set (2) has a non-trivial solution, provided

$$(\alpha - \mu e^{-2i\omega_1\tau})(\alpha^* - \mu e^{2i\omega_1\tau}) - \beta\beta^* = 0,$$

whence

$$\mu_{1,2} = \gamma \pm \sqrt{\gamma^2 - 1},$$

where

$$\gamma = \mathrm{Re}\,(\alpha e^{2i\omega_1\tau}) = \cos\omega_1\tau\cos\omega_2\tau - \frac{\omega_1^2+\omega_2^2}{2\omega_1\omega_2}\sin\omega_1\tau\sin\omega_2\tau.$$

After n periods the oscillation

$$x_{1,2} = A_{1,2}(e^{i\omega_1 t} + \lambda_{1,2} e^{-i\omega_1 t}), \quad 0 < t < \tau; \quad \lambda_{1,2} = \mu_{1,2}\frac{e^{-2i\omega_1\tau} - \alpha}{\beta^*}$$

has changed to

$$x_{1,2}(t) = \mu_{1,2}^n A_{1,2}(e^{i\omega_1 t'} + \lambda_{1,2} e^{-i\omega_1 t'}), \quad 0 < t' = t - 2n\tau < \tau.$$

Any oscillation is a superposition of oscillations such as $x_{1,2}$; in particular, a real oscillation (which is the only one which has a direct physical meaning)

$$x(t) = Ae^{i\omega_1 t} + A^* e^{-i\omega_1 t}, \quad 0 < t < \tau,$$

is the sum $x_1(t) + x_2(t)$ with

$$A_1 = \frac{A^* - \lambda_2 A}{\lambda_1 - \lambda_2}, \quad A_2 = \frac{\lambda_1 A - A^*}{\lambda_1 - \lambda_2}.$$

If $\gamma < 1$, $|\mu_{1,2}| = 1$ and the oscillations $x_{1,2}(t)$ (and at the same time $x(t)$) remain bounded.

If, however, $\gamma > 1$, we have $\mu_1 > 1$, and the amplitude of the oscillations increases without bound. This is the case of the onset of parametric resonance. One verifies easily that if the frequency difference is small, $|\omega_1 - \omega_2| \ll \omega_1$, this condition is satisfied if the frequencies lie close to $n\pi/\tau$:

$$|(\omega_1 + \omega_2)\tau - 2\pi n| < \frac{(\omega_1 - \omega_2)^2 \tau}{\omega_1 + \omega_2}.$$

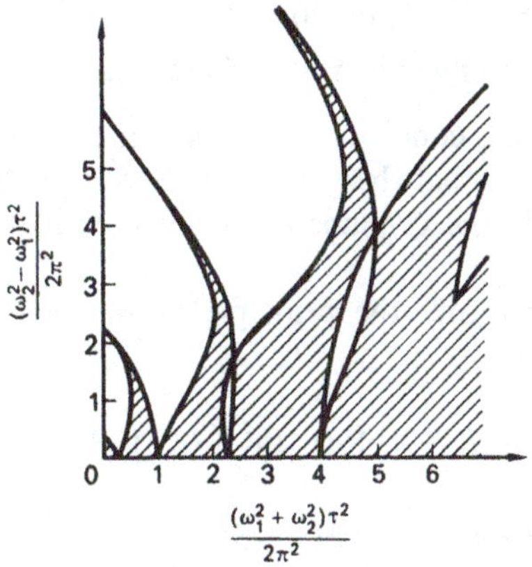

FIG. 114

We show in Fig. 114 the regions of instability against parametric resonance.

8.9.
$$\omega^2 = \frac{a^2\Omega^2}{2l^2} \pm \frac{g}{l}$$

(compare problem 1 in § 30 of Landau and Lifshitz, 1960).

8.10. (a)
$$U_{\text{eff}} = \frac{\alpha^2}{4m\omega^2}\left[\frac{a^2}{r^6} + \frac{3(\boldsymbol{a}\cdot\boldsymbol{r})^2}{r^8}\right]; \tag{1}$$

(b)
$$U_{\text{eff}} = \frac{\alpha^2}{4m(\omega^2-\omega_0^2)}\left[\frac{a^2}{r^6} + \frac{3(\boldsymbol{a}\cdot\boldsymbol{r})^2}{r^8}\right]. \tag{2}$$

We draw attention to the fact that the relation $U_{\text{eff}} \propto r^{-6}$ is characteristic for intermolecular forces. If we substitute into (1) the values $\alpha = e^2 \sim (5\times 10^{-10}\,\text{esu})^2$, $m \sim 10^{-27}$g, $a \sim 10^{-8}$ cm, $\omega \sim 10^{16}$ Hz, which are typical for atoms, we get $U_{\text{eff}} \sim 10^{-60}$ erg cm$^6/r^6$ which is close to the correct value for van der Waals interactions, as far as order of magnitude is concerned. This result may serve as an indication of the physical nature of this interaction. A complete calculation of the van der Waals forces is only possible using quantum mechanics.

8.11. The motion along the z-axis is nearly uniform, $z = vt$. In the xy-plane there acts upon the particle a fast oscillating force

$$f_x = 2Ax \sin kvt, \quad f_y = -2Ay \sin kvt.$$

The corresponding effective potential is

$$U_{\text{eff}} = \tfrac{1}{2}m\Omega^2(x^2+y^2) \quad \text{where} \quad \Omega = A/mkv.$$

According to the initial conditions, we have for the frequency of the force oscillations $kv \gg \Omega$ so that the force is, indeed, fast oscillating. The particle thus performs in the xy-plane a harmonic oscillation with frequency Ω around the z-axis.

This problem illustrates the principle of strong focusing of particle beams in accelerators.

9. Rigid-body Motion. Non-inertial Coordinate Systems

9.1. (a)

$$\begin{Vmatrix} 2a^2(m+M) & 2a^2(m-M) & 0 \\ 2a^2(m-M) & 2a^2(m+M) & 0 \\ 0 & 0 & 4a^2(m+M) \end{Vmatrix};$$

(b)

$$\begin{Vmatrix} 4ma^2 & 0 & 0 \\ 0 & 4Ma^2 & 0 \\ 0 & 0 & 4(m+M)a^2 \end{Vmatrix}.$$

9.2. For both cases one of the principal axes is the axis perpendicular to the plane of the figure going through the centre of mass of the figure (z-axis). The principal x-axis is orientated at an angle φ with respect to $0'x'$ of each of the two figures. The principal y-axis is perpendicular to the x-axis. Both these axes pass through the centre of mass of the figures.

(a) The coordinates of the centre of mass in the $0'x'y'$ system are: b, a;

$$I_{zz} = 2(M+m)(a^2+b^2);$$

$$I_{xx} = (M+m)(a^2+b^2)+\sqrt{(M+m)^2(b^2-a^2)^2+4(M-m)^2a^2b^2};$$

$$I_{yy} = (M+m)(a^2+b^2)-\sqrt{(M+m)^2(b^2-a^2)^2+4(M-m)^2a^2b^2};$$

$$\tan 2\varphi = \frac{(M+m)(b^2-a^2)}{2ab(M-m)}.$$

(b) The coordinates of the centre of mass in the $0'x'y'$ system are: a, a;

$$I_{zz} = 16ma^2; \quad I_{xx} = 4(2+\sqrt{2})ma^2; \quad I_{yy} = 4(2-\sqrt{2})ma^2;$$

$$\tan 2\varphi = -1; \quad \varphi = -\tfrac{1}{8}\pi.$$

9.3.

$$I_n = \sum_{i,k} I_{ik}n_k n_i.$$

9.4. The centre of mass is a point on the axis of symmetry at a distance $(R-r)r^3/(R^3-r^3)$ to the left of the centre of the sphere. The body is a symmetric top. With respect to the axis of symmetry we have (ϱ: density of the body)

$$I_z = \tfrac{4}{3}\pi\varrho \cdot \tfrac{2}{5}(R^5-r^5),$$

and with respect to any two perpendicular axes passing through the centre of mass:

$$I_x = I_y = \frac{4}{3}\pi\varrho\left[\frac{2}{5}(R^5-r^5)-\frac{(R-r)^2r^3R^3}{R^3-r^3}\right].$$

9.5.

$$D_{ik} = \delta_{ik}\sum_l I_{ll}-3I_{ik}$$

(see Landau and Lifshitz, 1962, § 96).

9.6. The centre of mass lies on the axis of the hemisphere at a distance $\frac{3}{8}R$ from the centre of the sphere, where R is the radius of the sphere. The moment of inertia around any axis perpendicular to the axis of symmetry is

$$I = \tfrac{2}{5}mR^2-(\tfrac{3}{8})^2mR^2 = \tfrac{83}{320}mR^2,$$

where m is the mass of the hemisphere. The centre of mass can only move along the vertical. Let φ be the angle over which the hemisphere is turned, and z the height of the centre of mass above the plane so that $z = R-\frac{3}{8}R\cos\varphi$.

The Lagrangian of the system is

$$L = \tfrac{1}{2}I\dot{\varphi}^2+\tfrac{1}{2}m\dot{z}^2-mgz,$$

or when φ is small,

$$L = \tfrac{1}{2}I\dot{\varphi}^2-\tfrac{3}{16}mgR\varphi^2.$$

The frequency of the small oscillations is thus given by

$$\omega^2 = \frac{120g}{83R}.$$

9.7. The moment of inertia of the ellipsoid with respect to the axis of symmetry is $I_3 = \frac{2}{5}Ma^2$; with respect to any axis perpendicular to that axis and passing through the centre of mass, we have $I_1 = \frac{1}{5}M(a^2+b^2)$, where M is the mass of the ellipsoid. The impinging particle of mass $m \ll M$ transfers to the ellipsoid a momentum $\boldsymbol{p} = (p_x, p_y, p_z) = mv(0, -1, 0)$ and an angular momentum $\boldsymbol{M} = mv(\varrho_1, 0, -\varrho_2)$. In the system of reference moving with a velocity $\boldsymbol{p}/(M+m)$, we find (compare Landau and Lifshitz, 1960, § 33) that the ellipsoid will rotate around the c-semi-axis with an angular velocity

$$\Omega_3 = \frac{M_z}{I_3} = -\frac{5mv\varrho_2}{2Ma^2},$$

while at the same time precessing around the direction of $\boldsymbol{M}$ with an angular velocity

$$\Omega = \frac{|\boldsymbol{M}|}{I_1} = \frac{5mv\sqrt{\varrho_1^2+\varrho_2^2}}{M(a^2+b^2)}.$$

9.8. Let $a = b \neq c$ be the semi-axes of the ellipsoid; R, Θ, and Φ the spherical coordinates of the centre of mass of the ellipsoid, and θ, φ, and ψ the Euler angles, and let the x_3-axis of the moving system of reference be along the c-semi-axis. The kinetic energy of the body is (see ter Haar, 1964, Ch. 4)

$$T = \tfrac{1}{2}m(\dot{R}^2 + R^2\dot{\Theta}^2 + R^2\dot{\Phi}^2 \sin^2\Theta) + \tfrac{1}{2}I_1(\dot{\varphi}^2 \sin^2\theta + \dot{\theta}^2) + \tfrac{1}{2}I_3(\dot{\varphi}\cos\theta + \dot{\psi})^2, \qquad (1)$$

where $I_1 = I_2 = \frac{1}{5}m(a^2+c^2)$ and $I_3 = \frac{2}{5}ma^2$ are the moments of inertia of the ellipsoid with respect to the x_1, x_2, and x_3 axes.

The potential energy for the interaction of the ellipsoid with the gravitational centre is, up to and including the quadrupole terms (compare Landau and Lifshitz, 1962, § 41; $\alpha = GmM$, where G is the gravitational constant),

$$U = -\frac{\alpha}{r} - \frac{\alpha}{10}(c^2-a^2)\frac{3\cos^2\beta - 1}{R^3}, \qquad (2)$$

where β is the angle between the radius vector $\boldsymbol{R}$ and the x_3-axis. The unit vector $\boldsymbol{e}_{x_3}$ which determines the direction of the x_3-axis has the components

$$\boldsymbol{e}_{x_3} = (\sin\theta\sin\varphi,\ -\sin\theta\cos\varphi,\ \cos\theta).$$

Hence we have

$$\cos\beta = \frac{(\boldsymbol{R}\cdot\boldsymbol{e}_{x_3})}{R} = \cos\Theta\cos\theta + \sin\Theta\sin\theta\sin(\varphi - \Phi). \qquad (3)$$

From (1), (2), and (3) we get finally the expression for the Lagrangian, $L = T - U$.

9.9.

$$\dot{M}_1 + \left(\frac{1}{I_2} - \frac{1}{I_3}\right) M_2 M_3 = K_1,$$

$$\dot{M}_2 + \left(\frac{1}{I_3} - \frac{1}{I_1}\right) M_3 M_1 = K_2,$$

$$\dot{M}_3 + \left(\frac{1}{I_1} - \frac{1}{I_2}\right) M_1 M_2 = K_3.$$

When $I_1 = I_2$, we get

$$M_1 = B\cos(\omega t + \varphi),$$
$$M_2 = B\sin(\omega t + \varphi) \quad \left(\omega = \left(\frac{1}{I_3} - \frac{1}{I_1}\right) M_3\right),$$
$$M_3 = \text{constant}$$

(compare ter Haar, 1964, Ch. 4, and also problem 11.7).

9.10. Let us consider the motion around an axis which lies close the the principal x_1-axis. From the Euler equations (ter Haar, 1964, eq. (4.206))

$$\Omega_1 + \frac{I_3 - I_2}{I_1} \Omega_2 \Omega_3 = 0,$$

we get $\Omega_1 = \text{constant}$, neglecting terms of order $\Omega_{2,3}/\Omega_1 \ll 1$. The two other equations become then linear in Ω_2 and Ω_3. Assuming that

$$\Omega_{2,3} \propto e^{st}, \tag{1}$$

we get for s the equation

$$s^2 = -\frac{(I_1 - I_3)(I_1 - I_2)}{I_2 I_3} \Omega_1^2.$$

When $I_2 < I_1 < I_3$ or $I_3 < I_1 < I_2$, equation (2) has real roots so that according to (1) the rotation around the x_1-axis is unstable.

If, however, I_1 is either the largest or the smallest moment of inertia, equation (2) has imaginary roots, that is, the changes in Ω_2 and Ω_3 are in the nature of oscillations and rotation around the x_1-axis is stable.

9.11. (a) We use as our generalised coordinates the X- and Y-coordinates of the centre of the disk and the Euler angles φ, θ, and ψ (see ter Haar, 1964, § 4.1). We take the Z-axis to be the vertical and the (moving) x_3-axis along the axis of the disk. The angle φ is the one between the intersection of the plane of the disk with the XY-plane and the X-axis. The Lagrangian is

$$L = \tfrac{1}{2}m(\dot{X}^2+\dot{Y}^2+a^2\dot{\theta}^2\cos^2\theta)+\tfrac{1}{2}I_1(\dot{\theta}^2+\dot{\varphi}^2\sin^2\theta) \\ +\tfrac{1}{2}I_3(\dot{\varphi}\cos\theta+\dot{\psi})^2-mga\sin\theta,$$

where $I_1 = I_2$ and I_3 are the principal moments of inertia of the disk and the x_1-, x_2-, and x_3-axes are along its principal axes; a is the radius of the disk and m its mass; the centre of the disk is at a distance $Z = a\sin\theta$ from the XY-plane. The generalised momenta

$$m\dot{X} = p_X, \quad m\dot{Y} = p_Y, \quad I_1\dot{\varphi}\sin^2\theta+I_3\cos\theta(\dot{\varphi}\cos\theta+\dot{\psi}) = p_\varphi \equiv M_Z, \\ I_3(\dot{\varphi}\cos\theta+\dot{\psi}) = p_\psi \equiv M_3, \tag{1}$$

together with the energy are integrals of motion. In the coordinate system moving with the constant velocity $(\dot{X}, \dot{Y}, 0)$ the centre of the disk moves only vertically. From (1) we have

$$\dot{\varphi} = \frac{M_Z-M_3\cos\theta}{I_1\sin^2\theta}, \quad \dot{\psi} = \frac{M_3}{I_3} - \frac{M_Z-M_3\cos\theta}{I_1\sin^2\theta}\cos\theta, \tag{2}$$

and substituting this into the energy we obtain

$$E = \tfrac{1}{2}(I_1+ma^2\cos^2\theta)\dot{\theta}^2+\frac{M_3^2}{2I_3}+\frac{(M_Z-M_3\cos\theta)^2}{2I_1\sin^2\theta}+mga\sin\theta. \tag{3}$$

From this equation we get θ as a function of t in the form of quadratures, after which one can get φ and ψ as functions of t from (2). The dip angle of the disk oscillates, and the precession velocity $\dot{\varphi}$ and the velocity of rotation around the axis of the disk $\dot{\psi}$ change at the same time. Equations (2) and (3) are similar to those for the motion of a heavy symmetric top (see, for instance, Landau and Lifshitz, 1960, § 35, problem 1, or ter Haar, 1964, p. 85).

The rolling of the disk is stable, if $\Omega_3^2 > mgaI_1/I_3^2$. The rotation is stable, if $\Omega_Z^2 > mga/I_1$.

(b) If the rolling is without slipping, in addition to the force of gravity mg and the reaction force $\boldsymbol{R}$, there is also a friction force $\boldsymbol{f}$ acting on the disk. It is convenient to write the equation of motion $\dot{\boldsymbol{M}}-[\boldsymbol{a}\wedge\boldsymbol{R}] = [\boldsymbol{a}\wedge\boldsymbol{f}]$ in its components along the Z-, x_3-, and ξ-axes, where the ξ-axis is the line of nodes†

† These equations are the Lagrangian equations of motion for the Euler angles when there is no friction force.

$$\dot{M}_Z = f_\eta a \cos \theta, \quad \dot{M}_3 = f_\xi a, \tag{4}$$

$$\frac{d}{dt}\frac{\partial L}{\partial \dot\theta} - \frac{\partial L}{\partial \theta} = = f_\xi a \sin \theta. \tag{5}$$

Here $\boldsymbol{a}$ is the vector from the centre of the disk to the point of contact. If we take the components of the equation $m\dot{\boldsymbol{V}} = \boldsymbol{f}+\boldsymbol{R}+m\boldsymbol{g}$ along the ξ-and η-axes (the η-axis is horizontal and at right angles to the ξ-axis) we have the following equations for f_ξ and f_η:

$$f_\xi = m\dot{V}_\xi = m(\dot{v}_\xi - \dot\varphi v_\eta), \quad f_\eta = m\dot{V}_\eta = m(\dot{v}_\eta - \dot\varphi v_\xi). \tag{6}$$

The condition of rolling without slipping, $\boldsymbol{v}+[\boldsymbol{\Omega} \wedge \boldsymbol{a}] = 0$, leads to the equations

$$v_\xi = -a(\dot\psi + \dot\varphi \cos \theta), \quad v_\eta = a\dot\theta. \tag{7}$$

Substituting (1), (6), and (7) into (4) and (5) we obtain a set of equations for the Euler angles. The disk can move along the plane without slipping and without leaving the plane, provided

$$|f| \leqq \mu m(g+\ddot{Z}), \quad g+\ddot{Z} \geqq 0,$$

where μ is the friction coefficient.

If we put $\dot\theta = 0$, we get $\ddot\varphi = \ddot\psi = 0$, and there exists the following relation between θ, $\dot\varphi$, and $\dot\psi$:

$$I_3'\dot\varphi(\dot\varphi \cos \theta + \dot\psi) \sin \theta - I_1\dot\varphi^2 \sin \theta \cos \theta + mga \cos \theta = 0 \tag{8}$$

(we put from now on $I_{1,3}' = I_{1,3} + ma^2$). The centre of the disk moves with a velocity, which has a constant absolute magnitude $V = a|\Omega_3| = a|\dot\psi + \dot\varphi \cos \theta|$, along a circle with radius $R = V/|\dot\varphi|$.

Condition (8) can also be expressed as follows:

$$I_3' R V^2 = |I_1 a V^2 \cos \theta + mga^2 R^2 \cot \theta|.$$

In particular, if the mass of the disk is concentrated in the centre ($I_1 = I_3 = 0$) we get the elementary relation

$$V^2 = gR|\cot \theta|.$$

Gyroscopic effects which appear when $I_{1,3}$ differ from zero may turn out to be important. For example when $R \gg a$, we have $\frac{3}{2}V^2 = gR\,|\cot \theta|$ for a uniform disk ($2I_1 = I_3 = \frac{1}{2}ma^2$), but $2V^2 = gR\,|\cot \theta|$ for a hoop ($2I_1 = I_3 = ma^2$).

If the disk is rolling vertically we have

$$\theta = \frac{\pi}{2}, \quad \dot\varphi = 0, \quad \dot\psi = \Omega_3 = \text{constant}. \tag{9}$$

In order to study the stability of this motion we put

$$\theta = \frac{\pi}{2} - \beta, \ \beta \ll 1, \ \dot{\varphi} \approx \dot{\beta} \ll \Omega_3, \ \ddot{\varphi} \sim \ddot{\beta} \sim \dot{\Omega}_3 \ll \dot{\varphi}\Omega_3$$

into equations (1) and (4) to (7), retaining only the first-order terms. We then get

$$M_Z = I_1\dot{\varphi} + I_3\Omega_3\beta = \text{constant}, \ \Omega_3 = \text{constant}, \ I_1'\ddot{\beta} + I_3'\Omega_3\dot{\varphi} - mga\beta = 0, \quad (10)$$

and hence

$$I_1'\ddot{\beta} + \left[\frac{I_3 I_3'}{I_1}\Omega_3^2 - mga\right]\beta = \frac{I_3'}{I_1} M_Z\Omega_3.$$

If

$$\Omega_3^2 > \frac{I_1 mga}{I_3 I_3'}, \quad (11)$$

small oscillations in β and $\dot{\varphi}$ occur with the angle θ differing from $\pi/2$:

$$\beta = \frac{I_3'\Omega_3 M_Z}{I_1\omega^2} + \beta_0 \cos(\omega t + \delta), \ \dot{\varphi} = -\frac{M_Z mga}{I_1^2\omega^2} - \frac{I_3\Omega_3\beta_0}{I_1}\sin(\omega t + \delta),$$

where

$$\omega^2 = \frac{I_3 I_3'}{I_1 I_1'}\Omega_3^2 - \frac{mga}{I_1'}.$$

The direction of motion also executes small vibrations; the motion is not about a straight line, but about a circle of radius $a\Omega_3 I_1^2\omega^2/mgaM_Z$. Therefore, if there are small deviations in the initial conditions from (9), we may have either small oscillations near an "equilibrium" motion along a straight line—if $M_Z = 0, \beta_0 \neq 0$—or a new "equilibrium" motion—if $M_Z \neq 0, \beta_0 = 0$.

If inequality (11) is not satisfied, the motion is not stable.

One can say that motion with θ = constant can occur, if in the θ-, $\dot{\varphi}$-, $\dot{\psi}$-space the representative point lies on the surface determined by equations (10). It can easily be seen that, if (11) holds, the motion is stable with respect to perturbations which remove the representative point from the surface (10) while it is neutral with respects to perturbations shifting the point along the surface. A similar situation holds for the stability of the motion of the disk along a smooth plane; we must merely replace $I_{1,3}'$ by $I_{1,3}$.

Rotation of the disk around its vertical diameter is stable, if $\Omega_Z^2 > mga/I_1'$.

(c) If there can be no rotation around a vertical axis, the following condition must be satisfied:

$$\Omega_Z = \dot{\varphi} + \dot{\psi} \cos \theta = 0. \tag{12}$$

In this case there is an additional, "frictional torque" N, which is directed along the vertical, acting on the disk. Instead of (4) we then have

$$\dot{M}_Z = f_\xi a \cos \theta + N, \quad \dot{M}_3 = f_\xi a + N \cos \theta. \tag{13}$$

The integration of the equations of motion can easily be reduced to quadratures (in contrast to the equations under (a)).

Motion with a constant angle of inclination is possible if (12) is satisfied as well as (8), which means that $\dot{\varphi}$ and $\dot{\psi}$ are completely determined by the angle θ.

In this case

$$R = a|\sin \theta \tan \theta|, \quad V^2 = \frac{mga^3 \sin \theta}{I_3' - I_1 \cot^2 \theta}.$$

Rolling of the disk in a vertical position is stable, if $\Omega_3^2 > mga/I_3'$.

(d) If there is a small inclination, the term $\delta L = -mg\alpha X$ must be added to the Lagrangian; the Y-axis lies in the plane and is horizontal, the X-axis lies in the place at right angles to the Y-axis, pointing upwards, and the Z-axis is at right angles to the plane. Substituting

$$\theta = \frac{\pi}{2} - \beta, \quad \beta \ll 1, \quad \dot{\psi} \sim \dot{\beta} \ll \Omega_Z, \quad \ddot{\psi} \sim \ddot{\beta} \sim \dot{\Omega}_Z \ll \dot{\psi}\Omega_Z$$

into (1) and (4) to (7), and adding the contribution from δL, we get

$$I_1'\ddot{\beta} + (I_1 - I_3')\Omega_Z^2\beta - I_3'\Omega_Z\dot{\psi} - mga\beta = mga\alpha \sin \Omega_Z t,$$
$$I_3'\ddot{\psi} + (I_3 + 2ma^2)\,\Omega_Z\dot{\beta} = -mga\alpha \cos \Omega_Z t,$$

and hence

$$\psi = -\left(2 + \frac{2ma^2}{I_3'} + \frac{mga}{I_3'\Omega_Z^2}\right) \alpha \cos \Omega_Z t, \quad \beta = -2\alpha \sin \Omega_Z t.$$

Substituting (7) and θ, φ, and ψ into the equations

$$\dot{X} = v_\xi \cos \varphi - v_\eta \sin \varphi, \quad \dot{Y} = v_\xi \sin \varphi + v_\eta \cos \varphi,$$

and averaging over one period of rotation, we find

$$\langle \dot{X} \rangle = 0, \quad \langle \dot{Y} \rangle = -\left(1 + \frac{ma^2}{I_3'} + \frac{mga}{I_3'\Omega_Z^2}\right) \alpha a \Omega_Z,$$

that is, the disk is displaced without losing height.

9.12. (a) The position of the sphere is determined by the coordinates of its centre of mass, X, Y, Z, and the Euler angles θ, φ, ψ which determine the orientation of the principal axes of the sphere. Let the Z-axis be vertical, and the x_3-axis be directed from the centre of mass to the geometric centre of the sphere; let $x_3 = b$ be the position of the geometric centre of the sphere and a be its radius. The analysis of the motion of the sphere is analogous to the analysis in the preceding problem.

If $M_Z \neq M_3$, there is a minimum in $U_{\text{eff}}(\theta)$ when $\theta \neq 0, \pi$, and if the energy $E = U_{\text{eff}}(\theta_0)$ we can have a steady rotation of the sphere with a constant angle $\theta = \theta_0$ and $Z = a - b\cos\theta_0$. The instantaneous point of contact of sphere and plane has a velocity $v = (b\dot{\varphi} + a\dot{\psi})\sin\theta_0$ along the direction of the line of nodes. Let us now take into account the dry friction force f. It is directed antiparallel to v and causes a change in θ_0, when $v \gtrless 0$, we have

$$\dot{M}_Z = \mp fb\sin\theta, \quad \dot{M}_3 = \mp fa\sin\theta_0. \tag{1}$$

Hence

$$M_Z a - M_3 b = C = \text{constant}. \tag{2}$$

If the sphere is rotating fast, $M \approx M_3$, $M_Z \approx M\cos\theta_0$, or, of we take (2) into account,

$$M(a\cos\theta_0 - b) = C. \tag{3}$$

It follows that the angular momentum decreases due to friction, while the angle θ_0 decreases, if $a\cos\theta_0 > b$, while it increases, if $a\cos\theta_0 < b$. From (1) and (3) we see that

$$\dot{\theta} = \frac{-fb}{aC(a\cos\theta - b)^2}.$$

The centre of mass moves slowly in the Z-direction while in the XY-plane the effect of the variable friction force $f_X = -f\cos\varphi$, $f_X = -f\sin\varphi$ is to produce a rotation of the centre of mass along a small circle with an angular velocity $\dot{\varphi}$. Of course, even the smallest friction force will eventually lead to a vanishing of the slipping so that the velocity of the lowest point of the sphere becomes zero.

(b) Let

$$\boldsymbol{R}_C = (X + b\sin\theta\sin\varphi,\ Y - b\sin\theta\cos\varphi,\ a)$$

be the coordinates of the geometrical centre of the sphere, and let

$$\begin{aligned}\boldsymbol{\Omega} &= (\Omega_X, \Omega_Y, \Omega_Z)\\ &= (\dot{\theta}\cos\varphi + \dot{\psi}\sin\theta\sin\varphi,\ \dot{\theta}\sin\varphi - \dot{\psi}\sin\theta\cos\varphi,\ \dot{\varphi} + \dot{\psi}\cos\theta)\end{aligned}$$

be the angular rotational velocity of the sphere, while $\boldsymbol{a} = (0, 0, -a)$ is the radius vector from the geometric centre of the sphere to the point where the sphere is in contact with the plane. The condition that the sphere rolls without slipping,

$$\dot{\boldsymbol{R}}_C + [\boldsymbol{\Omega} \wedge \boldsymbol{a}] = 0,$$

is the non-holonomic constraint

$$\dot{X} = \dot{\theta}(a-b\cos\theta)\sin\varphi-(a\dot{\psi}+b\dot{\varphi})\sin\theta\cos\varphi,$$
$$\dot{Y} = -\dot{\theta}(a-b\cos\theta)\cos\varphi-(a\dot{\psi}+b\dot{\varphi})\sin\theta\sin\varphi. \tag{4}$$

The equations of motion are (compare the preceding problem)

$$m\ddot{X} = \lambda_1, \quad m\ddot{Y} = \lambda_2, \tag{5}$$
$$\dot{M}_Z = (\lambda_1\cos\varphi+\lambda_2\sin\varphi)\, b\sin\theta, \tag{6}$$
$$\dot{M}_3 = (\lambda_1\cos\varphi+\lambda_2\sin\varphi)\, a\sin\theta, \tag{7}$$
$$\frac{d}{dt}\frac{\partial L}{\partial\dot{\theta}} - \frac{\partial L}{\partial\theta} = (-\lambda_1\sin\varphi+\lambda_2\cos\varphi)(a-b\cos\theta); \tag{8}$$

they contain the friction forces and the torques produced by these forces on the right-hand sides. Using (4) we can express the Lagrangian multipliers λ_1 and λ_2 in terms of the Euler angles. Indeed, the components of the friction force along the line of nodes, $f_\parallel$, and at right angles to it, $f_\perp$, are given by

$$f_\parallel = m\dot{\theta}\dot{\varphi}\,(a-b\cos\theta)-m\frac{d}{dt}[(a\dot{\psi}+b\dot{\varphi})\sin\theta], \tag{9}$$

$$f_\perp = -m\frac{d}{dt}[\dot{\theta}(a-b\cos\theta)]-m\dot{\varphi}(a\dot{\psi}+b\dot{\varphi})\sin\theta. \tag{10}$$

Note that equations (6) and (7) are the same as (1), if one substitutes into (1) the friction force $f_\parallel$ instead of the dry friction force $\mp f$. The quantity $M_Z a - M_3 b = C$ is an integral of motion, as before.

9.13. To solve this problem it is necessary to assume that that the height of the particle above the Earth, h, is small compared with the radius R of the Earth and that the centrifugal acceleration, $\Omega^2 R$ ($\boldsymbol{\Omega}$ is the angular velocity of the Earth), is small compared to the acceleration of free fall, g, towards the surface of the Earth. There are thus two small parameters in the problem:

$$\varepsilon_1 = \frac{R\Omega^2}{g} \sim 0.01, \quad \varepsilon_2 = \frac{h}{R}. \tag{1}$$

The equation of motion has the following form, if we take into account the dependence of $\boldsymbol{g}$ on the height $\boldsymbol{r}$ (up to second order in ε_2):

$$\boldsymbol{r} = \dot{\boldsymbol{V}} = \boldsymbol{g}\left[1-3\varepsilon_2\frac{(\boldsymbol{R}\cdot\boldsymbol{r})}{Rh}+\frac{15}{2}\varepsilon_2^2\frac{(\boldsymbol{R}\cdot\boldsymbol{r})^2}{R^2h^2}-\frac{3r^2}{2h^2}\varepsilon_2^2\right]$$

$$-g\varepsilon_2\frac{\boldsymbol{r}}{h}\left(1-3\varepsilon_2\frac{(\boldsymbol{R}\cdot\boldsymbol{r})}{Rh}\right)+g\varepsilon_1\frac{[\boldsymbol{\Omega}\wedge[\boldsymbol{R}\wedge\boldsymbol{\Omega}]]}{R\Omega^2}+g\varepsilon_1\varepsilon_2\frac{[\boldsymbol{\Omega}\wedge[\boldsymbol{r}\wedge\boldsymbol{\Omega}]]}{\Omega^2h}$$

$$+2g\sqrt{2\varepsilon_1\varepsilon_2}\frac{[\boldsymbol{V}\wedge\boldsymbol{\Omega}]}{\sqrt{2gh}\Omega}+o(\varepsilon_2^2,\varepsilon_1\varepsilon_2), \tag{2}$$

$$\boldsymbol{r}(0)=\boldsymbol{h};\quad \boldsymbol{V}(0)=0. \tag{3}$$

We choose the z-axis along the radius of the Earth, the x-axis along the meridian towards the Pole, and the y-axis along the latitude to the west. The (northern) latitude is denoted by λ. We then have

$$\begin{aligned}
&\boldsymbol{g}=(0,0,-g);\quad \boldsymbol{R}=(0,0,R);\quad \boldsymbol{\Omega}=\Omega(\cos\lambda,0,\sin\lambda);\\
&\boldsymbol{h}=h(\tfrac{1}{2}\varepsilon_1\sin2\lambda,0,1-\tfrac{1}{8}\varepsilon_1^2\sin^2 2\lambda);\\
&[\boldsymbol{\Omega}\wedge\boldsymbol{R}]=-\Omega R\cos\lambda(0,1,0);\\
&[\boldsymbol{\Omega}\wedge[\boldsymbol{R}\wedge\boldsymbol{\Omega}]]=\Omega^2R\cos\lambda(-\sin\lambda,\ 0,\cos\lambda).
\end{aligned} \tag{4}$$

The equation can be solved by the method of successive approximations:

$$\boldsymbol{r}=\boldsymbol{h}+\frac{1}{2}\boldsymbol{g}t^2+\frac{1}{2}\varepsilon_1gt^2\frac{[\boldsymbol{\Omega}\wedge[\boldsymbol{R}\wedge\boldsymbol{\Omega}]]}{R\Omega^2}$$

$$-2\varepsilon_2\cdot\frac{1}{2}\boldsymbol{g}t^2\left(1-\frac{gt^2}{12h}\right)+\sqrt{2\varepsilon_1\varepsilon_2}\frac{gt^3}{3}\frac{[\boldsymbol{\Omega}\wedge\boldsymbol{R}]}{\Omega R}\sqrt{\frac{g^2}{2h}}$$

$$+\frac{[\boldsymbol{\Omega}\wedge[\boldsymbol{R}\wedge\boldsymbol{\Omega}]]}{R\Omega^2}\frac{1}{2}gt^2\varepsilon_1\varepsilon_2\left(1+\frac{gt^2}{6h}\right)-\left(\boldsymbol{h}-\boldsymbol{R}\frac{(\boldsymbol{h}\cdot\boldsymbol{R})}{R^2}\right)\varepsilon_2\frac{gt^2}{2h}. \tag{5}$$

We then find for the time it takes to fall, t, and for the displacement:

$$t=\sqrt{\frac{2h}{g}}\left(1+\frac{1}{2}\varepsilon_1\cos^2\lambda-\frac{5}{6}\varepsilon_2\right);$$

$$x=-\tfrac{1}{2}\varepsilon_1h\sin2\lambda(4\varepsilon_2+\varepsilon_1\cos^2\lambda);\quad y=-\sqrt{2\varepsilon_1\varepsilon_2}\tfrac{2}{3}h\cos\lambda. \tag{6}$$

The minus signs show that the displacement is towards the east and the south.

9.14.

$$t = \sqrt{\frac{m}{2}} \int \frac{dr}{\sqrt{E+M\Omega-U_{\text{eff}}}}, \quad \varphi = \sqrt{\frac{m}{2}} \int \frac{(Mr^{-2}-\Omega)dr}{\sqrt{E+M\Omega-U_{\text{eff}}}},$$

where E is the energy, M the angular momentum in the rotating system of reference, $U_{\text{eff}} = U(r)+M^2/2mr^2$. We bear in mind that $E = E_0-M\Omega$, $M = M_0$, where E_0 and M_0 are the energy and angular momentum in the inertial system.

It is interesting to note that the centrifugal potential energy $-m\Omega^2 r/2$ does not enter into U_{eff}.

9.15. In the system of reference, which is fixed in the frame, the Lagrangian of the problem is the same as the one considered in problem 6.23, with $z = 0$ and with the parameters $\omega_H = -2\Omega$, $\omega_{1,2}^2 = \frac{2}{m}\left(\varkappa_{1,2}+\frac{f_{1,2}}{l}\right)-\Omega^2$. When $\omega_{1,2}^2 > 0$ the motion of the particles is the same as the motion of an anisotropic harmonic oscillator with a magnetic field $H = -2mc\Omega/e$. The orbits of the particle for the case $\omega_1 = \omega_2$ were shown in Fig. 71 of problem 2.28. In particular, if $\omega_1 = \omega_2 = 0$, the motion of the particle is the same as the motion of a free particle in a magnetic field:

$$x = x_0+a \cos \omega_H t, \quad y = y_0-a \sin \omega_H t,$$

that is, the particle moves uniformly along a circle with radius a and centre x_0, y_0. It is interesting to investigate what is the motion of the particle in the rest system which corresponds to the latter case, especially for $a = 0$ or for $x_0 = y_0 = 0$.

If the centrifugal force is larger than the restoring forces along the two springs, $\omega_{1,2}^2 < 0$, but the particle still executes small oscillations. Although the potential energy has a maximum at $x = y = 0$, the equilibrium position is stable because of the Coriolis force.

If ω_1 and ω_2 have opposite signs so that the point $x = y = 0$ is a saddle point of the potential energy, the equilibrium position is unstable.

Comparing these results with those of problem 5.4 one sees that in a system rotating with angular velocity Ω the point r_0, φ_0 lies on a ridge of the potential energy $U = -(\alpha/r^n)-\frac{1}{2}m\Omega^2 r^2$ which has a maximum in the direction of the radius vector but which does not change in the direction of the azimuth. In this case one of the eigen-frequencies is ω, but the other one vanishes: the equilibrium position is neutral with respect to some perturbations (for instance, a change in φ_0).

9.16. We shall consider the oscillations in a frame of reference which rotates together with the molecule. We obtain the Lagrangian from (1) of problem 6.37 by replacing $\dot{\boldsymbol{u}}_a$ by $\dot{\boldsymbol{u}}_a+[\boldsymbol{\Omega}\wedge\{\boldsymbol{r}_{a0}+\boldsymbol{u}_a\}]$ while the angular velocity $\boldsymbol{\Omega}$ of the system of reference is chosen to be equal to the angular rotational velocity of the molecule when there are no oscillations, that is,

$$\boldsymbol{\Omega} = \frac{\boldsymbol{M}}{m\Sigma_a r_{a0}^2}.$$

Instead of equation (3) of problem (6.37) we get

$$\sum_a \{[\boldsymbol{r}_{a0}\wedge\dot{\boldsymbol{u}}_a]+2(\boldsymbol{r}_{a0}\cdot\boldsymbol{u}_a)\boldsymbol{\Omega}\} = 0, \tag{1}$$

or

$$\dot{y}_1+\dot{y}_2+\dot{y}_3+\frac{2}{\sqrt{3}}\Omega l(x_1+x_2+x_3) = 0. \tag{2}$$

Introducing $q_4 = \frac{1}{2}(y_1+y_2+y_3)$ and neglecting terms† quadratic in Ω we can write the Lagrangian in the form

$$L = \tfrac{3}{2}m(\dot{q}_1^2+\dot{q}_2^2+\dot{q}_3^2+\dot{q}_4^2)-\tfrac{9}{2}\varkappa q_1^2-\tfrac{9}{4}\varkappa(q_2^2+q_3^2)+m\Omega(q_2\dot{q}_3-q_3\dot{q}_2)$$
$$+3m\Omega(q_1\dot{q}_4-q_4\dot{q}_1), \tag{3}$$

and condition (2) in the form

$$\dot{q}_4+2\Omega q_1 = 0. \tag{4}$$

The equations of motion lead to the following normal vibrations—which also satisfy condition (4):

$$q_1^{(1)} = A_1\cos(\omega_1 t+\varphi_1),\quad \omega_1 = \sqrt{3\varkappa/m};\quad q_4^{(1)} = -2\frac{\Omega}{\omega_1}A_1\sin(\omega_1 t+\varphi_1);$$

$$q_2^{(2,3)} = A_{2,3}\cos(\omega_{2,3}t+\varphi_{2,3}),\quad \omega_{2,3} = \sqrt{3\varkappa/2m}\pm\Omega;$$
$$q_3^{(2,3)} = \pm A_{2,3}\sin(\omega_{2,3}t+\varphi_{2,3}).$$

Moreover, the equations of motion and condition (4) are satisfied by $q_1 = C$, $q_4 = -2\Omega\, Ct+D$, but we must put $C = D = 0$ since this motion would move the atoms far from their equilibrium positions. The six arbitrary constants A_i, φ_i correspond to three vibrational degrees of freedom.

Describe the oscillations, when the initial displacements in the rotating system are those shown in Fig. 101, while the initial velocities are zero.

† If we take these corrections into account, we should make the substitution

$$\varkappa\to\varkappa-\tfrac{1}{6}m\Omega^2,\quad l\to l(1+m\Omega^2/2\varkappa),\quad \Omega\to\Omega(1-m\Omega^2/\varkappa).$$

10. The Hamiltonian Equations of Motion

10.1. Let $\boldsymbol{\epsilon}$ be a vector of an infinitesimal displacement; we then have

$$\boldsymbol{r}_a \to \boldsymbol{r}'_a = \boldsymbol{r}_a + \boldsymbol{\epsilon}, \quad \boldsymbol{p}_a \to \boldsymbol{p}'_a = \boldsymbol{p}_a, \quad H(\boldsymbol{r}_a, \boldsymbol{p}_a) = H(\boldsymbol{r}'_a, \boldsymbol{p}'_a).$$

Hence $\sum_a \nabla_a H = 0$. Using the Hamiltonian equations we get

$$\dot{\boldsymbol{P}} = \sum_a \dot{\boldsymbol{p}}_a = -\sum_a \nabla_a H = 0, \boldsymbol{P} = \text{constant}.$$

For an infinitesimal rotation $\boldsymbol{\delta\varphi}$ we have

$$\boldsymbol{r}_a \to \boldsymbol{r}'_a = \boldsymbol{r}_a + [\boldsymbol{\delta\varphi} \wedge \boldsymbol{r}_a], \boldsymbol{p}_a \to \boldsymbol{p}'_a = \boldsymbol{p}_a + [\boldsymbol{\delta\varphi} \wedge \boldsymbol{p}_a], H(\boldsymbol{r}_a, \boldsymbol{p}_a) = H(\boldsymbol{r}'_a, \boldsymbol{p}'_a),$$

$$\sum_a \left\{ (\nabla_a H \cdot [\boldsymbol{\delta\varphi} \wedge \boldsymbol{r}_a]) + \left(\frac{\partial H}{\partial \boldsymbol{p}_a} \cdot [\boldsymbol{\delta\varphi} \wedge \boldsymbol{p}_a] \right) \right\} = 0$$

$$= \sum_a \{ -(\dot{\boldsymbol{p}}_a \cdot [\boldsymbol{\delta\varphi} \wedge \boldsymbol{r}_a]) + (\dot{\boldsymbol{r}}_a \cdot [\boldsymbol{\delta\varphi} \wedge \boldsymbol{p}_a]) \} = -\left(\boldsymbol{\delta\varphi} \cdot \sum_a \frac{d}{dt} [\boldsymbol{r}_a \wedge \boldsymbol{p}_a] \right),$$

or,

$$\boldsymbol{M} = \sum_a [\boldsymbol{r}_a \wedge \boldsymbol{p}_a] = \text{constant}.$$

10.2.

$$H = \frac{p_\theta^2}{2I_1} + \frac{(p_\varphi - p_\psi \cos\theta)^2}{2I_1 \sin^2\theta} + \frac{p_\psi^2}{2I_3}.$$

10.3.

$$H = \frac{p^2}{2(1+2\beta x)} - \tfrac{1}{2}\omega^2 x^2 + \alpha x^3.$$

In particular, for small oscillations ($|\alpha x| \ll \omega^2$, $|\beta x| \ll 1$)

$$H = \tfrac{1}{2}p^2 - \tfrac{1}{2}\omega^2 x^2 + \alpha x^3 - \beta x p^2 + 2\beta^2 x^2 p^2 - \ldots,$$

and up to and including terms linear in α and β the extra term in the Hamiltonian of the harmonic oscillator is connected with the extra term in the Lagrangian through the equation $\delta H = -\delta L$ (see Landau and Lifshitz, 1960, § 40).

10.4.

$$x = a\cos(\omega t + \varphi), \quad p = -\omega_0 a \sin(\omega t + \varphi),$$

where

$$\omega = (1 + 2\lambda E_0)\omega_0, \quad E_0 = \tfrac{1}{2}\omega_0^2 a^2.$$

10.5.

$$\dot{\boldsymbol{r}} = \frac{c\boldsymbol{p}}{np} - \frac{cp}{n^2}\frac{\partial n}{\partial \boldsymbol{p}}, \quad \dot{\boldsymbol{p}} = \frac{cp}{n^2}\nabla n, \quad p = |\boldsymbol{p}|.$$

The given Hamiltonian describes the propagation of light in a transparent medium with refractive index $n(r)$ in the geometric optics approximation (see Landau and Lifshitz, 1960a, § 65). The "particle" is a wave packet, and $\boldsymbol{r}(t)$ gives the way it moves, $\dot{\boldsymbol{r}}$ its group velocity, while the vector $\boldsymbol{p}$ which is perpendicular to the wave front determines the wave vector. When $n(\boldsymbol{r}) = ax$, the trajectory is

$$x = c_1 \cosh\left(\frac{y}{c_1} + c_2\right),$$

where the c_i are determined by the initial and final points of the trajectory.

10.6. (a)

$$L = \tfrac{1}{2}m(\boldsymbol{v} - \boldsymbol{a})^2;$$

(b) $L = 0$: such "particles" cannot be described using a Lagrangian (compare Landau and Lifshitz, 1962, § 53).

10.7. The given vector potential determines a magnetic field $\boldsymbol{H}$ in the z-direction.

The Hamiltonian is

$$H(x, y, z, p_x, p_y, p_z) = \frac{p_x^2 + p_z^2}{2m} + \frac{1}{2m}\left(p_y - \frac{e}{c} Hx\right)^2.$$

Since H does not depend on y or z, we have p_y = constant and p_z = constant. If we write H in the form

$$H = \frac{p_x^2}{2m} + \frac{1}{2} m\omega^2 (x - x_0)^2 + \frac{p_z^2}{2m},$$

where $\omega = eH/mc$, $x_0 = cp_y/eH$, we see that x and p_x are obtained from the same Hamiltonian as that of a harmonic oscillator. Therefore we have

$$x = a\cos(\omega t + \varphi) + x_0, \quad p_x = -m\omega a \sin(\omega t + \varphi).$$

To determine y and z we use the equations

$$\dot{y} = -\frac{\partial H}{\partial p_y} = -\frac{1}{m}\left(p_y - \frac{e}{c} Hx\right) = \omega a \cos(\omega t + \varphi),$$

$$\dot{z} = \frac{p_z}{m},$$

whence

$$y = a \sin(\omega t + \varphi) + y_0, \quad z = \frac{p_z}{m} t + z_0.$$

The particle moves along a spiral with its axis parallel to $\boldsymbol{H}$. The generalised momentum p_y determines the distance of that axis from the yz-plane.

10.8.†

$$\dot{p} = eE + \frac{e}{c}[v \wedge H].$$

10.9.

$$p = p_0 + eEt; \quad \varepsilon(p) - e(E \cdot r) = \text{constant};$$
$$([r - r_0] \cdot eE) = \varepsilon(p_0 + eEt) - \varepsilon(p_0).$$

10.10. $\varepsilon(p) = E$, $p_H = \text{constant}$, p_H is the component of the momentum along the magnetic field H. The trajectory in momentum space is determined by the intersection of the two surfaces $\varepsilon(p) = \text{constant}$ and $p_H = \text{constant}$.

10.11. From the equation of motion,

$$\dot{p} = \frac{e}{c}[\dot{r} \wedge H],$$

it is clear that the projection of the electron orbit on a plane perpendicular to the magnetic field H is obtained from the orbit in momentum space by a rotation over $\pi/2$ around H and by changing the scale by a factor c/eH.

10.12.

$$T = \frac{-c}{eH}\oint \frac{dp}{|v_\perp|}, \quad S = \int_{E_{\min}}^{E} dE \oint \frac{dp}{|v_\perp|},$$

where $v_\perp$ is the component of the vector $\partial E/\partial p$ which is orthogonal to H.

11. Poisson Brackets. Canonical Transformations

11.1.‡ (a)

$$-\sum_k e_{ijk}x_k; \; -\sum_k e_{ijk}p_k; \; -\sum_k e_{ijk}M_k;$$

(b) $(a \cdot b)$; $\{(a \cdot M), (b \cdot r)\} = \left\{\sum_i a_i M_i, \sum_j b_j x_j\right\} = \sum_{ij} a_i b_j \{M_i, x_j\}$

$$= -\sum_{ijk} a_i b_j e_{ijk} x_k = -([a \wedge b] \cdot r); \qquad -([a \wedge b] \cdot M);$$

(c) $$0; \quad nrr^{n-2}; \quad 2a(a \cdot r).$$

† For details about the motion of electrons in a metal (problems 10.8 to 10.12) see, for instance, Haug 1971.

‡ e_{ijk} is the completely antisymmetric tensor: $e_{123} = e_{231} = e_{312} = 1$, $e_{132} = e_{213} = e_{321} = -1$, all other components of e_{ijk} vanish.

11.2.

$$\{A_i, A_j\} = -\sum_k e_{ijk}A_k; \quad \{A_j, A_4\} = 0,$$

where i, j, and k take on the values 1, 2, and 3 (compare problem 11.1a).

11.3.

$$\{M_i, \Lambda_{jk}\} = -\sum_l e_{ijl}\Lambda_{lk} - \sum_l e_{ikl}\Lambda_{lj};$$

$$\{\Lambda_{ik}, \Lambda_{jl}\} = \delta_{ij}M_{lk} + \delta_{ik}M_{lj} + \delta_{jl}M_{ik} + \delta_{kl}M_{ij},$$

where

$$M_{kl} = p_k x_l - p_l x_k.$$

11.4. When the system as a whole is rotated around the z-axis over an infinitesimal angle ε, the change $\delta\varphi$ in any function of the coordinates and momenta is in first order in ε given by

$$\delta\varphi = \varphi(x-\varepsilon y,\ y+\varepsilon x,\ z,\ p_x-\varepsilon p_y,\ p_y+\varepsilon p_x,\ p_z) - \varphi(x, y, z, p_x, p_y, p_z)$$
$$= \varepsilon\left(-\frac{\partial\varphi}{\partial x}y + \frac{\partial\varphi}{\partial y}x - \frac{\partial\varphi}{\partial p_x}p_y + \frac{\partial\varphi}{\partial p_y}p_x\right) = \varepsilon\{M_z, \varphi\}.$$

If φ is a scalar, this change under rotation must vanish, and thus $\{\varphi, M_z\} = 0$. If $\varphi = f_x$ is the component of a vector function, its change under rotation is $\delta f_x = -\varepsilon f_y$, and thus

$$\{M_z, f_x\} = -f_y, \quad \text{or,} \quad \{M_z, \boldsymbol{f}\} = [\boldsymbol{k}\wedge\boldsymbol{f}]$$

(compare problems 3 and 4 of § 42 of Landau and Lifshitz, 1960).

What is the value of the Poisson bracket $\{M_z, T_{xx}\}$, where T_{xx} is a component of a tensor function?

11.5.

$$\{\boldsymbol{f}, (\boldsymbol{a}\cdot\boldsymbol{M})\} = [\boldsymbol{f}\wedge\boldsymbol{a}];$$

$$\{(\boldsymbol{f}\cdot\boldsymbol{M}), (\boldsymbol{l}\cdot\boldsymbol{M})\} = ([\boldsymbol{f}\wedge\boldsymbol{l}]\cdot\boldsymbol{M}) + \sum_{i,k} M_i M_k \{f_i, l_k\}.$$

11.6. Substituting into the second formula of the preceding problem $\boldsymbol{f} = \boldsymbol{e}_\zeta$ and $\boldsymbol{l} = \boldsymbol{e}_\xi$ where $\boldsymbol{e}_\zeta$ and $\boldsymbol{e}_\xi$ are unit vectors along the ζ- and ξ-axes of the moving system of reference, we have

$$\{M_\zeta, M_\xi\} = M_\eta. \tag{1}$$

This equation differs in the sign of the right-hand side from the analogous relation for the components of the angular momentum along the axes of the fixed system of coordinates,

$$\{M_z, M_x\} = -M_y. \tag{2}$$

As was shown in problem 11.4 (see also ter Haar, 1964, § 5.3, and Goldstein, 1950, § 8.7) the Poisson bracket (2) characterises the change in the component M_x when the coordinate system is rotated as a whole over an infinitesimal angle ε (see Fig. 115a):

$$\delta M_x = \varepsilon\{M_z,\ M_x\} = -\varepsilon M_y.$$

The Poisson bracket (1), which is equal to

$$\{(\boldsymbol{e}_\zeta \cdot \boldsymbol{M}),\ (\boldsymbol{M} \cdot \boldsymbol{e}_\xi)\} = (\{M_\zeta,\ \boldsymbol{e}_\xi\} \cdot \boldsymbol{M}),$$

characterises the change in the component of the fixed vector $\boldsymbol{M}$ along the axis $\boldsymbol{e}_\xi$ when the moving coordinate system is rotated over an infinitesimal angle around the ζ-axis (see Fig. 115b; in the figure the ξ, η, ζ-axes are the same as the x, y, z-axes before the rotation).

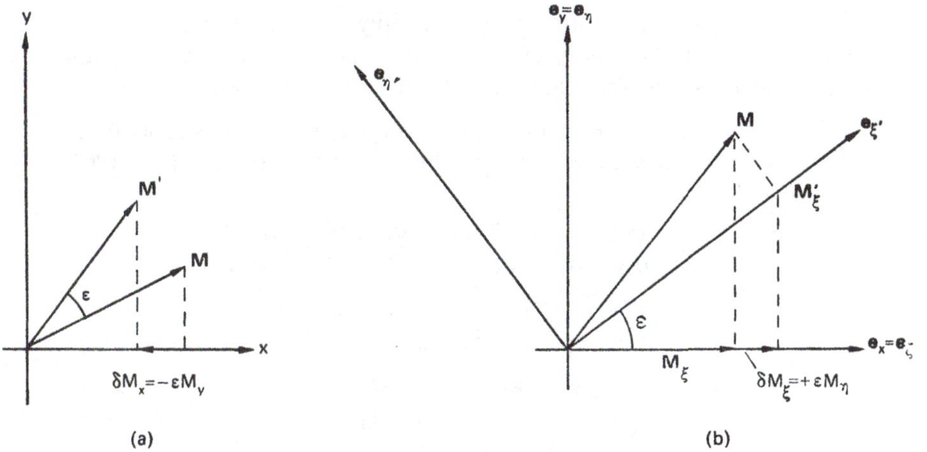

FIG. 115

11.7.

$$\dot{M}_\alpha = \sum_{\beta\gamma\delta} e_{\alpha\beta\gamma} I^{-1}_{\gamma\delta} M_\beta M_\delta .$$

In particular, if we choose the moving system of coordinates such that the inertial tensor $I_{\alpha\beta}$ is diagonal, we obtain the Euler equations (see ter Haar, 1964, § 4.2, using the relation $M_\alpha = I_\alpha \Omega_\alpha$).

11.8.

$$\dot{\boldsymbol{M}} = -\gamma[\boldsymbol{H} \wedge \boldsymbol{M}],$$

that is, the vector $\boldsymbol{M}$ processes around the direction of $\boldsymbol{H}$ with an angular velocity $-\gamma\boldsymbol{H}$ (compare the Larmor theorem; see § 45 of Landau and Lifshitz, 1962).

11.9.

$$\{v_i, v_j\} = -\frac{e}{m^2c}\sum_k e_{ijk}H_k.$$

11.10. (a)

$$\boldsymbol{p}(t) = \boldsymbol{p}+\boldsymbol{F}t,$$

$$\boldsymbol{r}(t) = \boldsymbol{r}+\frac{\boldsymbol{p}}{m}t+\frac{\boldsymbol{F}}{2m}t^2;$$

(b)

$$p(t) = p\cos\omega t - m\omega q\sin\omega t,$$

$$q(t) = q\cos\omega t+\frac{p}{m\omega}\sin\omega t.$$

Of course, these quantities can more simply be evaluated without using Poisson brackets. However, this method can easily be taken over in quantum mechanics (see, for instance, problem 3.20 in ter Haar, 1964a).

11.12. We can for the proof use, for instance, a generating function of the form $\Phi(q, P)$ (see Landau and Lifshitz, 1960, § 45, or ter Haar, 1964, § 5.2):

$$\{f, g\}_{p,q} = \frac{\partial(f, g)}{\partial(p, q)} = \frac{\partial(f, g)}{\partial(P, Q)}\,\frac{\partial(P, Q)}{\partial(P, q)}\bigg/\frac{\partial(p, q)}{\partial(P, q)}$$

$$= \frac{\partial(f, g)}{\partial(P, Q)}\left(\frac{\partial Q}{\partial q}\right)_{P=\text{const}}\bigg/\left(\frac{\partial p}{\partial P}\right)_{q=\text{const}}$$

$$= \frac{\partial(f, g)}{\partial(P, Q)}\,\frac{\partial^2\Phi}{\partial q\,\partial P}\bigg/\frac{\partial^2\Phi}{\partial P\,\partial q}$$

$$= \frac{\partial(f, g)}{\partial(P, Q)} = \{f, g\}_{P,Q}.$$

11.13. (a)

$$q = \sqrt{\frac{2P}{m\omega(t)}}\sin Q, \quad p = \sqrt{2m\omega(t)P}\cos Q,$$

$$\dot{Q} = \omega+\frac{\dot{\omega}}{2\omega}\sin 2Q, \quad \dot{P} = -P\frac{\dot{\omega}}{\omega}\cos 2Q.$$

In this case P and Q are action and angle variables. These variables are more convenient than p and q for solving the problem by the method of successive approximations, if the frequency $\omega(t)$ changes slowly, $\dot{\omega}/\omega^2 \ll 1$ (see problem 13.9).

(b)

$$q = \frac{F(t)}{m\omega^2} + \sqrt{\frac{2P}{m\omega}} \sin Q, \quad p = \sqrt{2m\omega P} \cos Q,$$

$$\dot{Q} = \omega + \dot{F} \sqrt{\frac{m\omega}{2P}} \cos Q, \quad \dot{P} = \dot{F} \sqrt{2m\omega P} \sin Q.$$

11.14.

$$\Psi(P, Q) = -Q \left[1 + \ln \frac{P^2}{4Q} \right].$$

11.15. The function $\Phi(q_1, q_2, \ldots, q_s, P_1, \ldots, P_s)$ determines a canonical transformation, provided

$$\det \frac{\partial^2 \Phi}{\partial q_i \, \partial P_k} \neq 0.$$

11.16. Let

$$Q = q \cos \alpha - p \sin \alpha,$$

and

$$P = q \sin \alpha + p \cos \alpha.$$

Then we have

$$\{P, Q\}_{p,\,q} = -\{q, p\}_{p,\,q} \sin^2 \alpha + \{p, q\}_{p,\,q} \cos^2 \alpha = 1.$$

For a system with one degree of freedom this is sufficient for the transformation to be canonical.

11.17. One sees easily (and subsequent calculations verify) that the canonical transformation must be close to the identity transformation, and that the terms ax^2P and bP^3 in the generating function are small. To solve the equations

$$p = P + 2axP, \quad Q = x + ax^2 + 3bP^2,$$

which determine the canonical transformation, for x and p, we replace x by Q and p by P in the small terms:

$$p = P + 2aQP, \quad x = Q - aQ^2 - 3bP^2.$$

We proceed in a similar fashion when we express the Hamiltonian in terms of the new variables:

$$H'(Q, P) = \tfrac{1}{2}P^2+\tfrac{1}{2}\omega^2Q^2+\alpha Q^3+\beta QP^2+2aQP^2-aQ^3-3bQP^2$$
$$+\text{terms of fourth degree in } P \text{ and } Q.$$

Putting $\alpha-a = 0$, $\beta+2a-3b = 0$, the third-order terms are made to vanish. In the approximation indicated in the problem we have thus $Q = A\cos\omega t$, $P = -\omega A\sin\omega t$, and from (1) (compare Landau and Lifshitz, 1960, § 28)

$$x = A\cos\omega t-\alpha A^2\cos^2\omega t-(\beta+2\alpha)\,\omega^2 A^2\sin^2\omega t.$$

11.18. Reducing the Hamiltonian to the form considered in problem 10.4 we get (compare Landau and Lifshitz, 1960, § 28)

$$x = Q-\frac{5\beta}{8\omega_0^2}Q^3-\frac{9\beta}{8\omega_0^4}QP^2,$$

where $\quad Q = A\cos\omega t,\quad P = -\omega_0 A\sin\omega t,\quad \omega = \omega_0+\dfrac{3\beta}{2\omega_0}A^2.$

11.19. $H'(P,Q) = H(P,Q)$; when $X = A\sin(\omega t+\varphi)$, $Y = 0$ the oscillator performs a motion along an ellipse:

$$x = A\cos\lambda\sin(\omega t+\varphi),\qquad y = A\sin\lambda\cos(\omega t+\varphi).$$

11.20. In order to make the notation less cumbersome it is convenient to put for the time being $m = \omega = e = c = 1$. One can easily reintroduce these factors in the final expressions. The transformation of problem 11.19 is a rotation in the x, p_y- and y, p_x-planes, which therefore leaves the form of that part of the Hamiltonian which is equal to $\tfrac{1}{2}(x^2+y^2+p_x^2+p_y^2)$ invariant. On the other hand, the correction due to the terms $\tfrac{1}{2}H^2x^2-Hxp_y$ is equal to

$$\tfrac{1}{2}H^2(X^2\cos^2\lambda+P_Y^2\sin^2\lambda+2XP_Y\sin\lambda\cos\lambda)+H(X^2-P_Y^2)\sin\lambda\cos\lambda$$
$$-H(\cos^2\lambda-\sin^2\lambda)\,XP_Y.$$

The off-diagonal term XP_Y vanishes, if we put

$$\sin^2\lambda-\cos^2\lambda+H\sin\lambda\cos\lambda = 0,\quad\text{that is,}\quad \cot 2\lambda = \tfrac{1}{2}H.$$

After a few simple transformations the Hamiltonian is reduced to the form

$$H = \frac{1}{2m}(P_X^2+P_Y^2\cot^2\lambda)+\tfrac{1}{2}m\omega^2(X^2\tan^2\lambda+Y^2). \tag{1}$$

The variables X and Y thus perform harmonic oscillations with frequencies which are, respectively, equal to

$$\omega_1 = \omega \tan\lambda = \left[\omega^2 + \left(\frac{eH}{2mc}\right)^2\right]^{\frac{1}{2}} - \frac{eH}{2mc},$$

$$\omega_2 = \omega \cot\lambda = \left[\omega^2 + \left(\frac{eH}{2mc}\right)^2\right]^{\frac{1}{2}} + \frac{eH}{2mc}$$

(compare Landau and Lifshitz, 1962, § 21). Each of the coordinates X and Y corresponds to a motion along an ellipse; an arbitrary oscillation is a superposition of two such motions (compare problems 6.23, 11.19).

It is interesting to note that when $H \to 0$, it turns out that $\lambda = \pi/4$ (and not $\lambda = 0$). This means, that even for very weak fields H the "normal" oscillations turn out to be "circularly polarised". On the other hand, oscillations corresponding to the coordinates X or Y with $\lambda = 0$ which if there were no field H would be linearly polarised, slowly change their direction of polarisation, as soon as there is a field H present.

If the magnetic field is variable, we must add to the Hamiltonian (1) the partial derivative with respect to the time of the generating function

$$\Phi = -m\omega xy \cot\lambda - \frac{P_X P_Y}{m\omega}\tan\lambda + \frac{xP_X + yP_Y}{\cos\lambda}$$

(expressing it in terms of X, Y, P_X, and P_Y; see also the footnote to problem 13.25).

11.21. Putting into the canonical transformation of the preceding problem

$$\omega = \omega_2, \quad \tan 2\lambda = \frac{2\omega_H \omega_2}{\omega_H{}^2 + \omega_1^2 - \omega_2^2},$$

we get

$$H' = \frac{1}{2m}\left(P_X^2 + \frac{\Omega_2^2}{\omega_2^2}P_Y^2 + p_Z^2\right) + \tfrac{1}{2}m(\Omega_1^2 X^2 + \omega_2^2 Y^2 + \omega_3^2 z^2),$$

where $\Omega_{1,\,2}$ was defined in problem 6.23.

11.22. The transformation ($\lambda = \pi/4$)

$$q_{s1} = \frac{1}{\sqrt{2}}\left(X_s + \frac{P_{Ys}}{Nm\omega_s}\right), \quad q_{s2} = \frac{1}{\sqrt{2}}\left(Y_s + \frac{P_{Xs}}{Nm\omega_s}\right)$$

leaves the form of the Hamiltonian

$$H = \frac{p_0^2}{2Nm} + \sum_{s=1}^{R} \left[\frac{p_{s1}^2 + p_{s2}^2}{2Nm} + \tfrac{1}{2}Nm\omega_s^2(q_{s1}^2 + q_{s2}^2) \right]$$

$$= \frac{p_0^2}{2Nm} + \sum_{s=1}^{R} \left[\frac{P_{Xs}^2 + P_{Ys}^2}{2Nm} + \tfrac{1}{2}Nm\omega_s^2(X_s^2 + Y_s^2) \right]$$

invariant (compare problem 11.19). The oscillation corresponding to $X_s = A \cos(\omega_s t + \beta)$ is

$$x_n = \frac{A}{\sqrt{2}} \sin(\omega_s t + n\varphi_s + \beta),$$

and the one corresponding to $Y_s = B \cos(\omega_s t + \beta)$ is

$$x = \frac{B}{\sqrt{2}} \sin(-\omega_s t + n\varphi_s - \beta).$$

11.23. The new Hamiltonian is $H' = \omega P_1$, and in the new variables the equations of motion have the form

$$\dot{P}_1 = \dot{P}_2 = \dot{Q}_2 = 0, \quad \dot{Q}_1 = \omega.$$

What is the change in the Hamiltonian H', if H depends on the time?

11.24. The transformation is $p = \alpha P$, $r = Q/\alpha$, which is a similarity transformation.

11.25. The gauge transformation

$$\boldsymbol{A}' = \boldsymbol{A} + \nabla f(\boldsymbol{r}, t), \quad \varphi' = \varphi - \frac{1}{c}\frac{\partial f}{\partial t}$$

can be written as a canonical transformation,

$$\boldsymbol{r}' = \boldsymbol{r}, \quad \boldsymbol{P}' = \boldsymbol{P} - \frac{e}{c}\nabla f(\boldsymbol{r}, t), \quad H' = H - \frac{e}{c}\frac{\partial f}{\partial t},$$

if one uses the generating function

$$\Phi(\boldsymbol{r}, \boldsymbol{P}') = (\boldsymbol{r} \cdot \boldsymbol{P}') - \frac{e}{c} f(\boldsymbol{r}, t).$$

11.26.

$$\Phi(q, P) = qP - f(q, t).$$

11.27.

(b) $$F_\tau(q, Q) = \frac{1}{2}F\tau(q+Q)+\frac{m}{2\tau}(q-Q)^2;$$

(c) $$F_\tau(q, Q) = \frac{m\omega}{2\sin\omega\tau}\left[2qQ-(q^2+Q^2)\cos\omega\tau\right]$$

11.28. (a)
$$\boldsymbol{Q} = \boldsymbol{r}+\delta\boldsymbol{a}, \quad \boldsymbol{P} = \boldsymbol{p}:$$
a shift of the system as a whole over $\delta\boldsymbol{a}$ (or a shift of the coordinate system over $-\delta\boldsymbol{a}$).

(b) Up to and including first-order terms, we have
$$\boldsymbol{Q} = \boldsymbol{r}+[\delta\boldsymbol{\varphi}\wedge\boldsymbol{r}], \quad \boldsymbol{P} = \boldsymbol{p}+[\delta\boldsymbol{\varphi}\wedge\boldsymbol{p}].$$
The transformation is a rotation of the coordinate system over an angle $-\delta\boldsymbol{\varphi}$.

(c)
$$Q(t) = q(t+\delta\tau), \quad P(t) = p(t+\delta\tau),$$
$$H'(P, Q, t) = H(p, q, t+\delta\tau).$$
The transformation is a shift in the time by $\delta\tau$ (compare Landau and Lifshitz, 1960, § 45).

(d) $$\boldsymbol{Q} = \boldsymbol{r}+2\boldsymbol{p}\delta\alpha, \quad \boldsymbol{P} = \boldsymbol{p}-2\boldsymbol{r}\,\delta\alpha.$$

The transformation is a rotation over an angle $2\delta\alpha$ in each of the x_ip_i-planes (i = 1, 2, 3) in phase space.

11.30. (a)
$$\Phi(\boldsymbol{r}, \boldsymbol{P}) = (\boldsymbol{r}\cdot\boldsymbol{P})+(\boldsymbol{n}\cdot\boldsymbol{P})\delta a+(\boldsymbol{n}\cdot[\boldsymbol{r}\wedge\boldsymbol{P}])\delta\varphi,$$
where δa is the displacement along the direction of $\boldsymbol{n}$ while $\delta\varphi = 2\pi\delta a/h$ is the angle of rotation around $\boldsymbol{n}$; h is the pitch of the screw;

(b) $$\Phi(\boldsymbol{r}, \boldsymbol{P}) = (\boldsymbol{r}\cdot\boldsymbol{P})+(\boldsymbol{V}\cdot\boldsymbol{P})t-m(\boldsymbol{r}\cdot\boldsymbol{V});$$

(c) $$\Phi(\boldsymbol{r}, \boldsymbol{P}) = (\boldsymbol{r}\cdot\boldsymbol{P})-t(\boldsymbol{\Omega}\cdot[\boldsymbol{r}\wedge\boldsymbol{P}]).$$

11.31.
$$\delta f(q, p) = \lambda\{W, f\}_{p, q}.$$
Indeed, substituting the values of the new variables,
$$P = p-\lambda\frac{\partial W}{\partial q}, \quad Q = q+\lambda\frac{\partial W}{\partial P},$$

into $f(Q, P)$ and expanding the expression obtained in powers of λ we get up to and including first-order terms

$$\delta f(q, p) = \lambda \frac{\partial f}{\partial q} \frac{\partial W(q, p)}{\partial p} - \lambda \frac{\partial f}{\partial p} \frac{\partial W(q, p)}{\partial q}.$$

11.32. Putting

$$\Phi = (\boldsymbol{r}\cdot\boldsymbol{P}) + \lambda(\boldsymbol{r}\cdot\boldsymbol{P})$$

in the preceding problem, we get a similarity transformation with $\alpha = 1+\lambda$ (see problem 11.24). The given Hamiltonian is such that $H'(\boldsymbol{P}, \boldsymbol{Q}) = \alpha^2 H(\boldsymbol{P}, \boldsymbol{Q})$ and therefore $\lambda\{H, (\boldsymbol{r}\cdot\boldsymbol{p})\} = H' - H = 2\lambda H (\lambda \to 0)$. On the other hand,

$$\{H, (\boldsymbol{r}\cdot\boldsymbol{p})\} = \frac{d}{dt}(\boldsymbol{r}\cdot\boldsymbol{p}),$$

and hence

$$(\boldsymbol{p}\cdot\boldsymbol{r}) - 2E = \text{constant}$$

(compare problem 4.13(b)).

11.34. Let $\delta_1 q$ and $\delta_1 p$ be the changes in the coordinates and momenta connected with the transformation defined by Φ_1.† Then we have

$$f(q+\delta_1 q,\ p+\delta_1 p) = f(q, p) + \lambda_1\{W_1(q, p), f(q, p)\}_{p,q} + \lambda_1^2 \varphi_1(q, p). \quad (1)$$

We now apply to each of the terms on the right-hand side of (1) another transformation, defined by the function Φ_2:

$$f(q+\delta_{21}q, p+\delta_{21}p) = f + \lambda_2\{W_2, f\} + \lambda_1\{W_1, f\} + \lambda_1\lambda_2\{W_2, \{W_1, f\}\} + \lambda_1^2\varphi_1 + \lambda_2^2\varphi_2. \quad (2)$$

The transformation of $\lambda_1^2\varphi_1(q, p)$ gives a correction of higher than second order. If we apply these transformation in the reversed order, the result is:

$$f(q+\delta_{12}q,\ p+\delta_{12}p) = f + \lambda_1\{W_1, f\} + \lambda_2\{W_2, f\} + \lambda_1\lambda_2\{W_1, \{W_2, f\}\} + \lambda_1^2\varphi_1 + \lambda_2^2\varphi_2. \quad (3)$$

The difference between (2) and (3) lies only in the second-order terms which are proportional to $\lambda_1\lambda_2$. Subtracting (3) from (2) we get

$$\lambda_1\lambda_2[\{W_2, \{W_1, f\}\} - \{W_1, \{W_2, f\}\}] = \lambda_1\lambda_2\{f, \{W_1, W_2\}\}.$$

† Let us as an example indicate the change in the momentum up to second-order terms:

$$\delta_1 p = P - p = -\lambda_1 \frac{\partial W_1(q, P)}{\partial q} = -\lambda_1 \frac{\partial W_1(q, p)}{\partial q} + \lambda_1^2 \frac{\partial^2 W_1(q, p)}{\partial p\, \partial q} \frac{\partial W_1(q, p)}{\partial q}.$$

Therefore, we see that, in particular, shifts $\lambda W = (\delta \boldsymbol{a} \cdot \boldsymbol{P})$ (see problem 11.28(a)) commute, while this is not the case for rotations around different axes, $\lambda W = (\delta \boldsymbol{\varphi} \cdot [\boldsymbol{q} \wedge \boldsymbol{P}])$.

Is the statement, which is the inverse of the one in the problem, correct?

11.35. (a) A canonical transformation with a variable parameter λ can be considered to be a "motion" where λ plays the role of the time and $W(q, p)$ the role of the Hamiltonian (compare problem 11.28c). The equations of "motion" are

$$\frac{dQ}{d\lambda} = \frac{\partial W(Q, P)}{\partial P}, \qquad \frac{dP}{d\lambda} = -\frac{\partial W(Q, P)}{\partial Q}.$$

One can also easily obtain these equations formally from the result of problem 11.31.

(b) The infinitesimal change in the coordinates and momenta under the given canonical transformation has the form

$$\delta \boldsymbol{r} = \frac{\lambda}{N}\{W, \boldsymbol{r}\} = \frac{2\lambda}{N} M\{(\boldsymbol{M}\cdot\boldsymbol{n}), \boldsymbol{r}\} = [\boldsymbol{n} \wedge \boldsymbol{r}]\delta\varphi,$$

$$\delta \boldsymbol{p} = [\boldsymbol{n} \wedge \boldsymbol{p}]\delta\varphi, \tag{1}$$

where

$$\boldsymbol{M} = [\boldsymbol{r} \wedge \boldsymbol{p}] = M\boldsymbol{n}, \quad \delta\varphi = -2\frac{\lambda}{N} M.$$

The transformation (1) is a rotation of the coordinate system over an angle $\delta\varphi$ around the direction of $\boldsymbol{M}$, that is, in the plane of the vectors $\boldsymbol{r}$ and $\boldsymbol{p}$. The vector $\boldsymbol{M}$ does not change under the transformation. If we take the z-axis along $\boldsymbol{M}$, we get finally

$$x(\varphi) = x_0 \cos\varphi - y_0 \sin\varphi, \quad y(\varphi) = y_0 \sin\varphi + x_0 \cos\varphi, \quad z(\varphi) = z_0,$$

and similar equations for the components of the momentum.

(c) $q(\varphi) = q_0 e^{\lambda}$, $p(\varphi) = p_0 e^{-\lambda}$.

11.36. (a) The volume specified in momentum space and in phase space does not change with time, but in coordinate space the volume is spread out. Thus, if at $t = 0$ the state of the system is represented by the rectangle ABCD (Fig. 116) it goes over to the parallelogram A′B′C′D′ (AD = A′D′) after a time t, and the distance in the x-direction between the points A′ and C′ is equal to $\Delta x = \Delta x_0 + \Delta p_0 t/m$. As time goes on this parallelogram degenerates into a narrow, very long strip.

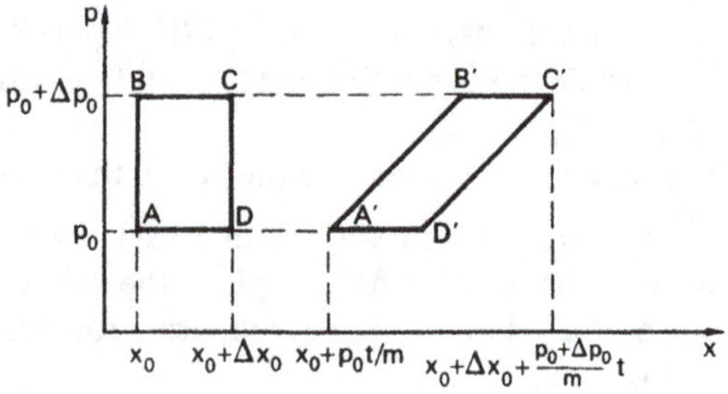

FIG. 116

(b) If there is a wall at the point $x = L$, the state of the system can no longer be represented by the parallelogram A′B′C′D′, but must have the form shown in Fig. 117a. When time marches on the initial phase volume ABCD changes into a number of very narrow parallel strips which are almost uniformly distributed inside two rectangles $0 \leqq x \leqq L$, $p_0 \leqq p \leqq p_0 + \Delta p_0$ and $0 \leqq x \leqq L$, $-p_0 - \Delta p_0 \leqq p \leqq -p_0$ (Fig. 117b).

(c) The phase orbit of an oscillator with energy E and frequency ω is the ellipse $(x^2/a^2)+(p^2/b^2) = 1$ with semi-axes $a = \sqrt{(2E/m\omega^2)}$, $b = \sqrt{(2E/m)}$. All points of the specified phase volume move along such ellipsis and return to their initial state after a period $T = 2\pi/\omega$. The dimensions of the specified "volume" in coordinate space, Δx, and in momentum space, Δp, oscillate with frequency 2ω. In contrast to the case sub (b) there is no spreading out of the specified phase volume into the whole of the available phase space.

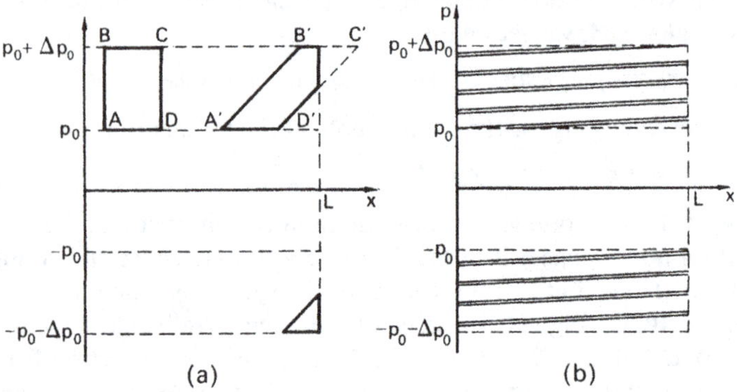

FIG. 117

(d) For an oscillator with friction (friction force $F_{fr} = -2m\lambda\dot{x}$) we have

$$x = ae^{-\lambda t}\cos(\omega t+\varphi),\ p = m\dot{x} = -mae^{-\lambda t}[\omega\sin(\omega t+\varphi)+\lambda\cos(\omega t+\varphi)],$$

and the oscillations are damped so that the phase orbit is a spiral,

$$\frac{x^2}{a^2}+\frac{(p+m\lambda x)^2}{m^2a^2\omega^2} = e^{-2\lambda t}.$$

The specified phase volume decreases until it vanishes. The non-conservation of phase volume is here connected with the fact that the system is not canonical: to describe it fully we need know not only the Lagrangian $L = \frac{1}{2}m(\dot{x}^2-\omega_0^2x^2)$ but also the dissipative function $F = \frac{1}{2}m\lambda\dot{x}^2$ (see Landau and Lifshitz, 1960, § 25).

If we choose for this system a "Lagrangian" in the form

$$L' = \tfrac{1}{2}me^{2\lambda t}(\dot{x}^2-\omega_0^2x^2)$$

(compare problem 4.17), the phase volume specified will be conserved for the appropriate canonical variables x and $p' = \partial L'/\partial\dot{x}$; however, in that case the generalised momentum $p' = m\dot{x}e^{2\lambda t}$ will not have a simple physical meaning, as before.

(e) Since the period of the motion in this case depends on the energy, the phase space volume is spread out with time, "filling" the whole of the available region of phase space (compare sub (b)).

Let the initial specified region be $x_0 < x < x_0+\Delta x$, $p_0 < p < p_0+\Delta p$. One can easily estimate the time which is such that during that period the fastest particles have made one more oscillation than the slowest ones:

$$\tau \sim \frac{T^2}{\Delta T},\quad \Delta T \sim \frac{dT}{dE}\Delta E,\quad \Delta E \sim \frac{p_0\Delta p}{m}+\left|\frac{dU(x_0)}{dx}\right|\Delta x.$$

(f) Let there be N particles such that the points in phase space which represent their state are at time $t = 0$ distributed with a density $Nw(x_0, p_0, 0)$ and that they move about according to the equations

$$x = f(x_0, p_0, t),\quad p = \varphi(x_0, p_0, t). \tag{1}$$

Here

$$f(x_0, p_0, t) = x_0+\frac{p_0}{m}t,\quad \varphi(x_0, p_0, t) = p_0,$$

for free motion and

$$f(x_0, p_0, t) = x_0\cos\omega t+\frac{p_0}{m\omega}\sin\omega t,\ \varphi(x_0, p_0, t) = -m\omega x_0\sin\omega t+p_0\cos\omega t,$$

for harmonic oscillators. The number of particles in the specified region of phase space, all points of which move according to the same law, remains constant; in particular, for an infinitesimal phase volume $dx\,dp$ we have

$$Nw(x, p, t)\,dx\,dp = Nw(x_0, p_0, 0)\,dx_0\,dp_0.$$

According to the Liouville theorem (see, for instance, ter Haar 1966, § 5.1) $\partial(x, p)/\partial(x_0, p_0) = 1$, and therefore

$$w(x, p, t) = w(x_0, p_0, 0). \tag{2}$$

Using (1) to get expressions for x_0 and p_0,

$$x_0 = f(x, -p, -t), \quad p_0 = \varphi(x, -p, -t),$$

and substituting this into (2), we get

$$w(x, p, t) = w(f(x, -p, -t), \varphi(x, -p, -t), 0),$$

or

$$w(x, p, t) = \frac{1}{2\pi\Delta p_0\,\Delta x_0}\, e^{-\alpha(x-X)^2-\beta(x-X)(p-P)-\gamma(p-P)^2},$$

where $X = f(X_0, P_0, t)$, $P = \varphi(X_0, P_0, t)$ while the coefficients α, β, γ are for free particles

$$\alpha = \frac{1}{2\Delta x_0^2}, \quad \beta = \frac{-t}{m\Delta x_0\,\Delta p_0}, \quad \gamma = \frac{1}{2\Delta p_0^2} + \frac{t^2}{2m^2\Delta x_0^2},$$

and for oscillators

$$\alpha = \frac{\cos^2 \omega t}{2\Delta x_0^2} + \frac{m^2\omega^2 \sin^2 \omega t}{2\Delta p_0^2}, \quad \beta = \sin \omega t \cos \omega t \left(\frac{m\omega}{\Delta p_0^2} - \frac{1}{m\omega\Delta x_0^2}\right),$$

$$\gamma = \frac{\cos^2 \omega t}{2\Delta p_0^2} + \frac{\sin^2 \omega t}{2m^2\omega^2\Delta x_0^2}.$$

We show in Figs. 118 and 119 how the regions in phase space in which $w(x, p, t) \geqq \frac{1}{2}$ (for free particles and for harmonic oscillators, respectively) move about. These regions are ellipses which are deformed as time marches on.† Their centres are displaced according to the same law (1) as the particles. In the case of free particles this ellipse is spread out without limit, but in the case of the oscillators, it only pulsates. We note

† If the scales along the p- and x-axes in the phase space of the harmonic oscillators are chosen such that $m\omega = 1$, the phase orbits are circles, and the specified region in phase space rotates around the origin without being deformed.

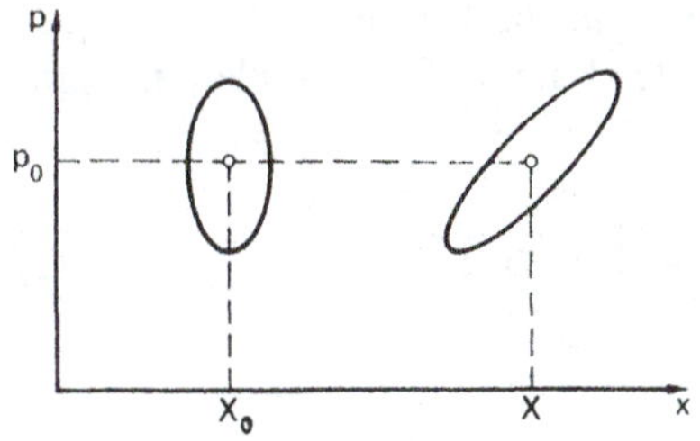

FIG. 118

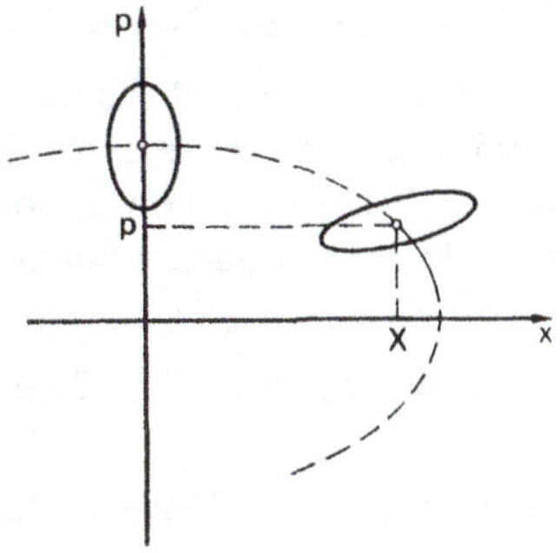

FIG. 119

that the distributions in coordinate and in momentum space are no longer independent ($w(x, p, t)$ cannot be split into two factors of the form $w_1(x, t)w_2(p, t)$).

It is interesting to consider the coordinate distribution function (independent of the values of the momenta)

$$w(x, t) = \int_{-\infty}^{+\infty} w(x, p, t)\, dp,$$

or the momentum distribution function

$$\tilde{w}(p, t) = \int_{-\infty}^{+\infty} w(x, p, t)\, dx.$$

These distributions turn out to be Gaussian with maxima at X and P, respectively,

$$w(x, t) = \frac{1}{\sqrt{2\pi}\, \Delta x} e^{-(x-X)^2/2(\Delta x)^2}, \quad \tilde{w}(p, t) = \frac{1}{2\pi \Delta p} e^{-(p-P)^2/2(\Delta p)^2},$$

where for the free motion

$$(\Delta x)^2 = (\Delta x_0)^2 + \frac{(\Delta p_0)^2}{m^2} t^2, \quad (\Delta p)^2 = (\Delta p_0)^2,$$

and for the oscillators

$$(\Delta x)^2 = (\Delta x_0)^2 \cos^2 \omega t + \frac{(\Delta p_0)^2}{m^2\omega^2} \sin^2 \omega t,$$

$$(\Delta p)^2 = (\Delta p_0)^2 \cos^2 \omega t + m^2\omega^2(\Delta x_0)^2 \sin^2 \omega t.$$

12. THE HAMILTON–JACOBI EQUATION

12.2. It is clear that the trajectory is a curve in a plane. If we use polar coordinates we can separate the variables in the Hamilton–Jacobi equation, provided we take the polar axis Oz along $\boldsymbol{a}$. The complete integral of the Hamilton–Jacobi equation is

$$S = -Et \pm \int \sqrt{\beta - 2ma\cos\theta}\, d\theta \pm \int \sqrt{2mE - \beta r^{-2}}\, dr. \qquad (1)$$

To fix the signs in (1) we use the relations

$$p_r = m\dot{r} = \frac{\partial S}{\partial r} = \pm\sqrt{2mE - \beta r^{-2}}, \qquad (2)$$

$$p_\theta = mr^2\dot{\theta} = \frac{\partial S}{\partial \theta} = \pm\sqrt{\beta - 2ma\cos\theta}. \qquad (3)$$

On the initial section of the trajectory† $\dot{r} < 0$, $\dot{\theta} > 0$. We must thus take the upper sign in front of the first radical in (1) and the lower sign in front of the second radical. The equation $\partial S/\partial\beta = B$ is the equation of the trajectory:

$$\int_0^\theta \frac{d\theta}{\sqrt{\beta - 2ma\cos\theta}} + \int_\infty^r \frac{dr}{r^2\sqrt{2mE - \beta r^{-2}}} = B; \qquad (4)$$

one can choose the lower limits of the integrals arbitrarily as long as the constant B is not determined. From our choice of lower limits and the condition that $\theta \to 0$ as $r \to \infty$, it follows that $B = 0$.

The constant β is an integral of motion of our problem and from (3) we have

$$\beta = p_\theta^2 + 2ma\cos\theta.$$

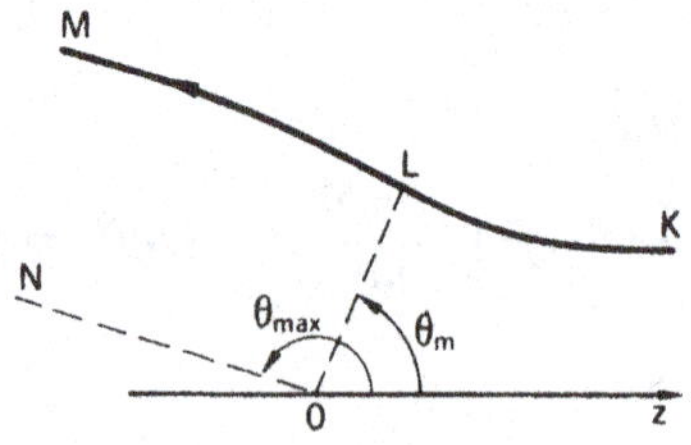

FIG. 120

† We assume that the trajectory lies above the z-axis (see Fig. 120).

It can be expressed in terms of the particle parameters when $r \to \infty$ and $\theta \to 0$, that is, before the collision, when $p_\theta = mv\varrho$ (ϱ is the impact parameter):

$$\beta = 2m(E\varrho^2 + a), \quad E = \tfrac{1}{2}mv^2.$$

When r changes from ∞ to

$$r_m = \sqrt{\frac{\beta}{2mE}} = \sqrt{\varrho^2 + \frac{a}{E}},$$

which is determined by the condition $p_r = 0$, θ changes from 0 to a value θ_m which is such that

$$\int_0^{\theta_m} \frac{d\theta}{\sqrt{\beta - 2ma\cos\theta}} + \int_\infty^{r_m} \frac{dr}{r^2\sqrt{2mE - \beta r^{-2}}} = 0. \tag{5}$$

A further increase in θ is accompanied by an increase in r; p_r then changes sign. The equation for the part LM of the orbit is

$$\int_{\theta_m}^{\theta} \frac{d\theta}{\sqrt{\beta - 2ma\cos\theta}} - \int_{r_m}^{r} \frac{dr}{r^2\sqrt{2mE - \beta r^{-2}}} = 0; \tag{6}$$

it is more convenient to use (5) and (6) and write it in the form

$$\int_0^{\theta} \frac{d\theta}{\sqrt{\beta - 2ma\cos\theta}} - \int_{r_m}^{\infty} \frac{dr}{r^2\sqrt{2mE - \beta r^{-2}}} - \int_{r_m}^{r} \frac{dr}{r^2\sqrt{2mE - \beta r^{-2}}} = 0. \tag{7}$$

As $r \to \infty$ the trajectory asymptotically approaches a straight line parallel to ON. The angle $\theta_{\max}$ can be found from the equation†

$$\int_0^{\theta_{\max}} \frac{d\theta}{\sqrt{\beta - 2ma\cos\theta}} = 2\int_{r_m}^{\infty} \frac{dr}{r^2\sqrt{2mE - \beta r^{-2}}} = \frac{\pi}{\sqrt{\beta}}. \tag{8}$$

The equation $\partial S/\partial E = A$ determines r as function of t. If we choose A such that $r(0) = r_m$, we get

$$r = \sqrt{v^2t^2 + r_m^2} = \sqrt{\varrho^2 + \frac{a}{E} + v^2t^2}. \tag{9}$$

The integrals over r in (4) and (7) can be evaluated elementarily, but those over θ reduce to elliptical integrals.

† We draw attention to the following method to avoid the calculation of the integral over r in (8). This integral is independent of a and must therefore equal the left-hand side of (8) also when $a = 0$. But in that case, clearly, $\theta_{\max} = \pi$, and the integral over θ is trivial.

If $E\varrho^2 \gg a$, we can expand the integrand in (4) and (7) in powers of $2ma/\beta \approx a/E\varrho^2$. Up to and including first-order terms we get

$$\theta + \frac{ma}{\beta}\sin\theta = \begin{cases} \arcsin(r_m/r), & 0 < \theta < \theta_m, \\ \pi - \arcsin(r_m/r), & \theta_m < \theta < \theta_{\max}, \end{cases} \tag{10}$$

or, with the same accuracy,

$$r\sin\theta = r_m\left(1 - \frac{a}{2E\varrho^2}\cos\theta\right) \tag{11}$$

(see Fig. 121). In this approximation, the angle over which the velocity of the particle is deflected after the scattering is equal to zero. This can be explained by the fact that the action of the force along different sections of the orbit (which to first approximation is the straight line $K'M'$) partially (and in first approximation completely) is self-cancelling.

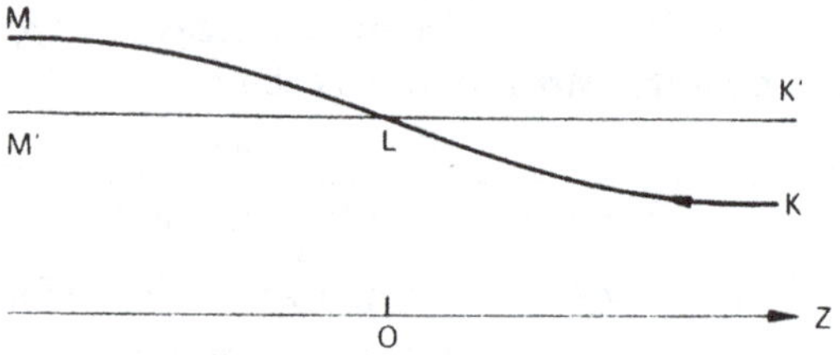

FIG. 121

12.3. (a) To determine the angle over which the particle is deflected we must expand in equation (8) of the preceding problem in powers of $a/E\varrho^2$ up to second order. We get the equation

$$\theta_{\max} + \frac{ma}{\beta}\sin\theta_{\max} + \frac{3}{4}\left(\frac{ma}{\beta}\right)^2\left(\theta_{\max} + \frac{1}{2}\sin 2\theta_{\max}\right) = \pi. \tag{1}$$

Solving this equation up to order $(ma/\beta)^2$, we find the angle of deflection†

$$\chi = \pi - \theta_{\max} = \frac{3}{4}\pi\left(\frac{ma}{\beta}\right)^2 = 3\pi\left(\frac{a}{4E\varrho^2}\right)^2. \tag{2}$$

† We look for $\theta_{\max}$ in the form $\theta_{\max} = \theta_0 + \theta_1 + \theta_2 + \ldots$, where $\theta_1 \sim (ma/\beta)\theta_0$. In zeroth approximation we get from equation (1) $\theta_0 = \pi$; in first approximation

$$\theta_1 + \frac{ma}{\beta}\sin\theta_0 = 0,$$

whence $\theta_1 = 0$; in second approximation

$$\theta_2 + \frac{ma}{\beta}\theta_1\cos\theta_0 + \frac{3}{4}\left(\frac{ma}{\beta}\right)^2\left(\theta_0 + \frac{1}{2}\sin 2\theta_0\right) = 0,$$

whence follows (2).

The scattering cross-section is

$$d\sigma = \pi\,|d\varrho^2| = \frac{\sqrt{3\pi a}\,d^2\omega}{16E\chi^{\frac{5}{2}}}.$$

The dependence on χ which we have obtained is the same as for small-angle scattering in the potential α/r^4, which decreases much faster than $U(\mathbf{r})$.

One obtains easily the result that when $\mathbf{v}_\infty$ is parallel to Oz the small-angle scattering cross-section is the same as (3).

In problem 3.12(b) we considered the scattering cross-section for particles for which $\mathbf{v}_\infty$ made an angle α with the dipole axis. For small α we can apply for some scattering angles χ (which ones?) equation (3), but for others we must use the equation from problem 3.12b.

(b) $$d\sigma = \frac{\pi b\,d^2\omega}{8E\chi^3}.$$

(c) When $E\varrho^2 \gg |b(\theta)|$ for all θ we have instead of equation (10) of problem 12.2

$$0 + \frac{m}{\beta}\int_0^\theta b(\theta)\,d\theta + \frac{3}{2}\frac{m^2}{\beta^2}\int_0^\theta b^2(\theta)\,d\theta = \begin{cases} \arcsin(r_m/r), & 0 < \theta < \theta_m, \\ \pi - \arcsin(r_m/r), & \theta_m < \theta < \theta_{\max}, \end{cases}$$

up to and including second-order terms.

If $$\int_0^\pi b(\theta)\,d\theta = \pi\langle b\rangle \neq 0,$$

we can limit ourselves to the first approximation for which

$$\chi = \pi - \theta_{\max} = \frac{m}{\beta}\pi\langle b\rangle,$$

and the small-angle scattering cross-section, $d\sigma = \pi\langle b\rangle d^2\omega/4E\chi^3$, is the same as in the central-field potential $U = \langle b\rangle/r^2$.

If, however, $\langle b\rangle = 0$, we must take the second-order terms into account and we get

$$\chi = \frac{3}{2}\frac{m^2}{\beta^2}\int_0^\pi b^2(\theta)\,d\theta = \frac{3}{2}\pi\frac{m^2\langle b^2\rangle}{\beta^2},$$

and the cross-section,

$$d\sigma = \frac{\sqrt{3\pi}}{8E\chi^{\frac{5}{2}}} \sqrt{\frac{1}{2}\langle b^2\rangle}\, d^2\omega,$$

is the same as the scattering-cross-section in the central-field potential $U = \alpha/r^4$ with $\alpha = \langle b^2\rangle/2E$.

Why can we neglect the possible contribution from small impact parameters?

12.4. (a) We can separate the variables in the Hamilton–Jacobi equation, if we choose spherical polars with the z-axis parallel to $\boldsymbol{a}$. The canonical momenta are

$$\left.\begin{aligned} p_r &= m\dot{r} = -\sqrt{2mE-\beta r^{-2}}, \\ p_\theta &= mr^2\dot{\theta} = \pm\sqrt{\beta - 2ma\cos\theta - (p_\varphi^2/\sin^2\theta)}, \\ p_\varphi &= mr^2\dot{\varphi}\quad \sin^2\theta = \text{constant}. \end{aligned}\right\} \tag{1}$$

One finds the constant

$$\beta = p_\theta^2 + \frac{p_\varphi^2}{\sin^2\theta} + 2ma\cos\theta$$

easily by noting that

$$p_\theta^2 + \frac{p_\varphi^2}{\sin^2\theta} = M^2,$$

where M is the total angular momentum of the particle; it is convenient to evaluate it for $r \to \infty$ and $\theta \to \pi - \alpha$ (α is the angle between $\boldsymbol{v}_\infty$ and $\boldsymbol{a}$), that is, before the collision.

According to (1) the particle can fall into the centre when $\beta < 0$, or

$$\varrho^2 < \frac{a}{E}\cos\alpha. \tag{2}$$

This is thus possible if $\alpha < \pi/2$, and in that case the cross-section is

$$\sigma = \frac{\pi a}{E}\cos\alpha.$$

Averaging over all possible values of $\boldsymbol{a}$ gives

$$\langle\sigma\rangle = \frac{1}{4\pi}\int_0^{\frac{\pi}{2}} \frac{\pi a}{E} 2\pi\cos\alpha\sin\alpha\, d\alpha = \frac{\pi a}{4E}.$$

It is interesting that the area defined by (2) is a circle with centre on the axis of the particle beam, although the potential is not symmetric with respect to that axis.

(b) $$\sigma = \begin{cases} \dfrac{\pi a}{E}\cos\alpha - \dfrac{\pi\lambda^2}{4E^2}, & 0 < \alpha < \alpha_m = \arccos\dfrac{\lambda^2}{4aE}; \\ 0, & \alpha_m < \alpha < \pi; \end{cases}$$

$$\langle\sigma\rangle = \frac{\pi a}{4E} + \frac{\pi\lambda^4}{64aE^3} - \frac{\pi\lambda^2}{8E^2};$$

(c) $$\sigma = \begin{cases} \dfrac{\pi a}{E}\cos\alpha + 2\pi\sqrt{\dfrac{\gamma}{E}}, & 0 < \alpha < \alpha_m = \pi - \arccos\dfrac{2\sqrt{\gamma E}}{a}; \\ 0, & \alpha_m < \alpha < \pi; \end{cases}$$

$$\langle\sigma\rangle = \frac{\pi a}{4E} + \sqrt{\frac{\gamma}{E}} + \frac{3\gamma}{a};$$

(d) $$\sigma = -\frac{\pi b(\pi - \alpha)}{E}, \quad \text{provided} \quad b(\pi - \alpha) < 0.$$

12.5.

$$\sigma = \begin{cases} \pi R^2 + \dfrac{\pi a}{E}\cos\alpha, & a\cos\alpha > -ER^2; \\ 0, & a\cos\alpha < -ER^2, \end{cases}$$

where α is the angle between $\boldsymbol{v}_\infty$ and $\boldsymbol{a}$.

12.6. (a) We use the same notation as in problem 12.2. The equation for the first part of the orbit ($r \to \infty$, $\theta \to \pi$) is

$$\int_\theta^\pi \frac{d\theta}{\sqrt{\beta - 2ma\cos\theta}} = \int_r^\infty \frac{dr}{r^2\sqrt{2mE - \beta r^{-2}}}, \tag{1}$$

with

$$\beta = 2m(E\varrho^2 - a). \tag{2}$$

When $\beta > 0$, the angle θ decreases when r changes from ∞ to r_m and then again increases to ∞.† The equation for the part of the orbit after

† The fact that there is no "stopping point" for θ is due to the inequality

$$\int_{\tilde\theta}^\pi \frac{d\theta}{\sqrt{1 - \lambda\cos\theta}} > \pi,$$

where

$$\tilde\theta = \begin{cases} 0, & 0 < \lambda < 1, \\ \arccos\dfrac{1}{\lambda}, & \lambda > 1 \end{cases}$$

(this inequality can easily be checked when $\lambda < 1$ and can be checked in a rather complicated way when $\lambda > 1$).

r has passed through the minimum distance from the centre is

$$\int_{\theta}^{\pi} \frac{d\theta}{\sqrt{\beta - 2ma\cos\theta}} = \frac{\pi}{2\sqrt{\beta}} + \int_{r_m}^{r} \frac{dr}{r^2\sqrt{2mE - \beta r^{-2}}}. \qquad (3)$$

It is clear that when $E\varrho^2 \gg a$ the orbit equations (1) and (3) are the same as equation (11) in problem 12.2.

When $\beta < 0$ the particle can fall into the centre (we note that it follows from (2) that only values $\beta \geqq -2ma$ are admissible). In that case r decreases monotonically from ∞ to 0. The angle θ decreases from π to the

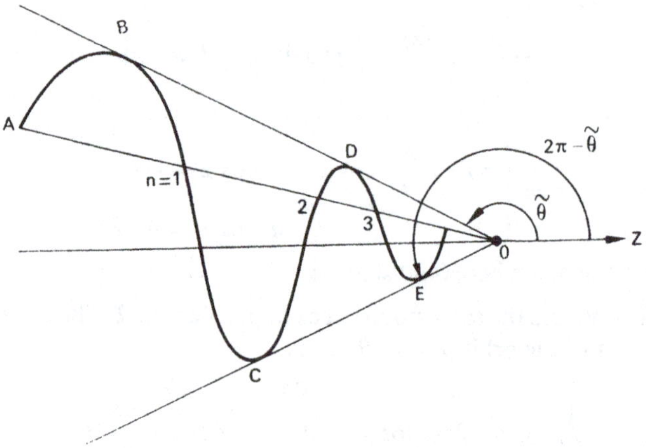

FIG. 122

value $\tilde{\theta}$ for which p_θ vanishes (the section AB of the orbit, see Fig. 122). We have then $\beta - 2ma\cos\tilde{\theta} = 0$. After that the angle increases until it reaches the value $2\pi - \tilde{\theta}$ (the section BC of the orbit):

$$\int_{r}^{\infty} \frac{dr}{r^2\sqrt{2mE - \beta r^{-2}}} = \int_{\tilde{\theta}}^{\pi} \frac{d\theta}{\sqrt{\beta - 2ma\cos\theta}} + \int_{\tilde{\theta}}^{\theta} \frac{d\theta}{\sqrt{\beta - 2ma\cos\theta}}. \qquad (4)$$

In the point C, p_θ again changes sign and θ decreases until it reaches the value $\tilde{\theta}$ in the point D, it then increases again, and so on.

The equation of the complete orbit can be written in the form

$$\int_r^\infty \frac{dr}{r^2\sqrt{2mE-\beta r^{-2}}} = (-1)^n \int_\theta^\pi \frac{d\theta}{\sqrt{\beta-2ma\cos\theta}} + 2n\int_{\tilde\theta}^\pi \frac{d\theta}{\sqrt{\beta-2ma\cos\theta}}, \quad n = 0, 1, 2, \ldots . \tag{5}$$

A single value of θ ($\tilde\theta < \theta < 2\pi-\tilde\theta$) corresponds to an infinite number of values of r (n can take on any non-negative integral value since the integral on the left-hand side of (5) increases without bound as $r \to 0$). The particle performs thus infinitely many oscillations between the lines BD and CE before it falls into the centre.

In the case of small impact parameters, $E\varrho^2 \ll a$, it turns out that $\pi-\tilde\theta \ll 1$ so that we can write in (5) $\cos\theta \approx -1+\frac{1}{2}(\pi-\theta)^2$. The final result is $\left(\operatorname{arsinh} x = \ln\left(x+\sqrt{1+x^2}\right)\right)$

$$\theta = \pi - \varrho\sqrt{\frac{2E}{a}} \sin\left[\frac{1}{\sqrt{2}} \operatorname{arsinh}\left(\frac{1}{r}\sqrt{\frac{a}{E}}\right)\right]. \tag{6}$$

The orbit $r(t)$ is determined in the same way as in problem 12.2, when $\beta > 0$ which justifies the relation (9) from problem 12.2. If $\beta < 0$, we have

$$r(t) = v\sqrt{t^2-\tau^2}, \quad -\infty < t < \tau = \frac{\sqrt{|\beta|}}{2E}, \tag{7}$$

and the particle falls into the centre at time τ.

(b) If $\beta > 0$ ($E\varrho^2 > a$), we have

$$\int_\theta^\pi \frac{d\theta}{\sqrt{1+(2ma/\beta)(1+\sin\theta)}} = \begin{cases} \arcsin\dfrac{r_m}{r}, & \theta_m < \theta < \pi, \\ \pi - \arcsin\dfrac{r_m}{r}, & \theta_{\min} < \theta < \theta_m. \end{cases}$$

If $\beta < 0$ ($E\varrho^2 < a$), we have

$$\left\{\int_{\theta_1}^\pi \pm \int_{\theta_1}^\theta + 2l\int_{\theta_1}^{\theta_2}\right\} \frac{d\theta}{\sqrt{\beta+2ma(1+\sin\theta)}} = \int_r^\infty \frac{dr}{r^2\sqrt{2mE-\beta r^{-2}}}$$

(see Fig. 123a), where l is the number of complete oscillations in angle (from θ_1 to θ_2 and back again) performed by the particle, and the + sign

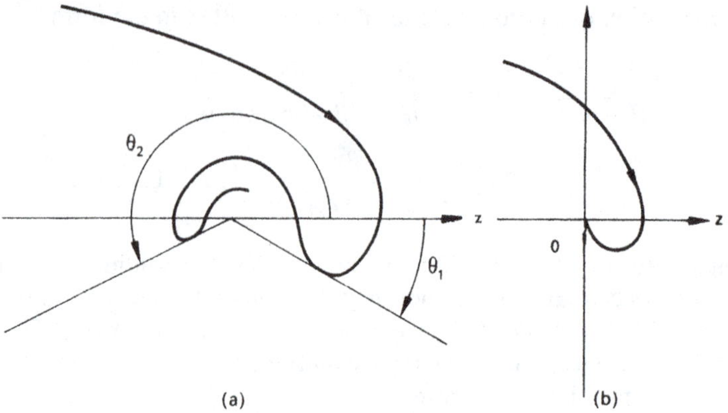

FIG. 123

(−sign) corresponds to counterclockwise (clockwise) motion, and

$$\theta_1 = -\arcsin\frac{E\varrho^2}{a}, \quad \theta_2 = \pi+\arcsin\frac{E\varrho^2}{a}.$$

If $\beta = 0$ ($E\varrho^2 = a$), we have

$$r = \frac{\varrho}{\sqrt{2}}\ln\frac{\tan(\frac{1}{8}\pi+\frac{1}{4}[\pi-\theta])}{\tan\frac{1}{8}\pi}, \quad -\frac{\pi}{2} < \theta < \pi.$$

The particle moves along the orbit of Fig. 123b, and we have $r = -\sqrt{2E/m}\,t$ ($t < 0$; the particle falls into the centre at $t = 0$).

12.7. The complete integral of the Hamilton–Jacobi equation is (see Landau and Lifshitz, 1960, § 48)

$$S = -Et+p_\varphi\varphi\pm\int\left[\beta-2ma\cos\theta-\frac{p_\varphi^2}{\sin^2\theta}\right]^{\frac{1}{2}}d\theta-\int\left[2mE-\frac{\beta}{r^2}\right]^{\frac{1}{2}}dr.$$

The generalised momenta are the same as in problem 12.4a. The particle can fall into the centre, if $\beta = 2m(E\varrho^2-a\cos\alpha) < 0$ (which is clearly satisfied if $\alpha^2 < 2E\varrho^2/a \ll 1$). In that case r decreases monotonically from ∞ to 0 (compare equation (7) of the preceding problem), and the angle φ increases monotonically from 0 to ∞. On the initial section of the orbit the angle θ decreases from a value $\theta_2 = \pi-\alpha$ to a value θ_1 where p_θ vanishes (if $\alpha^2 < 2E\varrho^2/a \ll 1$, it turns out that $\theta_1 = \pi-\sqrt{(2E\varrho/a)}$) after which it again increases to the value θ_2, and so on.

The equations for the orbit,

$$\varphi = \pm \int \frac{p_\varphi d\theta}{\sin^2\theta \sqrt{\beta - 2\,ma\cos\theta - (p_\varphi^2/\sin^2\theta)}}, \tag{1}$$

$$r = \mp r_0 \sinh \int \frac{\sqrt{|\beta|}\, d\theta}{\sqrt{\beta - 2ma\cos\theta - (p_\varphi^2/\sin^2\theta)}}, \quad r_0^2 = \frac{|\beta|}{2mE}, \tag{2}$$

can in general not be integrated to produce elementary functions. However, one can easily describe the motion qualitatively if one notes that equation (1) which gives a relation between the angles θ and φ is, apart from the notation, the same as the equation for the motion of a spherical pendulum (see problem 1 of § 14 of Landau and Lifshitz, 1960). The particle thus moves in such a way that the point where its radius vector intersects the surface of a sphere of radius l describes the same curve as does a spherical pendulum of length l, energy $\beta/2ml^2$, and angular momentum p_φ in the field of gravity $g = -a/ml^3$. This curve is enclosed between two "parallel" circles on the sphere corresponding to $\theta = \theta_1$ and $\theta = \theta_2$.

If $\alpha^2 < 2E\varrho^2/a \ll 1$, one can easily integrate equations (1) and (2):

$$\theta = \pi - \sqrt{(\varepsilon - \tfrac{1}{2}\alpha^2)\cos\left[2\sqrt{(ma/|\beta|)}\,\text{arsinh}\,(r_0/r)\right] + \varepsilon + \tfrac{1}{2}\alpha^2},$$

$$\theta = \pi - \frac{2\alpha\sqrt{\varepsilon}}{\sqrt{2\varepsilon + \alpha^2 + (2\varepsilon - \alpha^2)\cos 2\varphi}}, \quad \varepsilon = E\varrho^2/a. \tag{3}$$

It is clear from (3) that a particle when falling into the centre moves in the region between two conical surfaces $\theta_1 \leqq \theta \leqq \theta_2$ rotating around the z-axis, while one complete rotation around the z-axis corresponds to two complete oscillations in the angle θ. In this approximation the orbit is closed for a spherical pendulum (it is an ellipse).

12.8. (a) If the particle does not fall into the centre, the equation for a finite orbit is

$$\frac{p}{r} = 1 + e\cos[f(\theta)], \tag{1}$$

where

$$p = \frac{\beta}{m\alpha}, \quad e = \sqrt{1 + \frac{2E\beta}{m\alpha^2}}, \quad f(\theta) = \int \frac{d\theta}{\sqrt{1 - \dfrac{2ma}{\beta}\cos\theta}},$$

while the constants E and β satisfy the inequalities $E < 0$ and $\beta > 0$. If $0 < \beta < 2ma$, the orbit fills the region ABCDEF (Fig. 124),

$$r_1 \leqq r \leqq r_2, \quad r_{1,2} = \frac{p}{1 \pm e}, \quad \theta_1 \leqq \theta \leqq \theta_2, \quad \theta_1 = \arcsin\frac{\beta}{2ma}, \quad \theta_2 = 2\pi - \theta_1,$$

that is, it approaches any point in this arbitrarily closely.

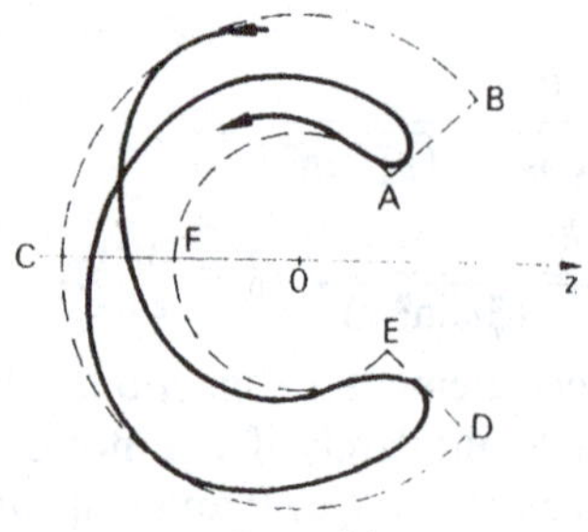

FIG. 124

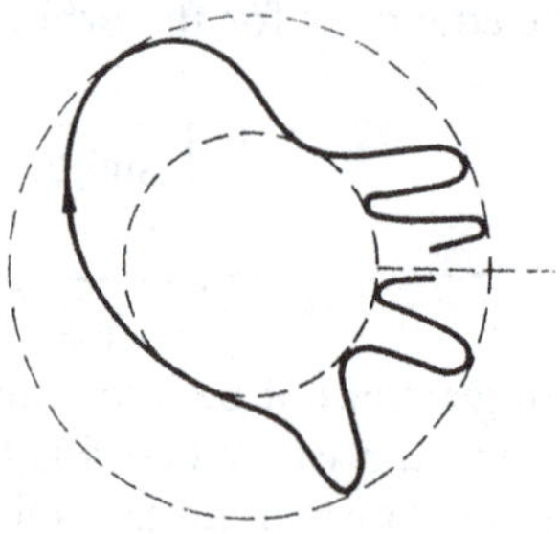

FIG. 125

If $\beta = 2ma$,

$$f(\theta) = \sqrt{2} \ln \tan \tfrac{1}{4}\theta + c_1, \tag{2}$$

and the orbit lies inside the ring $r_1 \leqq r \leqq r_2$ (Fig. 125).

If $\beta > 2ma$, the orbit fills the ring $r_1 \leqq r \leqq r_2$. In particular, if $\beta \gg 2ma$, we have

$$f(\theta) = \theta + \zeta \sin \theta + \tfrac{3}{4}\zeta^2\theta + \tfrac{3}{8}\zeta^2 \sin 2\theta + c_2, \tag{3}$$

where $\zeta = ma/\beta$. This is a slightly deformed ellipse, the nature of the deformation being determined by its orientation. Equation (3) can also be applied when $\theta \gtrsim \zeta^{-2}$. It is interesting to make a comparison with the results of problem 2.21.

12.9. If the motion lies inside the ring $r_1 \leqq r \leqq r_2$, when

$$\int_0^{2\pi} \frac{d\theta}{\sqrt{1-(2ma/\beta)\cos\theta}} = 2\pi \frac{n}{l},$$

and if the motion lies in the region $r_1 \leqq r \leqq r_2$, $\theta_1 \leqq \theta \leqq \theta_2$, when

$$\int_{\theta_1}^{\theta_2} \frac{d\theta}{\sqrt{1-(2ma/\beta)\cos\theta}} = \pi \frac{n}{l}$$

(n and l are integers).

12.10. One can separate variables in the Hamilton–Jacobi equation, if we take the z-axis along the vector $\boldsymbol{a}$ (see equation (48.9) of Landau and Lifshitz, 1960). The radial motion,

$$t = \sqrt{\frac{m}{2}} \int^{r} \frac{dr}{\sqrt{E-(\alpha/r)-(\beta/2mr^2)}},$$

is, when $\beta \geqq 0$, the same as the motion of a particle in a Coulomb potential $-\alpha/r$ with angular momentum β and energy E. When $\beta < 0$ the particle can fall into the centre. The equations of the orbit are $\partial S/\partial p_\varphi =$ constant, $\partial S/\partial \beta =$ constant. The first of these,

$$\varphi = \pm \int \frac{p_\varphi d\theta}{\sin^2\theta \sqrt{\beta - 2ma\cos\theta - (p_\varphi^2/\sin\theta)}},$$

is the same as the equation for the orbit of a spherical pendulum with energy $\beta/2ml^2$ and angular momentum $M_z = p_\varphi$ in the field of gravity $g = -a/ml^3$ (see problem 1 of § 14 in Landau and Lifshitz, 1960). The second equation connects r and θ. One can also use the analogy with a spherical pendulum for the analysis of that equation.

12.11.

(a) $|M_z| < \sqrt{\tfrac{1}{2}mb}$;

(b) A finite orbit is possible for any value of M_z.

12.12. (b) The complete integral of the Hamilton–Jacobi equation is (see Landau and Lifshitz, 1960, § 48, problem 1)

$$S = -Et + p_\varphi \varphi + \int p_\xi(\xi)\, d\xi + \int p_\eta(\eta)\, d\eta,$$

where

$$p_\xi = \pm\sqrt{\tfrac{1}{2}m[E - U_\xi(\xi)]}, \quad p_\eta = \pm\sqrt{\tfrac{1}{2}m[E - U_\eta(\eta)]},$$

$$\left.\begin{aligned} U_\xi(\xi) &= \frac{p_\varphi^2}{2m\xi^2} - \frac{m\alpha+\beta}{m\xi} - \frac{1}{2}F\xi, \\ U_\eta(\eta) &= \frac{p_\varphi^2}{2m\eta^2} - \frac{m\alpha-\beta}{m\eta} + \frac{1}{2}F\eta. \end{aligned}\right\}$$

The motion is determined by the equations

$$\frac{\partial S}{\partial \beta} = B; \quad \frac{\partial S}{\partial p_\varphi} = C; \quad \frac{\partial S}{\partial E} = A,$$

that is,

$$\int \frac{d\xi}{\xi p_\xi(\xi)} - \int \frac{d\eta}{\eta p_\eta(\eta)} = B,$$

$$\varphi - \frac{1}{2}p_\varphi \int \frac{d\xi}{\xi^2 p_\xi(\xi)} - \frac{1}{2}p_\varphi \int \frac{d\eta}{\eta^2 p_\eta(\eta)} = C,$$

$$-t + \frac{1}{4}m \int \frac{d\xi}{p_\xi(\xi)} + \frac{1}{4}m \int \frac{d\eta}{p_\eta(\eta)} = A.$$

When studying the character of the motion we must determine the region admissible for the values of ξ and η for given values of E, p_φ, and β. Figure 126 gives the shape of the effective potential energies $U_\xi(\xi)$ and $U_\eta(\eta)$. If $F = 0$, and when $-m\alpha < \beta < m\alpha$ (see curves a) and $E < 0$, the motion in both ξ and η is finite, but for $E > 0$ it is infinite. When a small force

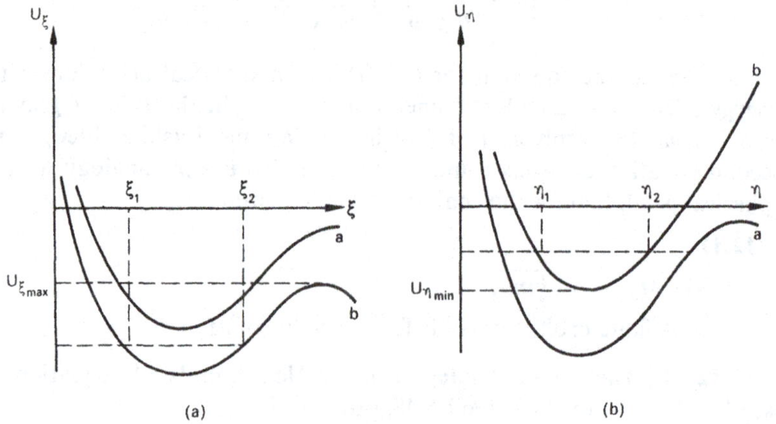

FIG. 126

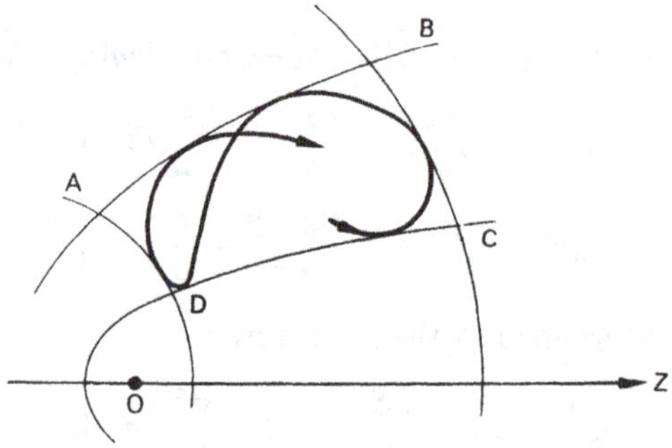

FIG. 127

$F > 0$ appears, the curve $U_\xi(\xi)$ shows a maximum (see curve b); when $U_{\eta\,\min} < E < U_{\xi\,\max}$, the motion is finite, as before. The motion is restricted to the region $\xi_1 < \xi < \xi_2$, $\eta_1 < \eta < \eta_2$ (see Fig. 127) in the ϱz-plane, while the ϱz-plane itself rotates around the z-axis with an angular velocity $\dot{\varphi}$. The orbit fills the region of space formed by rotating the figure ABCD around the z-axis (see also problem 2.32). When $U_{\xi\,\max} < E$, the motion is infinite.

When F increases the quantity $U_{\xi\,\max}$ decreases and $U_{\eta\,\min}$ increases. When $U_{\xi\,\max}$ becomes less than $U_{\eta\,\min}$ finite motion becomes impossible (when $\beta < -m\alpha+\frac{3}{2}(Fmp_\varphi^4)^{\frac{1}{3}}$ there are no extrema in $U_\xi(\xi)$).

12.13. In elliptical coordinates we have

$$\varrho = \sigma\sqrt{(\xi^2-1)(1-\eta^2)}, \quad z = \sigma\xi\eta, \quad \sigma = \sqrt{b^2-a^2}.$$

The potential,

$$U = \begin{cases} \infty, & \text{when} \quad \xi > \xi_0 = \dfrac{b}{\sigma}, \\ 0, & \text{when} \quad \xi < \xi_0, \end{cases}$$

depends only on ξ and we can separate the variables in the Hamilton–Jacobi equation (see Landau and Lifshitz, 1960, § 48).

The complete integral is

$$S = -Et+p_\varphi\varphi \pm \int \sqrt{2m\sigma^2E+\frac{\beta-2m\sigma^2A(\xi)}{\xi^2-1}-\frac{p_\varphi^2}{(1-\eta^2)^2}}\,d\xi$$

$$\pm\int\sqrt{2m\sigma^2E-\frac{\beta}{\xi^2-1}-\frac{p_\varphi^2}{(1-\eta^2)^2}}\,d\eta,$$

where

$$A(\xi) = (\xi^2-\eta^2)U(\xi) = U(\xi).$$

For a particle projected from the origin, $p_\varphi = 0$. From the above it follows that

$$p_\xi = \pm\sqrt{2m\sigma^2E+\frac{\beta-2m\sigma^2A(\xi)}{\xi^2-1}} = \frac{m\sigma^2(\xi^2-\eta^2)\dot{\xi}}{\xi^2-1},$$

$$p_\eta = \pm\sqrt{2m\sigma^2E-\frac{\beta}{1-\eta^2}} = \frac{m\sigma^2(\xi^2-\eta^2)\dot{\eta}}{1-\eta^2}.$$

In the origin ($\eta = 0$, $\xi = 1$) we have

$$= \pm\frac{\sqrt{2m\sigma^2E-\beta}}{m\sigma^2}, \quad \dot{\xi} = 0, \quad \dot{z} = \sigma(\dot{\xi}\eta+\dot{\eta}\xi) = \sigma\dot{\eta}$$

and from the condition

$$\sqrt{\frac{2E}{m}}\cos\alpha = \frac{\sqrt{2m\sigma^2E-\beta}}{m\sigma}$$

we find

$$\beta = 2m\sigma^2 E \sin^2 \alpha.$$

The region of the admissible values of η is determined by the condition

$$2m\sigma^2 E - \frac{\beta}{1-\eta^2} < 0,$$

or

$$|\eta| > |\cos \alpha|.$$

The motion thus takes place in the region

$$|\eta| < |\cos \alpha|, \quad 1 < \xi < \xi_0$$

(shaded region in Fig. 128).

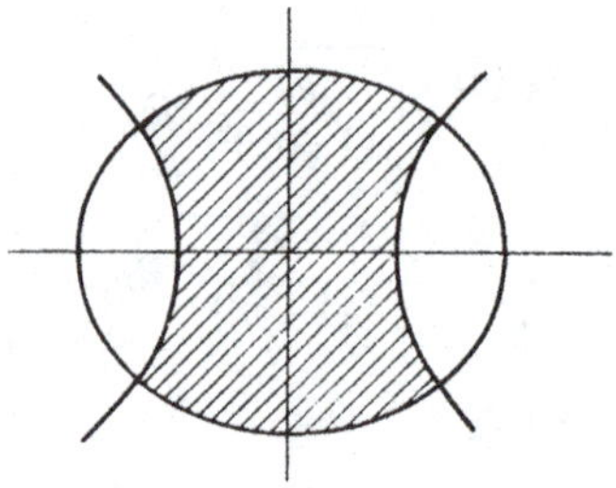

Fig. 128

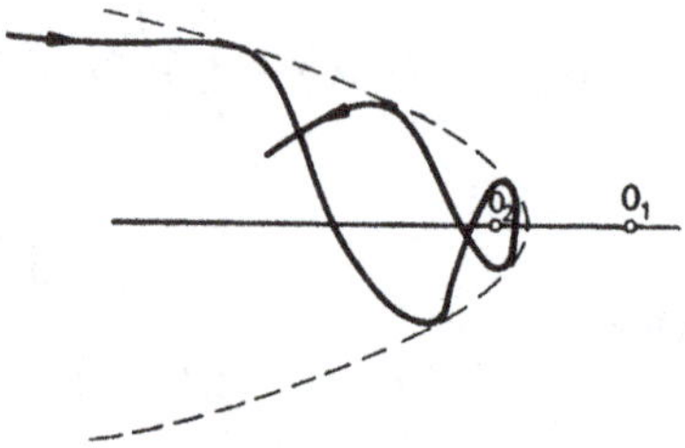

Fig. 129

12.14. One can separate the Hamilton–Jacobi equation in elliptical coordinates (see problem 2 of § 48 of Landau and Lifshitz, 1960, with $\alpha_1 = -\alpha_2 = \alpha$). For a particle coming from infinity along the z-axis, the constant $\beta = -2mE\varrho^2 + 4m\alpha\sigma$, where ϱ is the impact parameter.

If $\beta < 0$, the orbit is qualitatively the same as the orbit of a particle which is scattered in the potential of a point dipole (see problem 12.6b).

If $\beta > 0$ the particle "falls" onto the dipole (that is, it passes in its motion through the section O_1O_2) and then goes off again to infinity. If moreover $p_\eta(\eta_1) = 0$ when $\eta_1 < 0$, the particle moves in the region bounded by the hyperbola $\eta = \eta_1$ (Fig. 129).

12.15. In the Hamilton–Jacobi equation,

$$\frac{\partial S}{\partial t} + \frac{1}{2m}\left[\left(\frac{\partial S}{\partial z}\right)^2 + \left(\frac{\partial S}{\partial r}\right)^2 + \left(\frac{1}{r}\frac{\partial S}{\partial \varphi} + \frac{e}{2c}H(z)r\right)^2 = 0, \quad (1)$$

we can separate off the time and the angle φ:

$$S = -Et + p_\varphi \varphi + \bar{S}(r, z). \tag{2}$$

Considering in the following only orbits which intersect with the z-axis, we put $p_\varphi = 0$. It is not possible to separate the variables r and z and we shall look for the integral approximately, in the form of an expansion in r:

$$\bar{S}(r, z) = S_0(z) + r\psi(z) + \tfrac{1}{2}r^2\sigma(z) + \dots . \tag{3}$$

Since the radial momentum,

$$p_r = \frac{\partial S}{\partial r} = \psi(z) + r\sigma(z) + \dots, \tag{4}$$

for a particle flying along the z-axis (with $r = 0$) vanishes, for the particle beam considered we have $\psi(z) = 0$. Substituting (3) into (1) and comparing coefficients of the same powers of r (compare Landau and Lifshitz, 1962, § 56, problem 2), we get

$$S_0(z) = pz, \tag{5}$$

$$p\sigma'(z) + \sigma^2 + \frac{e^2}{4c^2} H^2(z) = 0. \tag{6}$$

Outside the lens (where $|z| > a$, $H(z) = 0$) we have from (6)

$$\sigma(z) = \frac{p}{z + c_1}, \quad \text{when} \quad z < -a, \tag{7}$$

$$\sigma(z) = \frac{p}{z + c_2}, \quad \text{when} \quad z > a. \tag{8}$$

The equation of the orbit,

$$\frac{\partial S}{\partial c_{1,2}} = -\frac{pr^2}{2(z + c_{1,2})^2} = B_{1,2}, \tag{9}$$

is an equation of straight lines intersecting the z-axis in the points $-c_{1,2}$,† that is, $z_0 = -c_1$ and $z_1 = -c_2$. From (6) we get

$$p\sigma(a) - p\sigma(-a) + \int_{-a}^{+a} \sigma^2\, dz + \frac{e^2}{4c^2} \int_{-a}^{+a} H^2(z)\, dz = 0. \tag{10}$$

† When z is close to $-c_{1,2}$, $\sigma \to \infty$ so that the expansion (3) becomes inapplicable. However, the equations (9) for the orbit remain valid also for that region.

Since $|z_{0,1}| \gg a$, it follows from (7) and (8) that

$$\sigma(\pm a) = -\frac{p}{z_{1,0}} \tag{11}$$

Let us estimate $\int_{-a}^{+a} \sigma^2\, dz$. According to (6), $\sigma(z)$ is a monotonic function. Therefore we have

$$\int_{-a}^{+a} \sigma^2\, dz \lesssim \frac{2ap^2}{z_{1,0}^2} \ll p\sigma(\pm a).$$

It thus follows from (10) that

$$\frac{1}{|z_0|} + \frac{1}{z_1} = \frac{e^2}{4c^2p^2} \int_{-a}^{+a} H^2(z)\, dz = \frac{1}{f}. \tag{12}$$

The condition $|z_{0,1}| \gg a$ is, indeed, satisfied when $a \ll cp/eH$.

12.16. The whole of the calculation of the preceding problem up to equation (6) is applicable also to this problem. The substitution $\sigma = f'/pf$ reduces (6) to the form

$$(1+\varkappa^2z^2)f''(z)+\frac{e^2H^2}{4c^2}f = 0,$$

and after that the substitution

$$\varkappa z = \tan\xi, \quad -\frac{\pi}{2} < \xi < \frac{\pi}{2}, \quad f(z) = \frac{\eta(\xi)}{\cos\xi}$$

gives

$$\eta''(\xi)+\lambda^2\eta(\xi) = 0,$$

where

$$\lambda^2 = 1+\frac{e^2H^2}{4c^2\varkappa^2p^2}.$$

Hence

$$\sigma = \sin\xi+\lambda\cos^2\xi\cot(\lambda\xi+\alpha),$$

and the equation for the orbit becomes

$$\frac{\partial S}{\partial\alpha} = -\frac{pr^2\lambda\cos^2\xi}{2\sin^2(\lambda\xi+\alpha)} = B,$$

or

$$r\cos\xi = B'\sin(\lambda\xi+\alpha).$$

When $r = 0$,

$$\lambda\xi_n+\alpha = n\pi,$$

and thus

$$\alpha = -\lambda \arctan \varkappa z_0,$$

so that the points where the beam is focused are given by

$$\varkappa z_n = \tan\left[\arctan \varkappa z_0 + \frac{n\pi}{\lambda}\right].$$

Depending on the magnitude of λ there will be one or several points of focusing.

12.17.

$$S(q, q, t, t_0) = f(q, \alpha(q, q_0, t, t_0), t) - f(q_0, \alpha(q, q_0, t, t_0), t_0),$$

where $f(q, \alpha, t)$ is the complete integral of the Hamilton–Jacobi equation, while the function $\alpha(q, q_0, t, t_0)$ is determined by the equation (or set of equations for the case of several degrees of freedom)

$$\frac{\partial f(q, \alpha, t)}{\partial \alpha} = \frac{\partial f(q_0, \alpha, t_0)}{\partial \alpha}.$$

13. Adiabatic Invariants

13.1. On the ring A there acts a force determined by the tension in the string. From Fig. 130 we see that for small φ, $F_x = mg\varphi$, $F_y = \frac{1}{2}mg\varphi^2$. Since the length of the string AB changes slowly, we can average the force

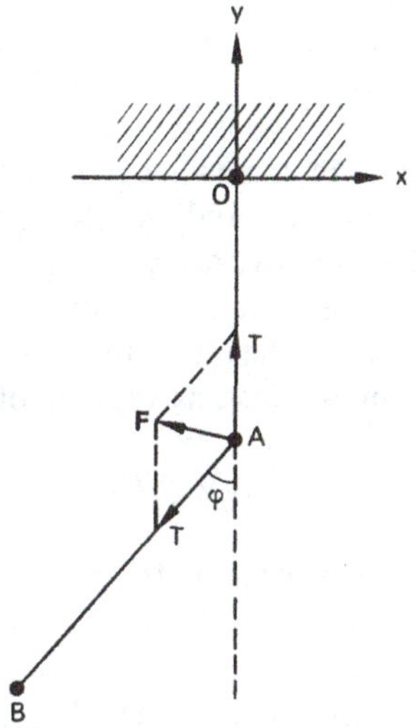

Fig. 130

over a period of the oscillations,

$$\varphi = \varphi_0 \cos \omega t, \quad \omega = \sqrt{\frac{g}{l}},$$

assuming the length of the string to be constant. We get

$$F_x = 0, \quad F_y = \tfrac{1}{4} m g \varphi_0^2.$$

When the ring is displaced over a distance $dy = dl$, the energy decreases by

$$F_y dy = \tfrac{1}{4} m g \varphi_0^2 \, dl.$$

Since

$$E = \tfrac{1}{2} m g l \varphi_0^2,$$

we have

$$dE = -\frac{1}{2} \frac{E}{l} \, dl.$$

Hence we have $El^2 =$ constant.

13.2. After the particle has collided with both walls its velocity v is changed by $2\dot{l}$. The condition that the change is slow means that $|2\dot{l}/v| \ll 1$. We choose a time interval Δt such that $\Delta t \gg 2l/v$ and $\Delta t \ll l/\dot{l}$. Such a Δt exists because of the slowness condition. During such a time interval there are $v\,\Delta t/2l$ pairs of collisions with the walls and the velocity is changed by

$$\Delta v = -v\dot{l}\,\frac{\Delta t}{l}. \tag{1}$$

Hence $vl =$ constant or $El^2 =$ constant.

It is interesting to study in somewhat more detail how the product vl changes. This is easily done by studying the functions $l(t)$ and $v(t)$ (see Fig. 131a, b). In Fig. 131c we have drawn the function $I = vl$. The quantity vl oscillates around the practically constant value $\langle vl \rangle$ while the amplitude of the oscillations has the relative magnitude $\Delta I/I \sim \dot{l}/v$. The deviation of $\langle vl \rangle$ from a constant value is of higher order:

$$\frac{d}{dt}\langle vl \rangle \sim \dot{l}^2.$$

13.3 If $g(t) = g - a$ were constant, the motion of the ball would be described by

$$z(t) = h - \tfrac{1}{2} g t^2 \quad \text{for} \quad -\sqrt{\frac{2h}{g}} < t < \sqrt{\frac{2h}{g}}. \tag{1}$$

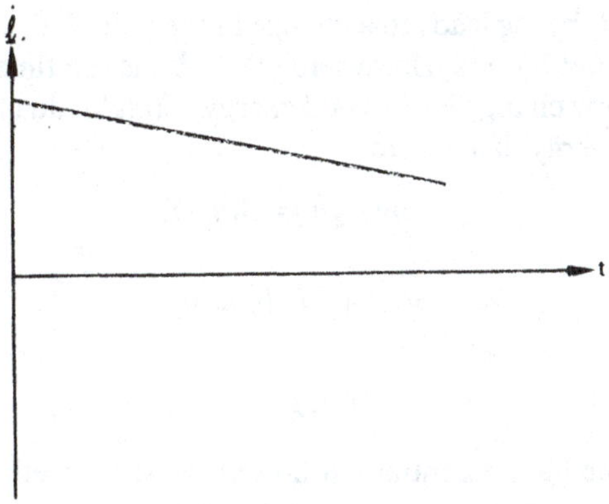

(a)

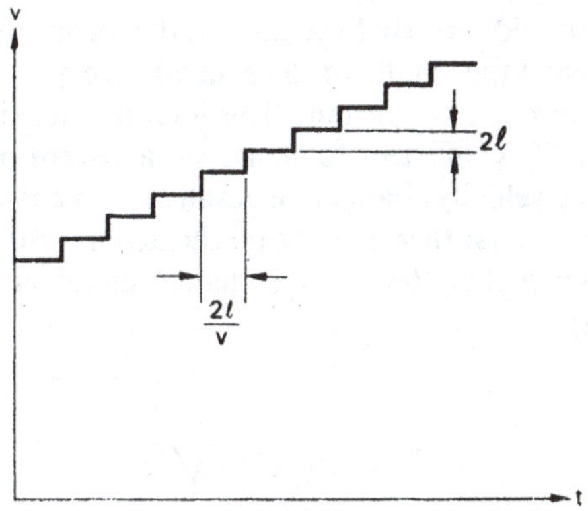

(b)

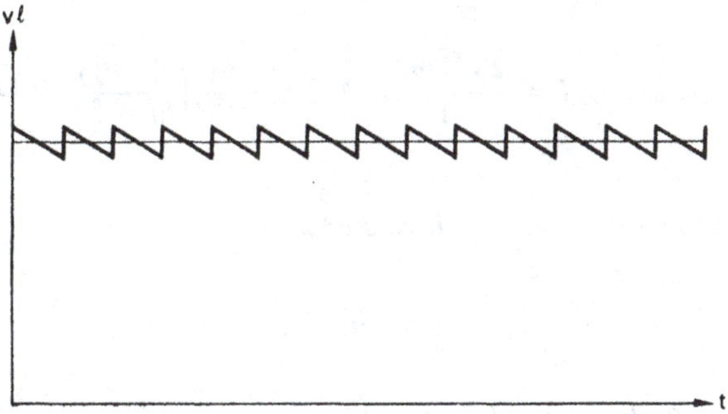

(c)

FIG. 131

A change in $g(t)$ by Δg leads to a change in the potential energy by $mz\,\Delta g$, and over a period by $m\langle z\rangle \Delta g$, where $\langle z\rangle = \frac{2}{3}h$ is the time average of z.

There is a slow change in the total energy, $\Delta(mgh)$, due to the change in the potential energy. Therefore

$$m\,\Delta g \cdot \tfrac{2}{3}h = \Delta(mgh),$$

or

$$g\,\Delta h + \tfrac{1}{3}h\,\Delta g = 0,$$

whence

$$h \propto g^{-\frac{1}{3}}.$$

In this proof we have essentially followed the same method which in the general case is applied to prove that $\oint p\,dq$ is constant (see Landau and Lifshitz, 1960, § 49, or ter Haar, 1964, § 6.3).

Of course, we could directly have used in this problem (and in the two preceding problems) the results of the general theory.

If the plate is raised, h = constant. This is clear when the velocity of the plate is constant (it is sufficient to change to a system of reference fixed in the plate). If the velocity changes the result cannot change as it depends, according to the general theory, only on the height of the support of the plate. It is assumed that the relative change in velocity during a time $\sqrt{(2h/g)}$ is small.

13.4. (a)

$$I = \frac{\sqrt{2m}}{\alpha}\left[\sqrt{U_0} - \sqrt{|E|}\right];$$

(b)

$$I = \frac{\sqrt{2m}}{\alpha}\left[\sqrt{E+U_0} - \sqrt{U_0}\right];$$

(c)

$$I = \frac{2\sqrt{2m}}{\pi n} A^{-\frac{1}{n}} E^{\frac{1}{n}+\frac{1}{2}} \frac{\Gamma(1/n)\Gamma(\frac{3}{2})}{\Gamma[(1/n)+\frac{3}{2}]} \propto TE.$$

13.5.

$$h \propto \sin^{\frac{2}{3}}\alpha.$$

13.6.

$$x \propto \sin^{-\frac{1}{4}}\alpha.$$

13.7.

$$I = \frac{8ml\sqrt{gl}}{\pi}\left[E\left(\sin\frac{1}{2}\varphi_0\right) - \cos^2\frac{1}{2}\varphi_0 K\left(\sin\frac{1}{2}\varphi_0\right)\right].$$

13.8. (a) Let the coordinates of the particles m and M, reckoned from O be x and X. The motion of the light particle can be considered approximately as the motion between two walls, one of which is moving. As the condition

$$|\dot{x}| \gg |\dot{X}| \tag{1}$$

is satisfied, the average over one period of the product $|\dot{x}|X = C$ is conserved (see problem 13.2). Eliminating $\dot{x}$ from the energy conservation law,

$$\tfrac{1}{2}m\dot{x}^2+\tfrac{1}{2}M\dot{X}^2 = E,$$

we find that the effect of the light particle upon the motion of the heavy one is equivalent to the appearance of a potential energy $U(X) = mC^2/2X^2$. The equation

$$\tfrac{1}{2}M\dot{X}^2+U(X) = E$$

leads to the following equation for the orbit:

$$X = \sqrt{\frac{mC^2}{2E}+\frac{2E}{M}(t-\tau)^2}\,.$$

The constants E, C, and τ can be determined from the initial values of X, $\dot{X}$ and $\dot{x}$ (they are independent of $x(0)$). This method of solving the problem becomes inapplicable when condition (1) is not satisfied.

Similar approximations (which are called adiabatic approximations) are widely applied, for instance, in the theory of molecules.

(b) If at the moment of contact of the heavy particles ($x_1 = x_2$) the energy of the light particle $E < -\frac{2}{3}V$, a "molecule" may exist.

13.9. We expand the frequency in a series in t in the equations for P and Q,

$$\dot{Q} = \omega+\frac{\dot{\omega}}{2\omega}\sin 2Q, \quad \dot{P} = -P\frac{\dot{\omega}}{\omega}\cos 2Q.$$

Restricting ourselves to first-order corrections we get for P and Q the equations

$$\dot{Q} = \omega_0+\dot{\omega}_0 t+\frac{\dot{\omega}_0}{2\omega_0}\sin 2Q, \tag{1}$$

$$\dot{P} = -P\frac{\dot{\omega}_0}{\omega_0}\cos 2Q, \tag{2}$$

where ω_0 and $\dot{\omega}_0$ are the values of the frequency and its derivative at time

$t_0 = 0$, and we have $\dot{\omega}_0 = \varepsilon^2\omega_0^2$ with $\varepsilon \ll 1$. From (1) and (2) we get

$$Q = \omega_0 t + \varphi + \tfrac{1}{2}\,\dot{\omega}_0 t^2 + \frac{\dot{\omega}_0}{2\omega_0}\int_0^t \sin 2Q(t)\,dt, \tag{3}$$

$$P = P_0\left[1 - \frac{\dot{\omega}_0}{\omega_0}\int_0^t \cos 2Q\,dt\right], \tag{4}$$

that is, the phase Q and the amplitude $A = \sqrt{2P/m\omega}$ of the perturbed motion differ relatively little from their initial values $Q_0 = \omega_0 t + \varphi$ and $A_0 = \sqrt{2P_0/m\omega_0}$ even for time intervals which are much longer than the

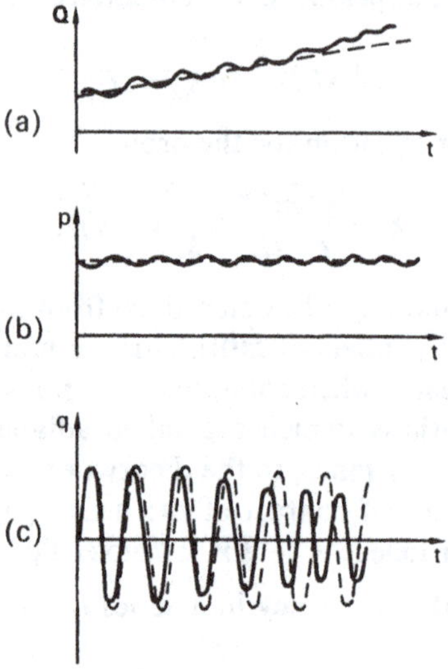

FIG. 132

period $2\pi/\omega$ of the oscillations (see Fig. 132). Thus for a time $t \sim 1/\varepsilon\omega_0$ the second term in (3) is of order unity, and the third one of order ε, and thus

$$Q = \omega_0 t + \varphi + \tfrac{1}{2}\dot{\omega}_0 t^2, \quad P = P_0.$$

However, this change in phase leads to the fact that the perturbed motion in terms of the variables p and q,

$$q(t) = A_0 \cos(\omega_0 t + \varphi + \tfrac{1}{2}\dot{\omega}_0 t^2),$$

will differ appreciably from the unperturbed motion,

$$q_0(t) = A_0 \cos(\omega_0 t + \varphi),$$

in such a way that

$$q(t)-q_0(t) \sim q_0(t).$$

When one tries to construct a perturbation theory for the variables q and p one obtains for the first-order correction $q_1(t)$ the equation

$$\ddot{q}_1+\omega_0^2 q_1 = -2\omega_0\dot{\omega}_0 t A_0 \cos(\omega_0 t+\varphi),$$

which has a resonance force which increases with time. The solution obtained in such a theory is thus applicable only for small time intervals of the order of a few periods of the oscillations $2\pi/\omega_0 \ll 1/\varepsilon\omega_0$.

13.10.

$$I(t) = I(-\infty)+\frac{1}{2m\omega^3}\left|\int_{-\infty}^{t} F'(\tau)e^{-i\omega\tau}\,d\tau\right|^2-\frac{a}{\omega}\int_{-\infty}^{t} F'(\tau)\sin(\omega\tau-\varphi)d\tau,$$

$$I(-\infty) = \tfrac{1}{2}m\omega a^2.$$

13.11. We transform the Hamiltonian of the system,

$$H(x, p, t) = \frac{p^2}{2m}+\tfrac{1}{2}m\omega^2x^2-xF(t) = E(t), \tag{1}$$

to the form

$$\tfrac{1}{2}m\omega^2\left(x-\frac{F}{m\omega^2}\right)^2+\frac{p^2}{2m}-\frac{F^2}{2m\omega^2} = E.$$

From this it is clear that the orbit in phase space is an ellipse which is displaced along the x-axis over a distance $F/m\omega^2$ with semi-axes

$$a = \sqrt{\frac{2E}{m\omega^2}+\frac{F^2}{m^2\omega^4}}, \quad b = \sqrt{2mE+\frac{F^2}{\omega^2}}.$$

Apart from a factor $1/2\pi$ the adiabatic invariant is the area of this ellipse

$$I = \tfrac{1}{2}ab = \frac{E+F^2/2m\omega^2}{\omega}. \tag{2}$$

Here the meaning of $E+F^2/2m\omega^2$ is that of the energy of oscillations near the displaced equilibrium position (compare problem 5.16). Substituting the value of E from (1) into (2) we can write the result in the form

$$I = \frac{m}{2\omega}\left|\dot{x}+i\omega\left(x-\frac{F}{m\omega^2}\right)\right|^2$$

$$= \frac{m}{2\omega}\left|\frac{1}{m}\int_0^t e^{i\omega(t-\tau)}F(\tau)d\tau+e^{i\omega t}[\dot{x}(0)+i\omega x(0)]-\frac{iF(t)}{m\omega}\right|^2.$$

We can use here equations (22.9) and (22.10) from Landau and Lifshitz, 1960, for the quantity $\dot{x}+i\omega x$.

Integrating by parts we get

$$I(t) = I(0)+\frac{\dot{x}(0)}{\omega^2}\int_0^t F(t)\sin\omega t\,dt-\frac{1}{\omega}\left[x(0)-\frac{F(0)}{m\omega^2}\right]\int_0^t \dot{F}(t)\cos\omega t\,dt$$
$$+\frac{1}{2m\omega}\left|\int_0^t \dot{F}(t)e^{i\omega t}\,dt\right|^2.$$

If the force changes slowly, $I(t)$ will thus oscillate near $I(0)$. If $F(t)\to$ constant as $t\to\infty$, the total change in the adiabatic invariant, $I(\infty)-I(0)$, can be very small (see problem 5.18).

13.12. $PV^{\frac{5}{3}}$ = constant.

13.13. (a)

$$E=\frac{2\pi_2}{m}\left[\frac{I_1^2}{a^2}+\frac{I_2^2}{b^2}+\frac{I_3^2}{c^2}\right],$$

where a, b, and c are the lengths of the edges of the parallelepiped, and I_k = constant. The dependence of the energy on a, b, and c is determined not only by their initial values, but also by the initial distribution of energy over the different degrees of freedom.

(b) The position of the parallelepiped is determined by three angles (for instance, the Euler angles). These angles will occur as parameters in the Hamiltonian and will change slowly when the parallelepiped is rotated. In a system of coordinates with axes parallel to its edges, we can separate the variables in the Hamilton–Jacobi equation. The form of the Hamiltonian is in that system of coordinates independent of the above-mentioned parameters. The invariance of the appropriate adiabatic invariants thus leads to the invariance of the absolute magnitudes of the components of the velocity along each of the edges. The angles of incidence of the particle on each of the sides are also invariant.

13.14. In spherical coordinates the variables separate. The angular momentum $\boldsymbol{M}$ is strictly conserved. (Moreover, M_z is an adiabatic invariant corresponding to the angle φ.) The adiabatic invariant for the radial motion is

$$I_r=\frac{1}{2\pi}\int_{r_{min}}^{R}\sqrt{2mE-M^2r^{-2}}\,dr. \qquad (1)$$

We can find the function $E(R)$ without evaluating the integral (1). The substitution $r = Rx$ gives

$$I_r = \frac{1}{2\pi}\int_{x_{\min}}^{1} \sqrt{2mER^2 - M^2x^{-2}}\,\frac{dx}{x} = I_r(ER^2, M),$$

whence $ER^2 =$ constant. We get thus for the angle of incidence

$$\sin\alpha = \frac{r_{\min}}{R} = \frac{M}{\sqrt{2mE}\,R} = \text{constant}.$$

13.15. (a) $E \propto \gamma^{2/(2-n)}$;

(b) $E \propto \gamma^{-\frac{1}{2}}$.

13.17. Equating the values of the adiabatic invariant before and after the switching on of the field,

$$\int_{r_{\min}}^{r_{\max}} \sqrt{E - (M^2/2mr^2) - U(r)}\,dr$$
$$= \int_{r_{\min}}^{r_{\max}} \sqrt{E + \delta E - (M^2/2mr^2) - U(r) - \delta U(r)}\,dr,$$

we get

$$\delta E = \langle \delta U \rangle = \frac{2}{T}\int_{r_{\min}}^{r_{\max}} \frac{\delta U(r)\,dr}{\sqrt{(2/m)\,[E - (M^2/2mr^2) - U]}}$$

(compare problem 13.3).

13.18.

$$E = I_1\Omega_1 + I_2\Omega_2$$

(in the notation of problem 6.4a). The orbit fills the rectangle

$$|Q_1| \leqq \sqrt{I_1/\Omega_1}, \quad |Q_2| \leqq \sqrt{I_2/\Omega_2}.$$

The condition that the theory of adiabatic invariants is applicable is

$$\dot{\Omega}_i \ll \Omega_i^2, \quad \Omega_i \ll \Omega_i \dot{\Omega}_i, \quad i = 1, 2.$$

Outside the region of degeneracy these conditions reduce to the same ones for $\omega_1(t)$. In the region of degeneracy $|\omega_1^2 - \omega_2^2| \sim \alpha$, and the second condition is more restrictive and gives $\dot{\omega}_1 \ll \alpha$ (the region of degeneracy is traversed during a time which is considerably longer than the period of the beats).

13.19. When the coupling αxy is not present, the system splits into two independent oscillators with coordinates x and y. The corresponding adiabatic invariants are $I_x = E_x/\omega_1$ and $I_y = E_y/\omega_2$, where E_x and E_y are the energies of these oscillators.

When the coupling is taken into account the system consists of two independent oscillators with coordinates Q_1 and Q_2. If the frequency changes sufficiently slowly, the quantities $I_1 = E_1/\Omega_1$ and $I_2 = E_2/\Omega_2$ are invariant.

Outside the region of degeneracy the normal oscillations are strongly localised, and when $\omega_1 < \omega_2$ it turns out that $Q_1 = x$, $Q_2 = y$, while when

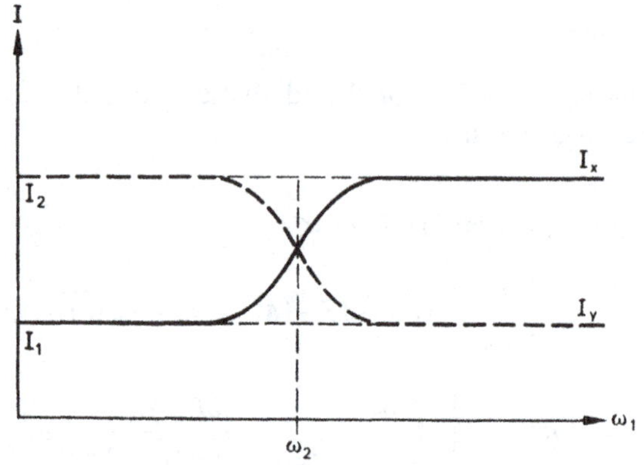

FIG. 133

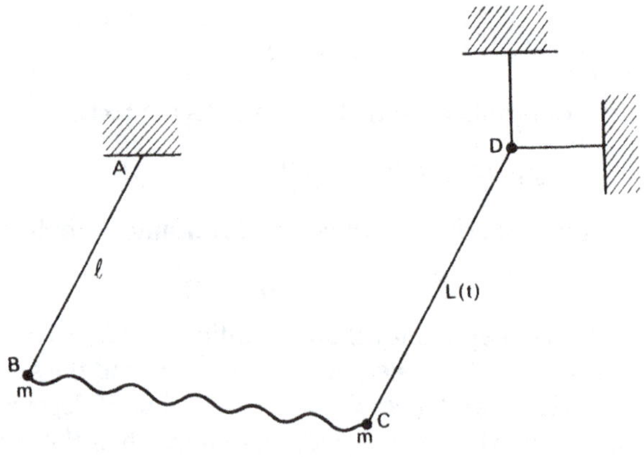

FIG. 134

$\omega_1 > \omega_2$, we have $Q_1 = y$, $Q_2 = -x$. Thus, when $\omega_1 < \omega_2$, $I_x = I_1$, $I_y = I_2$, while when $\omega_1 < \omega_2$, we have $I_x = I_2$, $I_y = I_1$ (see Fig. 133).

We shall illustrate this by the following example. Two pendulums, the length of one of which can be changed slowly, are coupled by a spring with a small stiffness (Fig. 134). When the lengths l and L of the pendulum are appreciably different, the normal oscillations are practically the same as the oscillations of one or the other pendulum. Let the pendulum AB initially oscillate with amplitude φ_0, and the pendulum CD with a very small amplitude. When L is decreased the amplitude of the oscillations of the pendulum CD remains small until its length becomes almost equal to l. When $L \approx l$, its amplitude increases (and when $l = L$ both pendulums will oscillate with the same amplitude, $\varphi_0/\sqrt{2}$, in antiphase). When L is decreased further, practically all the energy transfers to the pendulum CD and its amplitude becomes $\varphi_1 = \varphi_0(l/L)^{\frac{3}{4}}$, as for a separate pendulum.

If we traverse the degeneracy region relatively fast, $\alpha \ll \dot{\omega}_1$, such a transfer of energy between the oscillators will not take place. If, moreover, $\dot{\omega}_1 \ll \omega_1^2$, $\ddot{\omega}_1 \ll \dot{\omega}_1\omega_1$, I_x and I_y will be invariant.

13.20. From the equations of motion,

$$\ddot{x}+\omega_1^2x+2\beta xy = 0, \tag{1}$$

$$\ddot{y}+\omega_2^2y+\beta x^2 = 0, \tag{2}$$

we see easily that the coupling between the oscillators leads to a large energy transfer when $2\omega_1 \approx \omega_2$.

Let

$$x = a(t)\cos(\omega_1 t+\varphi), \quad y = b(t)\cos(\omega_2 t+\psi).$$

If $a \gg b$, the term

$$\beta x^2 = \tfrac{1}{2}\beta a^2+\tfrac{1}{2}\beta a^2\cos(2\omega_1+2\varphi)$$

in (2) will play the role of an applied force, leading to a resonance increase in y. If, however, $a \ll b$, the term

$$2\beta xy = 2\beta bx\cos(\omega_2+\psi)$$

leads to a parametric building-up of the oscillations in x.

The region of resonance interaction (see problem 8.7) is

$$|2\omega_1-\omega_2| \lesssim \beta b/\omega_1.$$

In general, a strong resonance interaction between the oscillators occurs when $n\omega_1 = m\omega_2$, where n and m are integers. However, the width of the regions of frequencies in which these resonances occur is for not too small n and m extremely small (see Landau and Lifshitz, 1960, § 29). We can therefore neglect their influence on the motion of the oscillators for not too small values of $\dot{\omega}_1$ (provided they are sufficiently small that we can use the theory of adiabatic invariants).

13.21. Let the particle moving in the xy-plane at a small angle to the y-axis ($|\dot{x}| \ll |\dot{y}|$) be reflected from the x-axis and from the curve $y_0(x)$ (Fig. 135). If we assume that we know how the particle moves in the x-direction, we can study the motion in the y-direction by taking $x(t)$ to be a slowly

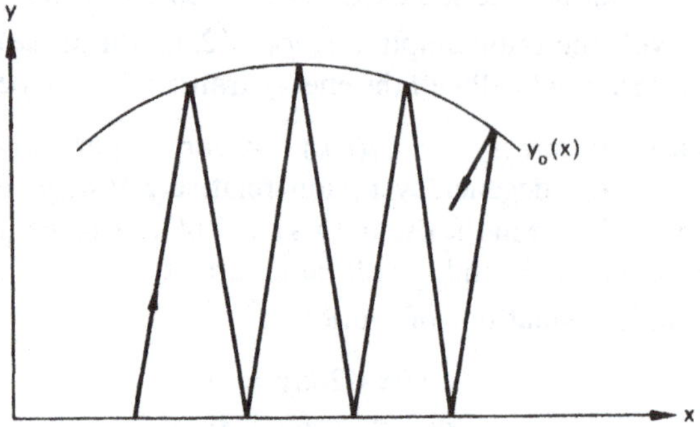

FIG. 135

changing parameter. The adiabatic invariant,

$$\oint p_y \, dy = |p_y| \, y_0(x) = 2\pi I,$$

will remain constant and that equation determines the function $p_y(x)$. To determine $x(t)$ we can use the energy conservation law

$$m^2\dot{x}^2 + p_y^2(x) = 2mE.$$

The minimum distance x_{min} is determined by the condition

$$p_y^2(x_{min}) = 2mE.$$

Substituting

$$y_0(x) = x \tan\alpha, \quad 2\pi I = \sqrt{2mE}\, l \tan\alpha \cos\varphi_0,$$

we get

$$x_{min} = l \cos\varphi_0.$$

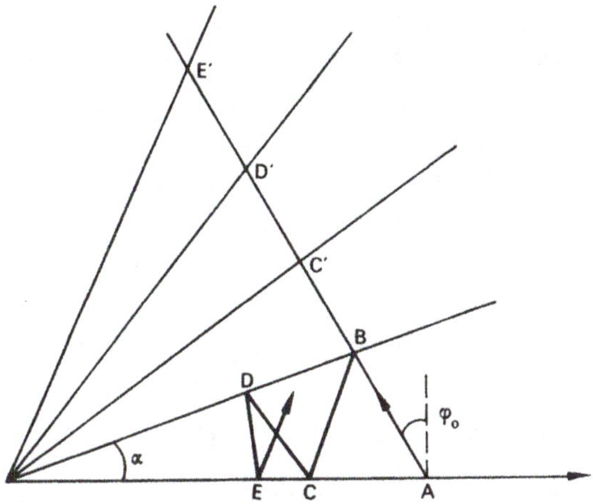

FIG. 136

The solution by means of the reflection method is clear from Fig. 136. This method gives an exact solution applicable to any angles α and φ_0 but it cannot be generalised to the case when $y_0(x)$ is not a straight line.

13.22. $\tan \alpha x_m = \tan \varphi,\ T = \dfrac{2\pi}{\alpha v\sqrt{\cos 2\varphi}}.$

13.23. (a) The problem of the motion of a particle in a magnetic field reduces for the given choice of vector potential to the problem of the motion of a harmonic oscillator (see problem 10.7). The adiabatic invariant is

$$I = \frac{E - p_z^2/2m}{\omega} \propto \frac{v_\perp^2}{H} \propto \pi a^2 H,$$

where $a = cmv_\perp/eH$ is the radius of the electron orbit (compare Landau and Lifshitz, 1962, § 21). The relation $I \propto \pi a^2 H$ can be interpreted simply: the radius of the orbit changes in such a way that the magnetic field flux through the area circumscribed by it remains constant. The distance of the centre of the orbit from the yz-plane is equal to $x = cp_y/eH$, and decreases with increasing H.

The occurrence of a drift of the orbit is connected with the appearance of an electric field,

$$\boldsymbol{E} = -\frac{1}{c}\dot{\boldsymbol{A}} = (0, -\frac{1}{c}x\dot{H}, 0),$$

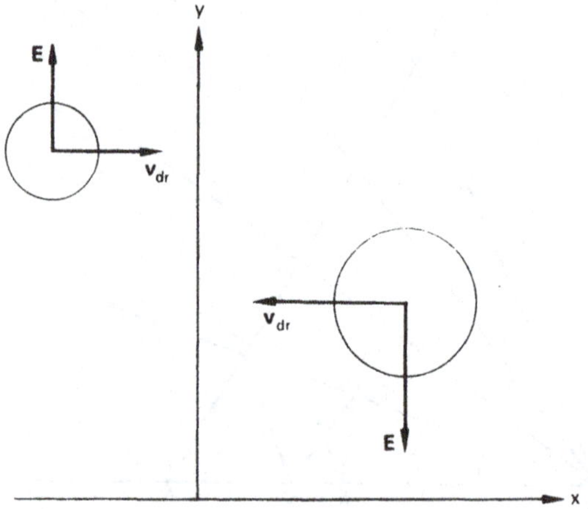

FIG. 137

when the magnetic field changes (compare Landau and Lifshitz, 1962, § 22) (the electrical field vector $\boldsymbol{E}$ and the drift velocity $\boldsymbol{v}_{dr}$ are shown in Fig. 137 for different orbit positions).

(b) The Hamiltonian is in cylindrical coordinates

$$H = \frac{p_z^2}{2m}+\frac{p_r^2}{2m}+\frac{1}{2mr^2}\left(p_\varphi-\frac{eH}{2c}r^2\right)^2.$$

The quantities p_z and p_φ are integrals of motion. The adiabatic invariant for the radial motion is

$$\pi I_r = \int_{r_{max}}^{r_{min}} \sqrt{2mE_\perp-\frac{1}{r^2}\left(p_\varphi-\frac{eH}{2c}r^2\right)^2}\,dr,$$

which after the substitution $r = H^{-\frac{1}{2}}\xi$ becomes

$$\pi I_r = \int_{\xi_{min}}^{\xi_{max}} \sqrt{(2mE_\perp/H)-\xi^{-2}\left(p_\varphi-\frac{e}{2c}\xi^2\right)^2}\,d\xi = \pi I_r(p_\varphi, E_\perp/H).$$

Therefore, $E_\perp/H =$ constant, that is, the energy of the transverse motion changes in the same way as under (a). The distance r_0 of the centre of the orbit to the origin is

$$r_0 = \frac{1}{2}(r_{max}+r_{min}) = \frac{\xi_{max}+\xi_{min}}{2\sqrt{H}} \propto \frac{1}{\sqrt{H}}.$$

When H increases, the centre of the orbit approaches the origin (Fig. 138).

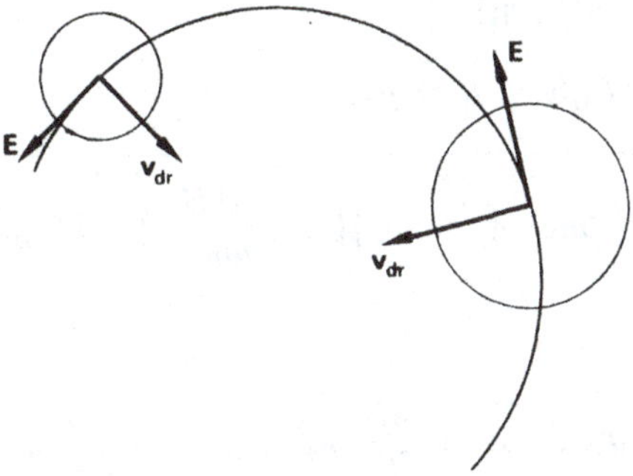

FIG. 138

When H changes there occurs an electric field

$$E_\varphi = -\frac{r}{2c}\dot{H}, \quad E_r = E_z = 0,$$

the field lines of which are closed circles (Fig. 138).

In real conditions a uniform magnetic field can exist only in a limited region of space. The electrical field occurring when the magnetic field is changed depends very strongly on the shape of that region and the conditions at its boundaries (compare Landau and Lifshitz, 1962, § 21). For instance, the field considered under (a) could occur near a conducting plane in which there was a current, while the field under (b) could be produced in a solenoid.†

The strong dependence of the nature of the motion of the particle on the weak field $\boldsymbol{E}$ even in the case of infinitesimal $\dot{\boldsymbol{H}}$ can be explained by the presence of degeneracy (when $\boldsymbol{H}$ = constant the periods in the two coordinates x and y, or r and φ are the same).

We note that the quantity $E_\perp/H$ turned out to be an adiabatic invariant in both cases. One can prove that this result is independent of the choice of the form of A (see Landau and Lifshitz, 1962, § 21, or Bogolyubov and Mitropolskii, 1958, § 25).

13.24. Choosing the vector potential in the form

$$A_\varphi = \tfrac{1}{2}rH(t), \quad A_r = A_z = 0, \tag{1}$$

† The change in the electric field $\boldsymbol{E}$ connected with the change in the choice of the form of A would not occur if we had simultaneously changed the scalar potential by $\Delta\varphi = c^{-1}(\partial/\partial t)(\frac{1}{2}Hxy)$ (gauge transformation).

we get the adiabatic invariants

$$I_z = E_z/\omega, \quad I_\varphi = p_\varphi,$$

$$I_r = \frac{I}{\pi}\int_{\xi_{\min}}^{\xi_{\max}} \sqrt{\left(2mE_\perp + \frac{e}{c}Hp_\varphi\right)\left(\omega^2 + \frac{e^2H^2}{4m^2c^2}\right)^{-\frac{1}{2}}\xi^2 - p_\varphi^2 - m^2\xi^4}\,\frac{d\xi}{\xi}. \tag{2}$$

Therefore

$$E_z \propto \omega, \quad E_\perp + \frac{eH}{2mc}p_\varphi \propto \left[\omega^2 + \left(\frac{eH}{2mc}\right)^2\right]^{\frac{1}{2}}. \tag{3}$$

As we showed in the preceding problem, if we give $\boldsymbol{H}(\boldsymbol{r}, t)$ in the region where the motion of the particle takes place, we have not determined uniquely the physical conditions of the problem: $\boldsymbol{E}(\boldsymbol{r}, t)$ is not determined uniquely. However, if we give the vector potential $\boldsymbol{A}(\boldsymbol{r}, t)$ (we assume that the scalar potential is equal to zero) the fields $\boldsymbol{E}$ and $\boldsymbol{H}$ are completely determined.

The vector potential (1) gives a magnetic field which is symmetric with respect to the z-axis going through the centre of the oscillator. If we make a different choice for $\boldsymbol{A}$,

$$A_x = A_z = 0, \quad A_y = xH(t), \tag{4}$$

we get practically a different physical problem. The Lagrangians for these two problems differ by

$$\delta L = \frac{d}{dt}\left(\frac{e}{2c}Hxy\right) - \frac{e}{2c}\dot{H}xy, \tag{5}$$

that is, their difference is very small, if we drop in (5) the inessential total derivative with respect to time. In the preceding problem, where the motion was degenerate, just this extra term led to a complete change in the direction and drift velocity of the orbit. In the present case, however, the motion of the oscillator is not degenerate when $\boldsymbol{H} \neq 0$ and we can neglect the extra term δL (compare problem 13.19). The relation (3) is thus valid also for a different choice of $\boldsymbol{A}$. When one passes through the degeneracy region ($\boldsymbol{H} = 0$) equation (3) remains valid only when we choose the axially symmetric field (1). For instance, the behaviour of the oscillator in the field (4) when $\boldsymbol{H}$ passes through zero requires additional study.

Would I_r from (2) and $I_z = E_z/\omega_z$ for an harmonic oscillator with an elastic constant in the z-direction different from the constants $m\omega^2$ in the

xy-plane be invariant when the magnetic field passes through values such that one of the frequencies of the transverse oscillations,

$$\omega_{1,2} = \sqrt{\omega^2 + \left(\frac{eH}{2mc}\right)^2} \pm \frac{eH}{2mc},$$

turns out to be equal to ω_z?

13.25. (a) Using a canonical transformation one can reduce the Hamiltonian to a sum of two independent oscillator Hamiltonians (for X and Y; see problem 11.21). For each of the oscillators the ratio of the energy to the frequency is an adiabatic invariant. We remind ourselves that the oscillations of each of them corresponds to motion along an ellipse (see problem 6.23). In terms of the amplitudes a_k of the oscillations in the x-direction, for instance, the adiabatic invariants are equal to

$$I_k = \frac{ma_k^2}{2\Omega_k} \frac{\Omega_k^4 - \omega_1^2\omega_2^2}{\Omega_k^2 - \omega_2^2}, \quad k = 1, 2.$$

When the parameters of the system are changing we must also add to the new Hamiltonian the partial derivative with respect to the time of the generating function which is equal to $\dot{\lambda}(m\omega_2 XY + P_X P_Y/m\omega_2)$.† This correction term is small ($\dot{\lambda} < \Omega_k$) and can be neglected provided the eigen-frequencies are not the same (compare problem 13.19). One must consider separately the degenerate case when $\omega_1 = \omega_2$ and a magnetic field which can vanish.

If we choose a different vector potential which leads to the same magnetic field, but to a different electric field, as $\boldsymbol{E} = -c^{-1}\,\partial \boldsymbol{A}/\partial t$, the adiabatic invariants turn out to be unchanged (we must again exclude the case when $\omega_1 = \omega_2$ and $\boldsymbol{H} = 0$).

(b) To fix the ideas let $\omega_1 > \omega_2$. The motion is along a circle of radius $a\sqrt{\omega_1/\omega_H}$ with a frequency ω_H, but the centre of the circle moves

† One can simplify the calculation of this partial derivative by the following considerations. When we go from t to $t+\delta t$ we must perform an additional canonical transformation corresponding to changing from λ to $\lambda+\delta\lambda$. Such a transformation is produced by the generating function (see problem 11.29)

$$\Phi(X, Y, P'_X P'_Y) = XP'_X + YP'_Y + \delta\lambda(m\omega_2 XY + P'_X P'_Y/m\omega_2).$$

Therefore

$$\left.\frac{\partial \Phi}{\partial t}\right|_{\delta\lambda \to 0} = \dot{\lambda}(m\omega_2 XY + P_X P_Y/m\omega_2).$$

along an ellipse with semi-axes in the x- and y-directions and equal to $b\omega_2\sqrt{\omega_1\omega_H}$ and $b\sqrt{\omega_1/\omega_H}$, with a frequency $\omega_1\omega_2/\omega_H$.

(c) The oscillation will proceed almost in the y-direction; its amplitude is increased by a factor $\sqrt{\omega_1/\omega_2}$ (compare problem 13.19).

13.27. (a) The motion of the particle in the xy-plane takes place under the action of a magnetic field which is slowly varying as the particle moves along the z-direction. The adiabatic invariant $I_\perp = E_\perp/(eH(z)/mc)$ is then conserved (see problem 13.23). From the energy conservation law we have

$$\tfrac{1}{2} m\dot{z}^2 + I_\perp \frac{eH(z)}{mc} = E.$$

The particle moves in the z-direction as if it moved in a potential $U(z) = I_\perp eH(z)/mc$. The period of the oscillations is (compare problem 2b from Landau and Lifshitz, 1960, § 12)

$$T = \frac{2\pi a}{v\sqrt{\lambda \sin^2\alpha - \cos^2\alpha}},$$

where α is the angle between the velocity v of the particle and the z-axis. Particles for which $\cot^2\alpha > \lambda$ are not contained in the trap. The condition for the applicability of the theory of adiabatic invariants consists in the requirement that the change in the magnetic field during one period of revolution of the particle be small. This gives $mc\lambda v_z \ll aeH_0$.

The motion of a particle the centre of the orbit of which is not on the z-axis is more complicated. The centre of its orbit both moves in the z-direction and slowly rotates around the z-axis at a constant distance.

As an example of a magnetic trap we can mention the radiation belts of the Earth.

(b) $T = \dfrac{2\pi a}{v \sin\alpha}.$

13.28. (a) $(\lambda E_\perp - E_z)a^2 = \text{constant}, \quad E_\perp/H_0 = \text{constant},$
$E = E_\perp + E_z;$

(b) $E_\perp/H_0 = \text{constant}, \quad E_z\sqrt{H_0/a} = \text{constant}.$

13.29. If we neglect in the Hamiltonian

$$H = \frac{p_r^2}{2m} + \frac{p_\theta^2}{2mr^2} + \frac{p_\varphi^2}{2mr^2\sin^2\theta} - \frac{eHp\varphi}{2mc} + \frac{eH^2r^2\sin^2\theta}{8mc^2}$$

the last term which is quadratic in H we can separate the variables in the Hamilton–Jacobi equation. The adiabatic invariants have the form

$$I_\varphi = p_\varphi,\; I_\theta = \frac{1}{\pi}\int_{\theta_1}^{\theta_2} [\beta-(p_\varphi^2/\sin^2\theta)]^{\frac{1}{2}}\, d\theta = I_\theta(p_\varphi, \beta),$$

$$I_r = \frac{l}{\pi}\int_{r_1}^{r_2}\left\{2m\left[E+\frac{eHp_\varphi}{2mc}-U(r)\right]-\frac{\beta}{r^2}\right\}^{\frac{1}{2}} dr = I_r\left(E+\frac{eHp_\varphi}{2mc}, \beta\right).$$

When H is slowly changed, the quantities p_φ, β, and $E+eHp_\varphi/2mc$ thus remain constant.

13.30. (a) Apart from the obvious integrals of motion E and M the following quantities are also conserved (we consider at once planar motion):

$$E_x = \frac{p_x^2}{2m}+\tfrac{1}{2}\varkappa x^2, \quad E_y = \frac{p_y^2}{2m}+\tfrac{1}{2}\varkappa y^2.$$

The number of independent integrals (three, when we bear in mind that $E_x+E_y = E$) is larger than the number of degrees of freedom (two).

Of course, there are yet other integrals of motion—such as, for instance, $\{M_z, E_x\}$—but they are not independent.

(b) Apart from

$$\frac{p_x^2}{2m}+\tfrac{1}{2}m\omega^2x^2 = E_x, \quad \frac{p_y^2}{2m}+\tfrac{1}{2}m\omega^2y^2 = E_y,$$

the quantity $B = \tan(2w_x-w_y)$ is also a unique integral of motion; $w_x = \arctan(p_x/m\omega x)$, $w_y = \arctan(p_y/2m\omega y)$ are angle variables (Landau and Lifshitz, 1960, § 50; ter Haar, 1964, § 6.2):

$$B = \frac{4m^2\omega^2xyp_x-m^2\omega^2x^2p_y+p_x^2p_y}{2m^3\omega^3x^2y-2m\omega yp_x^2+2m\omega xp_xp_y}.$$

13.31. (a)

$$w = \arctan\frac{p}{m\omega q}, \quad I = \frac{p^2}{2m\omega}+\tfrac{1}{2}m\omega q^2.$$

These variables are convenient, for instance, to develop perturbation theory (see problem 13.9; see also ter Haar, 1964, Ch. 7).

(b) Let initially the particle move to the right from the point $x = 0$; we shall choose S such that $S = 0$ for $x = 0$.

In that case

$$S = \int_0^x |p|dx = \pi I - \pi a \left[\left(\frac{I}{a} \right)^{2/3} - Fx \right]^{3/2},$$

where

$$I = \frac{1}{\pi} \int_0^{x_m} |p|dx = aE^{3/2}, \quad a = \frac{2\sqrt{2m}}{3\pi F}, \quad x_m = \frac{E}{F}, \quad |p| = \sqrt{2m(E - xF)}.$$

If the motion is to the left

$$S = \left\{ \int_0^{x_m} - \int_{x_m}^{x} \right\} |p|dx = \pi I + \pi a \left[\left(\frac{I}{a} \right)^{2/3} - Fx \right]^{3/2},$$

and so on. For the nth oscillation

$$S = (2n-1) I \mp \pi a \left[\left(\frac{I}{a} \right)^{2/3} - Fx \right]^{3/2}$$

(the upper (lower) sign corresponds to motion to the right (left); Fig. 139).

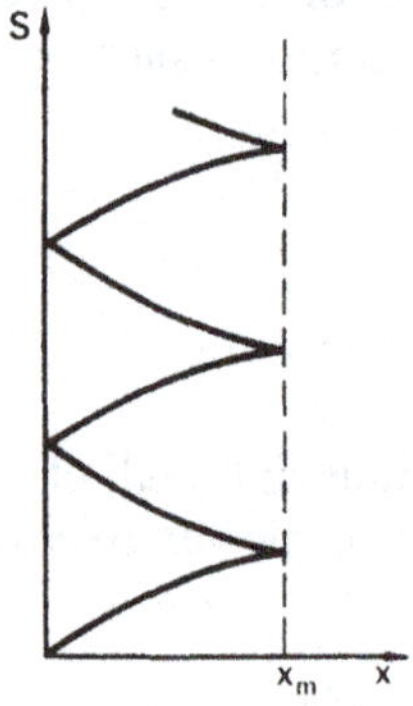

FIG. 139

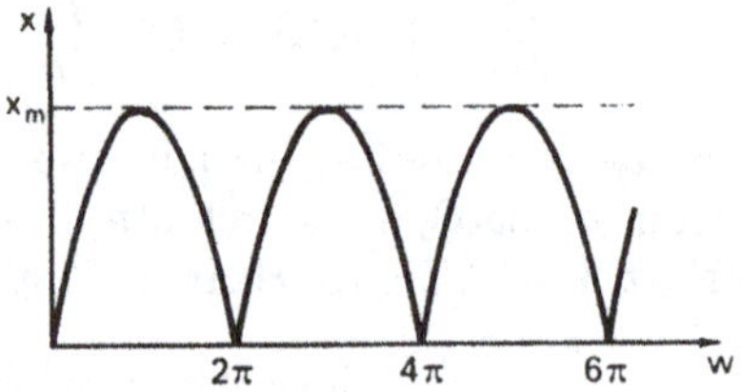

FIG. 140

One can use $S(x, I)$ as a generating function to change to new canonical action and angle variables (see Landau and Lifshitz, 1960, § 49). The new variables are connected with the old ones in the following way:

$$x = \frac{1}{\pi^2 F} \left(\frac{I}{a} \right)^{2/3} \{\pi^2 - [(2n-1)\pi - w]^2\}, \quad p = \tfrac{3}{2} a \left(\frac{I}{a} \right)^{2/3} [(2n-1)\pi - w],$$

where w is a periodic function of x (but w is a multivalued function of x; Fig. 140).

13.32. From the relation

$$P = \int_0^a \sqrt{2m(E-U)}\, dx$$

we find

$$E = \frac{P^2}{2ma^2} + \tfrac{1}{2}V + \frac{mV^2a^2}{8P^2}.$$

The action is

$$S_0 = \int_0^x p\, dx \begin{cases} \sqrt{2mE}\, x + (n-1)P, & \text{when } na < x < (n+\tfrac{1}{2})a, \\ \sqrt{2m(E-V)}(x-\tfrac{1}{2}a) + \sqrt{2mE}\,\dfrac{a}{2} + (n-1)P, & \text{when } (n+\tfrac{1}{2})a < x < (n+1)\, a. \end{cases}$$

Eliminating E we get the generating function for the canonical transformation under consideration

$$S_0(x, P) = \begin{cases} \left(\dfrac{P}{a} + \dfrac{amV}{2P}\right) x + (n-1)P, & \text{when } na < x < (n+\tfrac{1}{2})a, \\ \dfrac{ma^2V}{2P} + \left(\dfrac{P}{a} - \dfrac{amV}{2P}\right) x + (n-1)P, & \text{when } (n+\tfrac{1}{2})\, a < x < (n+1)a. \end{cases}$$

From the equations $Q = \partial S_0/\partial P$, $p = \partial S_0/\partial x$ we get

$$p(P,Q) = \begin{cases} \dfrac{P}{a} + \dfrac{amV}{2P}, \\ \dfrac{P}{a} - \dfrac{amV}{2P}; \end{cases} \quad x(P,Q) = \begin{cases} \dfrac{Q+1-n}{1-(ma^2V/2P^2)}\, a, & \text{when } n-1 < Q < n-\tfrac{1}{2}, \\ \dfrac{Q+\frac{1}{2}-n}{1+(ma^2V/2P^2)}\, a + \tfrac{1}{2}a, & \text{when } n-\tfrac{1}{2} < Q < n. \end{cases}$$

The variables P and Q are analogous to action and angle variables and the quantity $a\dot{Q}$ is the average particle velocity.

References

ABRAMOWITZ, M. and STEGUN, I. A. (1965) *Handbook of Mathematical Functions*, Dover, New York.

BOGOLYUBOV, N. N. and MITROPOLSKII, YU. A. (1958) *Asymptotic Methods in the Theory of Non-linear Oscillations*, Noordhoff, Groningen.

GOLDSTEIN, H. (1950) *Classical Mechanics*, Addison-Wesley, Reading, Mass.

TER HAAR, D. (1964) *Elements of Hamiltonian Mechanics*, North Holland, Amsterdam.

TER HAAR, D. (1964a) *Selected Problems in Quantum Mechanics*, Academic Press, New York.

TER HAAR, D. (1966) *Elements of Thermostatistics*, Holt, Rinehart, & Winston, New York.

HAUG, A. (1971) *Theoretical Solid State Physics*, Pergamon, Oxford.

KITTEL, C. (1968) *Introduction to Solid State Physics*, Wiley, New York.

LANDAU, L. D. and LIFSHITZ, E. M. (1960) *Mechanics*, Pergamon, Oxford.

LANDAU, L. D. and LIFSHITZ, E. M. (1960a) *Electrodynamics of Continuous Media*, Pergamon, Oxford.

LANDAU, L. D. and LIFSHITZ, E. M. (1962) *Classical Theory of Fields*, Pergamon, Oxford.

RAYLEIGH, LORD (1890) *Theory of Sound.*

WANNIER, G. H. (1959) *Elements of Solid State Theory*, Cambridge University Press.

Index

The numbers refer to the problems; for instance, 4.12 is problem 12 of § 4.

Index

OTHER TITLES IN THE SERIES IN NATURAL PHILOSOPHY

Vol. 1. DAVYDOV – Quantum Mechanics
Vol. 2. FOKKER – Time and Space, Weight and Inertia
Vol. 3. KAPLAN – Interstellar Gas Dynamics
Vol. 4. ABRIKOSOV, GOR'KOV and DZYALOSHINSKII – Quantum Field Theoretical Methods in Statistical Physics
Vol. 5. OKUN' – Weak Intraction of Elementary Particles
Vol. 6. SHKLOVSKII – Physics of the Solar Corona
Vol. 7. AKHIEZER *et al.* – Collective Oscillations in a Plasma
Vol. 8. KIRZHNITS – Field Theoretical Methods in Many-body Systems
Vol. 9. KLIMONTOVICH – Statistical Theory of Non-equilibrium Processes in a Plasma
Vol. 10. KURTH – Introduction to Stellar Statistics
Vol. 11. CHALMERS – Atmospheric Electricity (2nd Edition)
Vol. 12. RENNER – Current Algebras and their Applications
Vol. 13. FAIN and KHANIN – Quantum Electronics, Volume 1 – Basic Theory
Vol. 14. FAIN and KHANIN – Quantum Electronics, Volume 2 – Maser Amplifiers and Oscillators
Vol. 15. MARCH – Liquid Metals
Vol. 16. HORI – Spectral Properties of Disordered Chains and Lattices
Vol. 17. SAINT JAMES, THOMAS and SARMA – Type II Superconductivity
Vol. 18. MARGENAU and KESTNER – Theory of Intermolecular Forces
Vol. 19. JANCEL – Foundations of Classical and Quantum Statistical Mechanics
Vol. 20. TAKAHASHI – An Introduction to Field Quantization
Vol. 21. YVON – Correlations and Entropy in Classical Statistical Mechanics
Vol. 22. PENROSE – Foundations of Statistical Mechanics
Vol. 23. VISCONTI – Quantum Field Theory, Volume 1
Vol. 24. FURTH – Fundamental Principles of Theoretical Physics
Vol. 25. ZHELEZNYAKOV – Radioemission of the Sun and Planets
Vol. 26. GRINDLAY – An Introduction to the Phenomenological Theory of Ferroelectricity
Vol. 27. UNGER – Introduction to Quantum Electronics
Vol. 28. KOGA – Introduction to Kinetic Theory Stochastic Processes in Gaseous Systems
Vol. 29. GALASIEWICZ – Superconductivity and Quantum Fluids
Vol. 30. CONSTANTINESCU and MAGYARI – Problems in Quantum Mechanics

Made in the USA
Monee, IL
04 February 2025

11495345R00164